S0-BBO-485

The Human Body

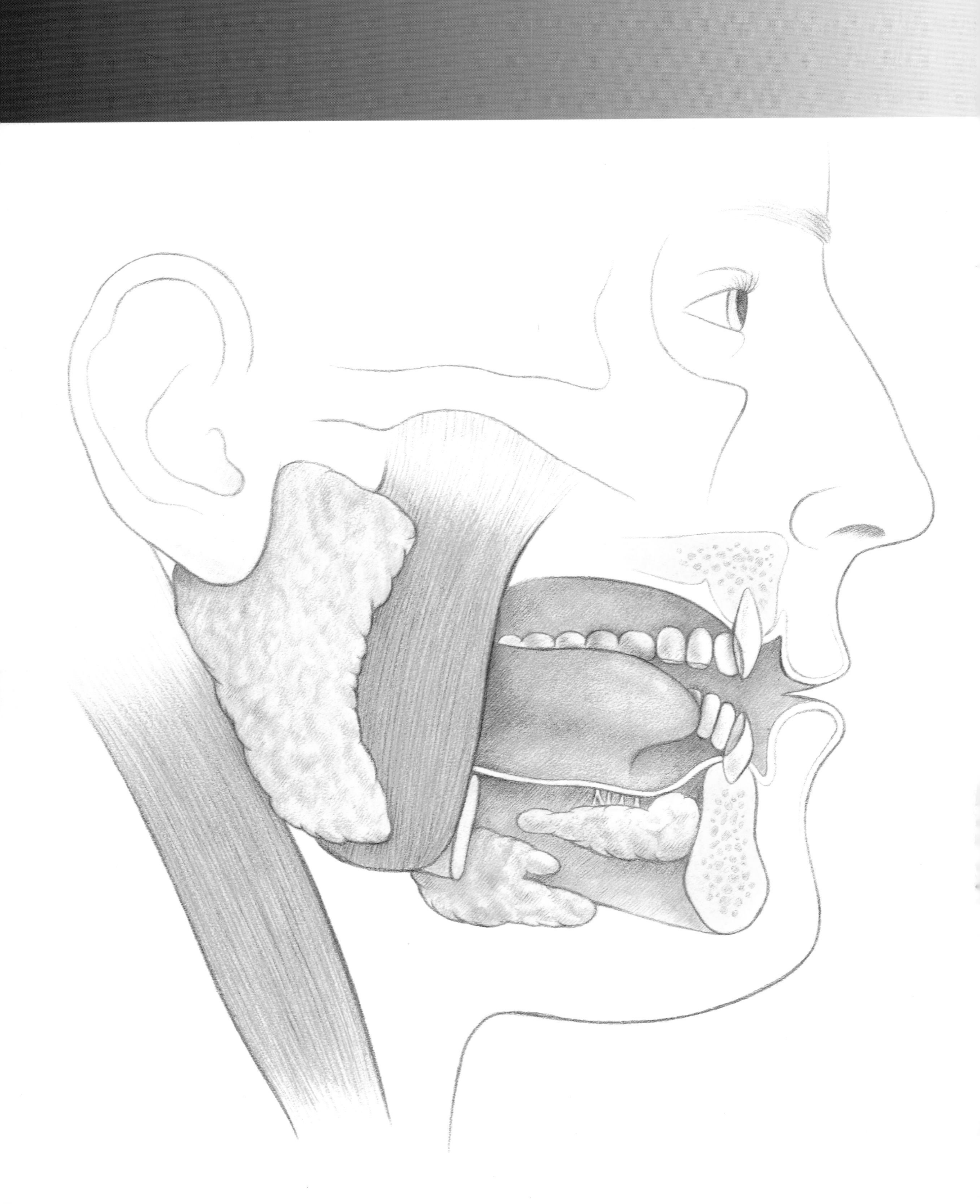

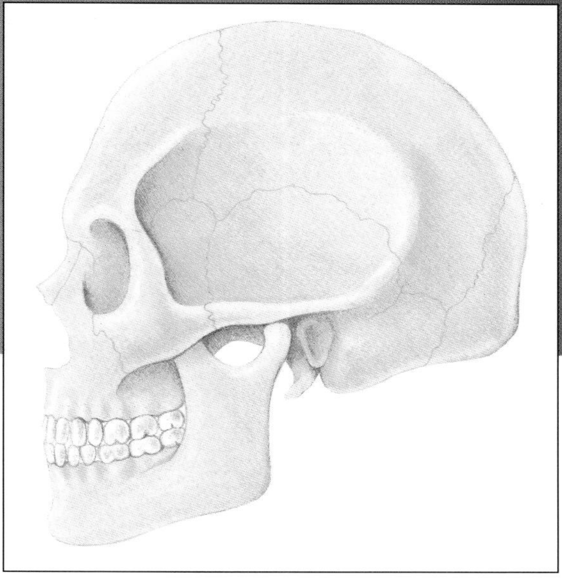

The Human Body

William Clevenger

Illustrations
by Laura Pardi Duprey,
George Gilliland,
and Laurie van der Steelink

Friedman Group

A FRIEDMAN GROUP BOOK

ISBN 1–56799-045–2

THE HUMAN BODY
was prepared and produced by
Michael Friedman Publishing Group, Inc.
15 West 26th Street
New York, New York 10010

Editor: Sharyn Rosart
Art Director: Jeff Batzli
Designer: Patrick McCarthy
Diagram Labels: Eugene M. Bak, Patrick McCarthy
Photography Designer: Christopher C.Bain

Typeset by Bookworks Plus
Printed in Hong Kong and bound in China by Leefung–Asco Printers Ltd.

Illustrations

George Gilliland: pages 10–16, 17(top), 38 (top), 42 (top), 49 (top, middle, and bottom), 50, 51 (middle), 55, 57, 60 (top), 65 (middle), 69, 97(bottom), 99, 111 (top and middle), 112 (bottom left and right).

Laura Pardi Duprey: pages 9, 29 (bottom), 30–31 (bottom), 38, 39, 40, 41, 42 (bottom), 43, 52 (top), 53, 56 (top and bottom), 59 (top), 61 (top), 66, 67, 68, 71, 72 (top, bottom, and middle), 81, 83, 86, 91, 92, 94, 97(top), 100, 101, 109, 115, 118, 123.

Laurie van der Steelink: pages 17 (bottom), 19, 20, 21, 22, 23, 27, 29 (top), 31 (top), 32, 33, 34, 37, 45, 47, 48, 51(top), 52 (bottom), 54, 58 (top, middle, and bottom), 59 (bottom), 60 (bottom), 61 (middle), 63 (middle and bottom), 64, 65 (top), 74, 75, 76–77, 78, 79, 84, 87, 88, 89, 93, 96, 102, 103, 105, 107, 116, 119, 121 (top and bottom), 122.

Acknowledgments

My sincere appreciation goes out to Sharyn Rosart for her talent and expertise in putting this book together. Also, a million thanks to Professor William S. Bradshaw for provoking me to think for myself.

Dedication

This book is for JoJo, my flesh and blood, and so much more.

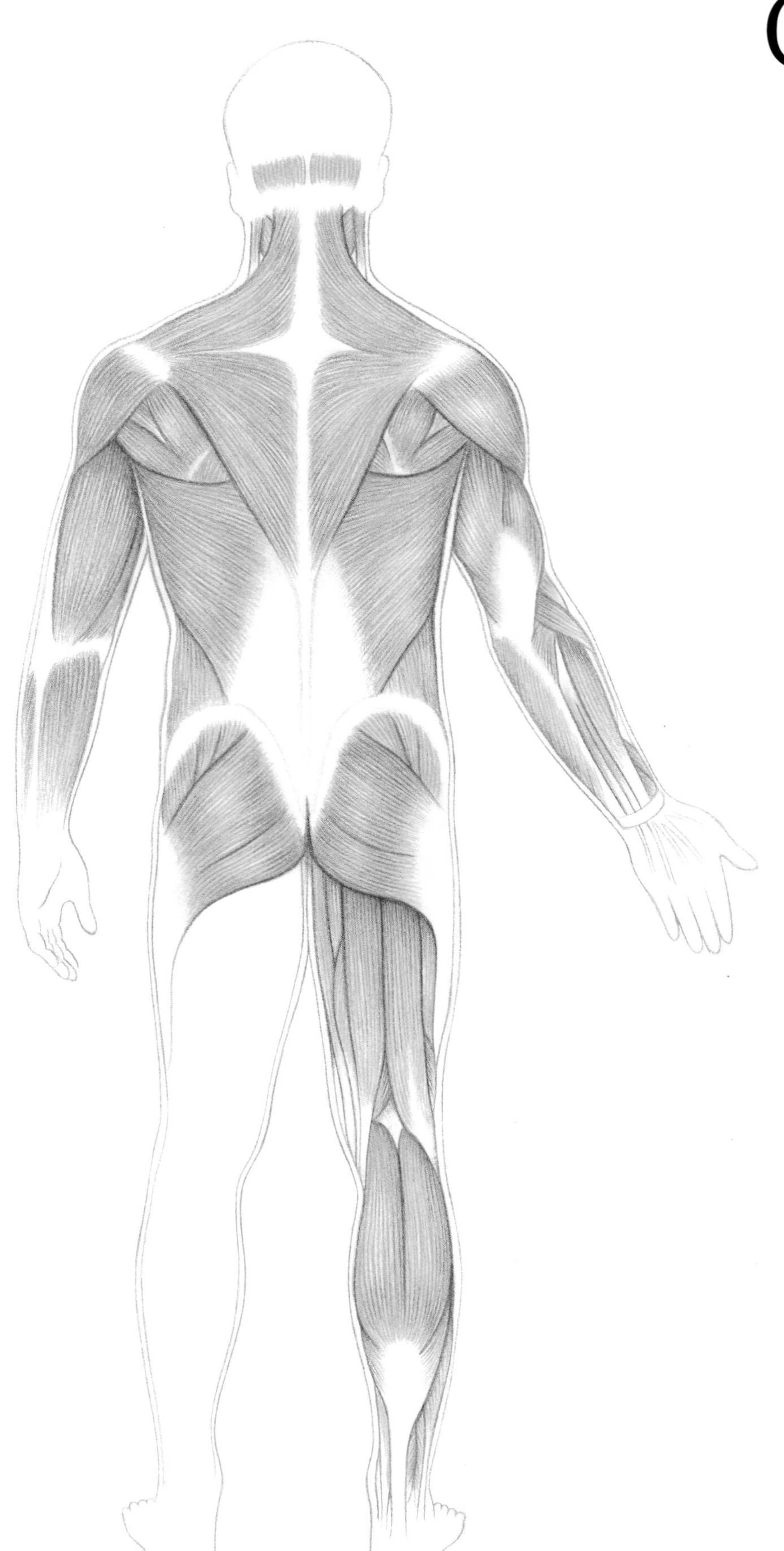

Contents

Chapter 1
Cells–The Basic Units of Life
9

Chapter 2
The Integumentary System
19

Chapter 3
The Skeletal System
27

Chapter 4
The Muscular System
37

Chapter 5
The Nervous System
47

Chapter 6
The Circulatory System
63

Chapter 7
The Respiratory System
71

Chapter 8
The Digestive System
81

Chapter 9
The Urinary System
91

Chapter 10
The Endocrine System
99

Chapter 11
The Immune System
107

Chapter 12
The Reproductive System
115

Further Reading
124

Index
125

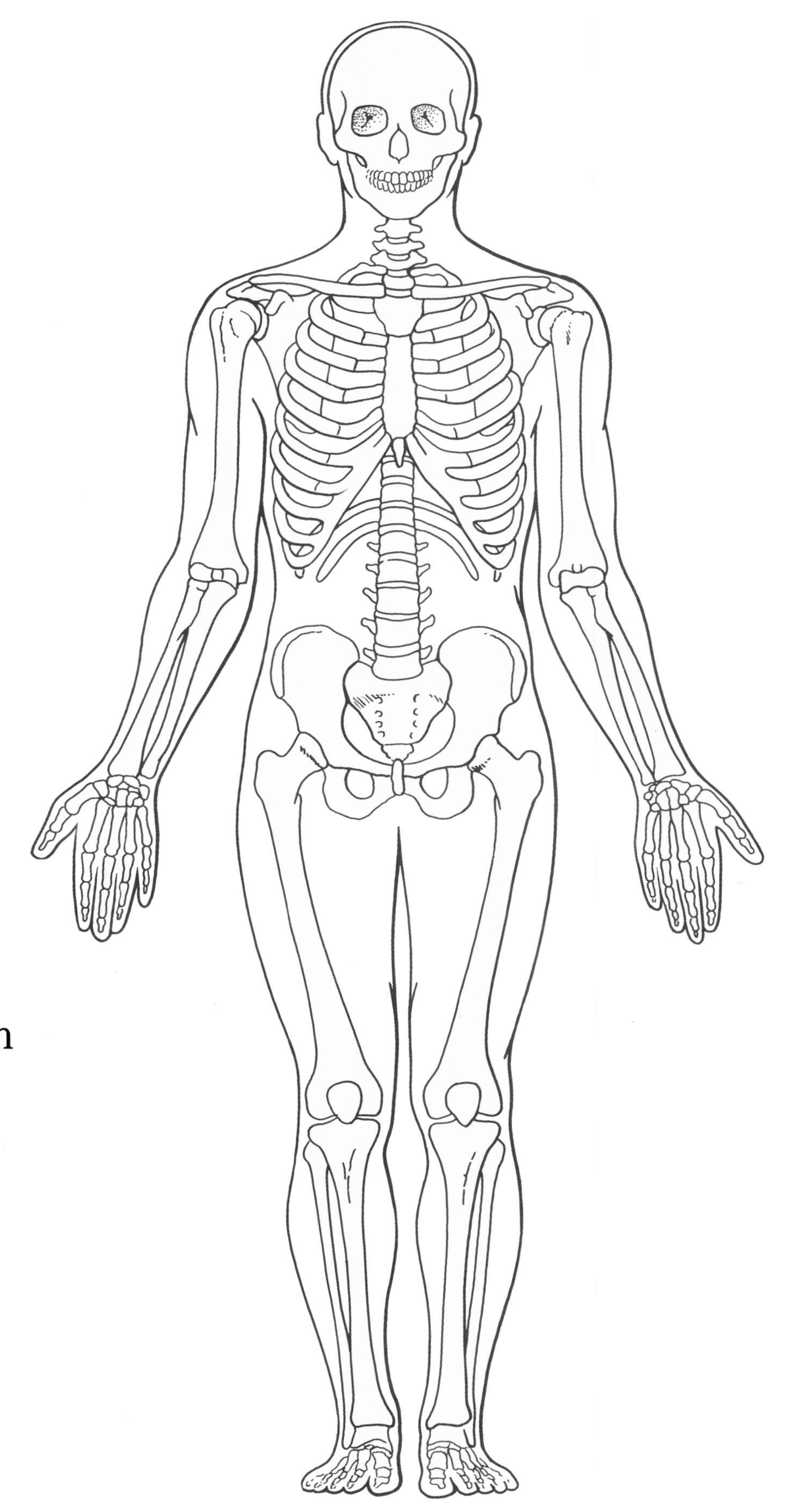

Chapter 1

CELLS–THE BASIC UNITS OF LIFE

The human body is made up of many different parts, including muscles, bones, skin, nerves, and blood vessels. These separate parts can be grouped into twelve systems, each of which performs a specific task that benefits the body as a whole. For example, the circulatory system, made up of the heart and blood vessels, delivers nutrients and vital oxygen to all areas, while another system, the immune system, protects against invading microorganisms such as viruses and bacteria.

Each of these systems is composed of structures called organs. The lungs are the main organ of the respiratory system, while the digestive system includes several organs: the stomach, intestines, liver, and pancreas. Such organs, in turn, are made up of two or more **tissues**, which are layers of material that fit together to form larger structures. The skin, for example, is composed of several layers of different kinds of tissues.

An even closer look reveals that tissues, organs, and systems—the entire body, in fact—is made up of very small individual units called **cells**. A cell is too small to see without a microscope, but not by much. If magnified about twenty times, which is within the range of even the simplest microscope, human cells can easily be observed.

Cells are the basic building blocks of the human body. They are the smallest units to exhibit the characteristics of life, such as growing, dividing to create new cells, and repairing themselves. Indeed, human cells can, under special conditions, be removed from the body and grown in the laboratory. The number of cells in a fully grown human being is an incredibly large figure—about one thousand trillion in all. Let's now consider in detail the structure of the individual cell.

OPPOSITE PAGE: Structure of DNA Space-filling model of the chemical structure of deoxyribonucleic acid. Each sphere represents one atom. Notice how the sugar-phosphate backbone (lighter-colored spheres) forms an outer double helix, while the attached bases (darker spheres) are tucked inside the center of the chain where they pair with one another.

CELL ANATOMY

A typical human cell is roughly spherical in shape. It has an outer covering called the **plasma membrane**, which holds the cell together and separates it from the surrounding environment. Inside the

CELL STRUCTURE

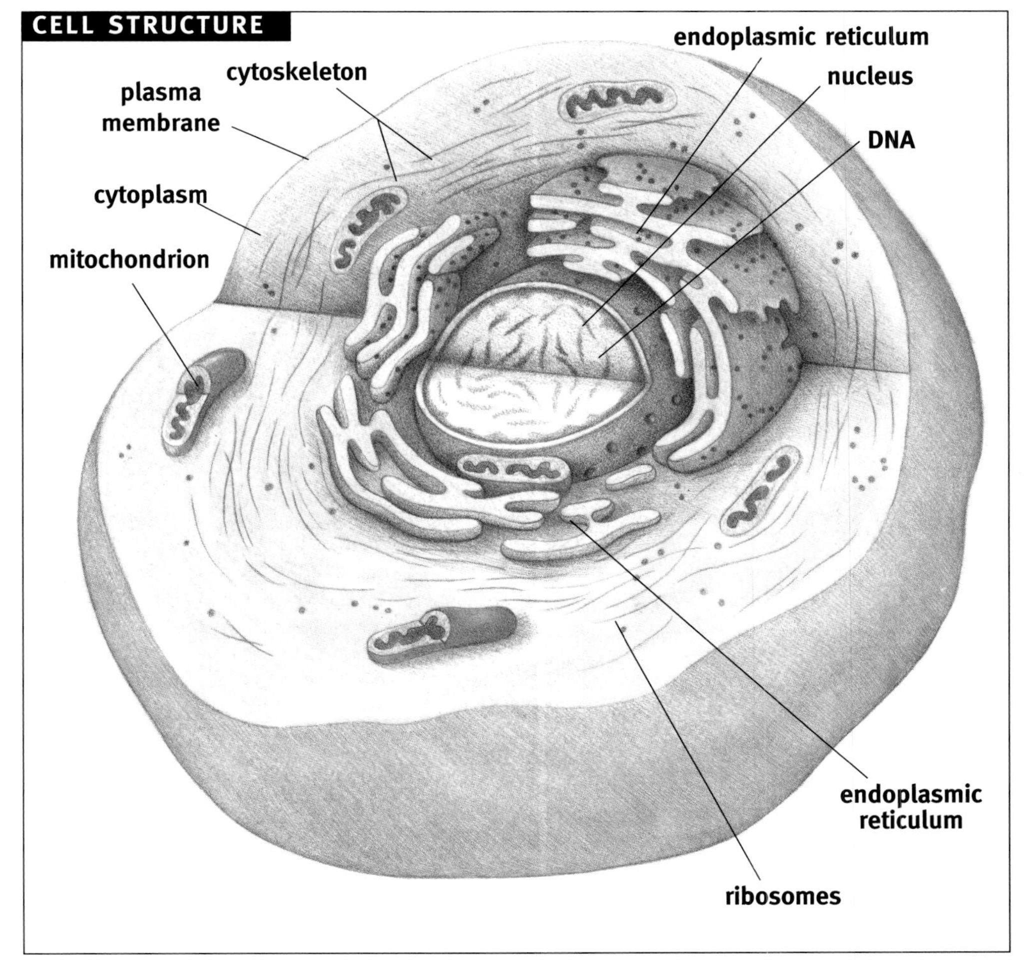

plasma membrane is the **cytoplasm**, a thick fluid made up of water and small molecules that the cell needs for survival. Floating in the cytoplasm are a host of structures known as **organelles**. These include **mitochondria**, oblong bodies that act as tiny powerhouses, producing energy for cellular reactions. There are also thousands of small dense structures called **ribosomes**, which are responsible for making proteins, a special class of molecules that carry out a number of different functions.

The largest structure within the cytoplasm is the **nucleus**, which is the headquarters of the cell. The nucleus contains large amounts of **deoxyribonucleic acid** (DNA), extremely long molecules that direct all cellular activities. Another prominent feature within the cell is a series of tubes and chambers called the **endoplasmic reticulum**—the cell's highway system—through which molecules travel to various locations within the cell. Overall structure is maintained by the **cytoskeleton**, a crisscrossing network of thin fibers that help the cell maintain its shape.

To understand how these organelles work within the cell, it is important to first know something about their composition and structure. Let's now briefly examine the finest detail within the cell, the actual chemicals that make up the organelles described above, to see how these separate components interact to carry out the fascinating process of life.

A. bases in DNA

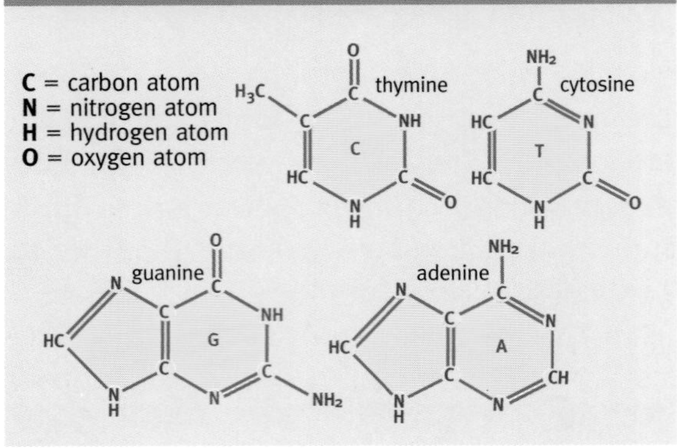

C = carbon atom
N = nitrogen atom
H = hydrogen atom
O = oxygen atom

B. base linkage

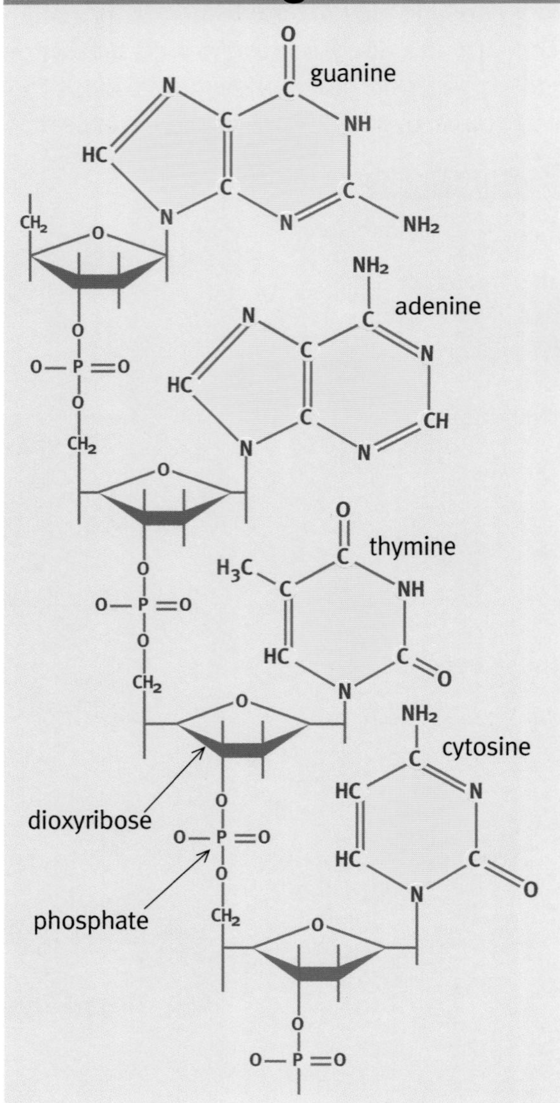

THE CHEMISTRY OF LIFE

All matter, both living and nonliving, is made up of atoms, tiny particles too small to observe with even the most powerful microscopes. There are about one hundred different known atoms, also called elements, but only a handful of these make up the bulk of a living cell. In fact, just six elements, carbon, hydrogen, nitrogen, oxygen, phosphorus, and sulfur, make up more than 99 percent of a cell's weight.

Atoms can be linked together to form larger structures called molecules. For example, two hydrogen atoms linked to one oxygen atom form a very common molecule: water. The chemical formula for water is written as H_2O, where O stands for an oxygen atom, and H for hydrogen, with the figure 2 showing that there are two hydrogens linked to one oxygen. Water is the most common small molecule within the

BASE PAIRING

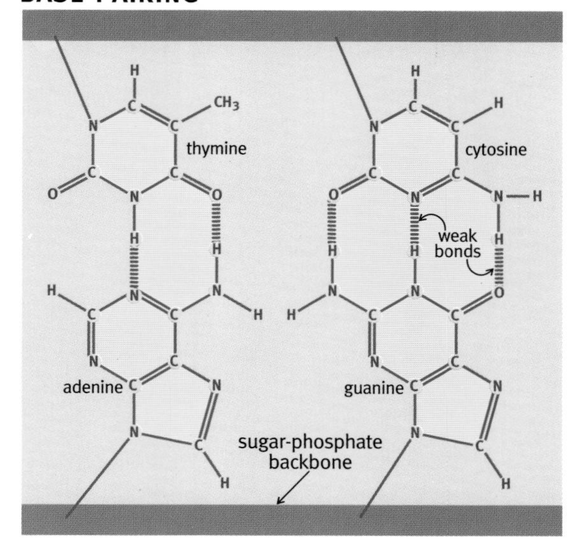

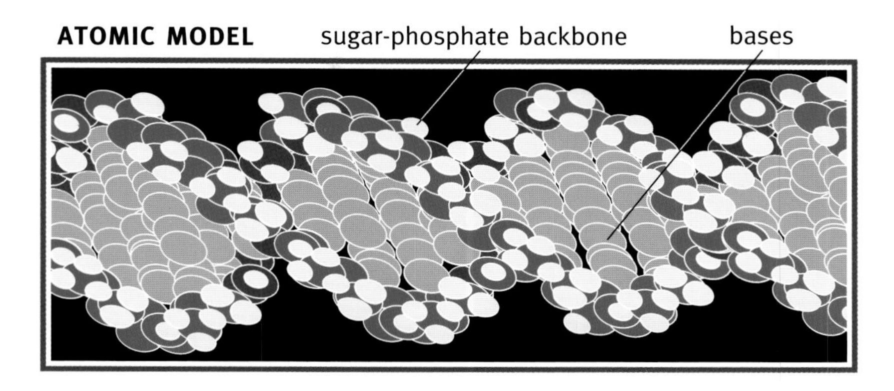

cell, accounting for about 70 percent of the cell's total weight.

What is interesting and special about cells is their ability to join hundreds, thousands, and even millions of atoms together to form very large molecules called macromolecules. There are four types of macromolecules within living cells: DNA, proteins, carbohydrates, and fatty acids.

DNA DNA (deoxyribonucleic acid) is made up of four molecules called bases: **adenine, guanine, cytosine,** and **thymine**. In the chemical structure of these bases, C stands for a carbon atom, N for nitrogen, H for hydrogen, and O for oxygen. The lines drawn between atoms represent chemical bonds holding the atoms together. DNA is formed when these bases are linked into a chain, with two other molecules, **phosphate** and **deoxyribose**, forming the backbone.

A typical DNA molecule contains millions of bases linked together in a row, forming a thin, extremely long molecule. If you stretched the DNA in one cell from end to end, it would be about three feet (almost a meter) long. Of course, cells are not this long, which means the DNA must be coiled up and condensed within the cell. An individual DNA molecule is too thin to see with a regular microscope, but it can be photographed with a special type of instrument called an electron microscope, which has the power to magnify samples about one million times. This reveals DNA fibers as thin, extremely long threadlike structures that are usually looped and coiled within the nucleus.

The actual DNA molecule contains two strings of bases wound around each other to form a double helix. The bases are arranged on the inside of the helix, facing each other, and form weak chemical bonds in a specific way: A (adenine) always pairs with T (thymine), and G (guanine) always pairs with C (cytosine). Thus, if the sequence of the bases on one strand is known, the sequence of the matching strand can be figured out, too.

The position of bases along the DNA strand is very important—the As, Gs, Cs, and Ts are not strung together randomly. This is because DNA is an informational molecule: the order of the bases along the helix contains information that controls every feature of the cell. Thus DNA serves as a blueprint, spelling out messages the cell uses to survive and perform its duty in the body. This information is called the genetic code, because the sequence of bases codes for other kinds of cellular macromolecules—proteins.

PROTEINS The second class of large molecules within cells, proteins are also long

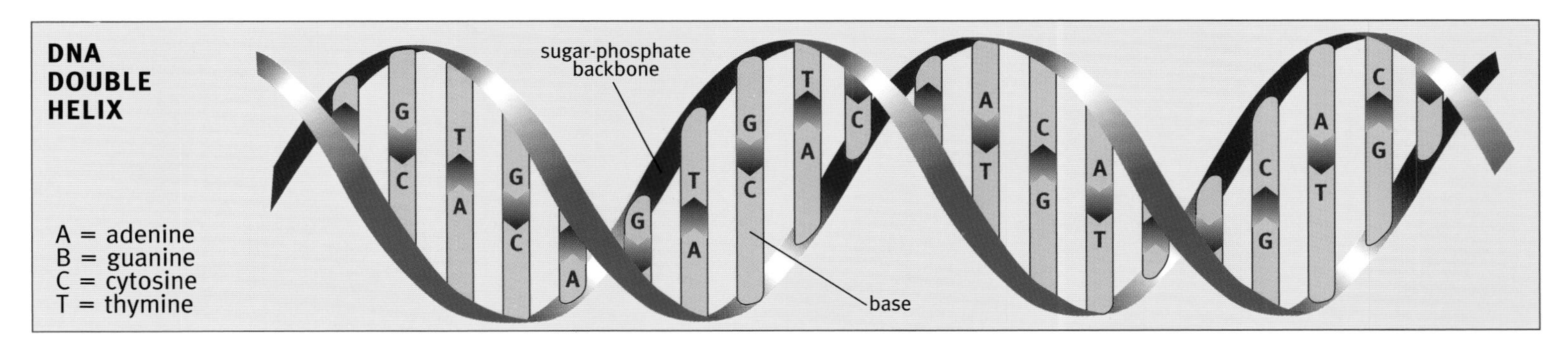

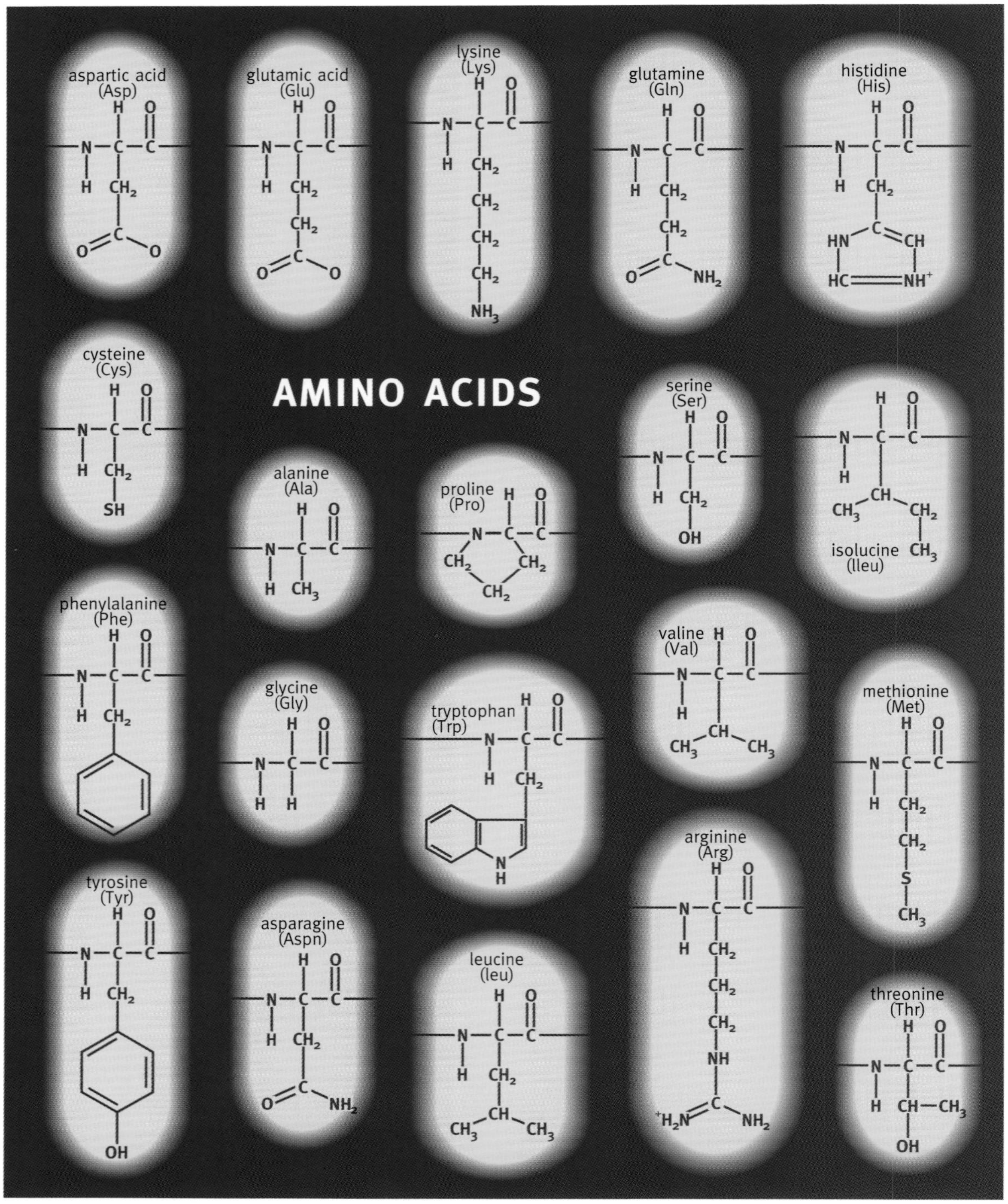

AMINO ACIDS

aspartic acid (Asp)
glutamic acid (Glu)
lysine (Lys)
glutamine (Gln)
histidine (His)
cysteine (Cys)
serine (Ser)
isolucine (Ileu)
alanine (Ala)
proline (Pro)
phenylalanine (Phe)
valine (Val)
glycine (Gly)
tryptophan (Trp)
methionine (Met)
arginine (Arg)
tyrosine (Tyr)
asparagine (Aspn)
leucine (leu)
threonine (Thr)

strings of individual units hooked together. Instead of bases, though, the building blocks of proteins are **amino acids**. And while DNA has just four different bases, there are twenty different amino acids, which means proteins display a large degree of variety.

The fact that protein and DNA are both long strings of connected units is not simply a coincidence. Indeed, these two types of macromolecules are related in a special way: the sequence of DNA determines the sequence of proteins. This is because the order of bases in DNA, the genetic code, specifies the order of amino acids hooked together to form a protein. A section of DNA that codes for one protein is called a **gene.**

When a protein is to be made, a segment of DNA unwinds, allowing a special molecule called **polymerase** to read the strand and make a copy of the gene. This copy is made of **ribonucleic acid** (RNA), which is related to DNA but has a slightly different structure. The RNA message, which contains the same order of bases as the gene, leaves the nucleus and travels into the cytoplasm, where it attaches to ribosomes.

Ribosomes then scan along the RNA fiber, decoding the information in the bases three at a time and linking amino acids together. For example, the bases A, T, and G in sequence signal the ribosome to hook the amino acid methionine onto the growing protein chain, while three Gs in a row code for a different amino acid, glycine.

THE GENETIC CODE

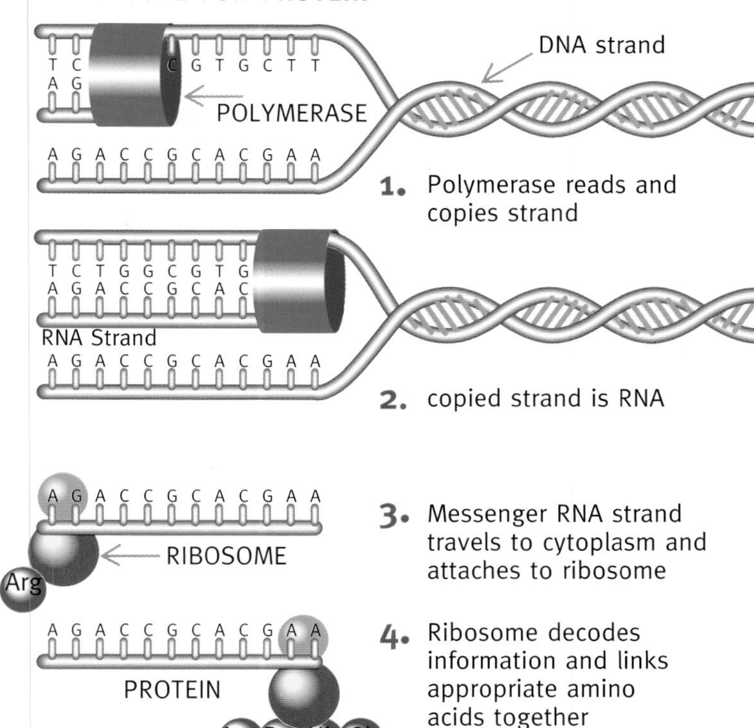

Some amino acids have more than one triplet code: serine, for example, is specified by six different combinations. Following this code, then, the sequence AGA, CCG, CAC, GAA would code for arginine, proline, histidine, and glutamic acid. Notice there are also stop signals that occur at the end of genes to alert the ribosomes that the new protein is finished.A typical gene is about 1,500 bases long, coding for an average protein of about 500 amino acids in length. It is estimated that there are approximately 100,000 genes in human DNA.

The role of DNA, then, is to code for proteins, and it is proteins that determine

LIFE-STYLE AND CANCER RISK

Scientific research has demonstrated a link between the incidence of cancer and certain features of life-style such as diet, exercise, and stress level.

Studies suggest that foods with high fiber content and little or no fat tend to decrease the risk of developing some types of cancer. The reason for this may be that many of the cancer-inducing chemicals or carcinogens we come into contact with enter our systems in the foods we eat. The human body is equipped with numerous mechanisms to detoxify incoming food and eliminate harmful chemicals, but there are limits. In this regard, fibrous foods are beneficial because they provide roughage that helps move food along through the digestive track, so that carcinogens have less opportunity to penetrate. Substances that are difficult to digest, including fatty foods, tend to remain in the digestive system a long time, slowing down the entire process so that harmful substances are retained inside the body.

Regular exercise is another factor that decreases the likelihood of developing cancer. Physical activity stimulates the digestive system and helps move waste products containing carcinogens out of the body. In addition, exercise activates organ systems and tones muscles, making the entire body stronger and more resistant to diseases of all kinds.

There is also an apparent connection between stress and the frequency of cancer. Mental and emotional stress produce many biochemical changes inside our bodies and upset the delicate balance required for health. The immune system—those cells and tissues that protect us from diseases, including cancer—is particularly sensitive to stress-induced chemical imbalances. A life-style that produces high levels of stress and irritation can reduce the immune response that normally destroys cancerous cells, increasing the risk of contracting this disease.

For these reasons, medical professionals recommend diets rich in natural fiber and low in fat. Foods in this category include vegetables, legumes, grains, and fruits. Doctors also advise that following a steady program of exercise, along with activities that help us to unwind and release stress, are important in maintaining good health. The strong connection between life-style and physical health is obvious to most of us, and is now supported by scientific evidence as well.

all of the characteristics of the cell. Once made, new proteins fold up into specific shapes and carry out specialized tasks. The protein hemoglobin, for example, which is the major protein in red blood cells, folds into a structure that captures oxygen for transport throughout the body. Another protein, crystallin, forms into a transparent sheet that makes up the lens of the eye. Many proteins are **enzymes,** a special type of molecule that carries out chemical reactions within the cell. The polymerase that copies a DNA segment to create an RNA message is an example of an enzyme.

Some proteins are present in many different kinds of cells. Polymerase, for example, is found in every cell type in the body, which makes sense because all cells must produce RNA to make proteins. But many other proteins are more restricted. The protein hemoglobin is found only in maturing red blood cells, while crystallin is confined to cells that form the lens of the eye. This is not because certain cells contain only certain genes. Every cell in the body has exactly the same DNA and the same set of genes, except for a few special cases.

The reason for the differences in the proteins that are present in a cell is that in a specific cell type, only some of the genes are active. This means that in eye lens cells, the crystallin gene is turned on, while the hemoglobin gene is turned off. The situation is reversed in maturing red blood cells, where the hemoglobin gene is going full speed while the crystallin gene is motionless. Every cell type has a set of genes that is expressed, while the rest are shut down. The cell has many ways to regulate the expression of its genes, and carefully selects and controls which proteins are made.

CARBOHYDRATES The third type of large molecules, carbohydrates are made of sub-

WHAT CAUSES CANCER?

Scientists have known for many years that cancer occurs when groups of the body's own cells grow rapidly out of control, crowding out normal cells until the new growth interferes with some important body function. Today research is uncovering the puzzle behind this chain of events.

Specific genes have been identified that are involved in cancer—genes that make the proteins that control cell growth. In mature cells, growth-promoting genes are mostly inactive, since most cells in the adult body grow very slowly or not at all. But if for some reason these genes are accidentally reactivated, they signal the cell to grow and divide again and again, producing a mass of cells called a tumor. In the most dangerous cancers, some cells break off from the tumor and travel through the bloodstream to other parts of the body where they invade and create more tumors (a process known as metastasis). Eventually the tumor cells crowd out vital tissues and organs, which causes death.

There are many different causes of cancer. For example, we know that exposure to cigarette smoke, ultraviolet rays from the sun, asbestos (a substance used for insulation), and many industrial chemicals leads to this disease. The common link in all these causative factors is that they can make changes in the order of bases in DNA. Any change in the sequence of DNA is called a mutation. When the bases in DNA mutate, the protein product can also be altered, or the amount of protein that is made can change. If a mutation occurs in a growth-promoting gene, too much of the protein product might be made, or the protein might be altered so that it reactivates cells to grow and divide. This can lead to the formation of a tumor and the onset of cancer.

Currently, cancer is treated with drugs that are somewhat more toxic to cancerous cells than to normal cells, with radiation that is targeted to kill tumorous growths, or with surgery to cut out tumors when possible. Such treatments are effective in some types of cancer but have serious side effects, and are not effective in other types.

As scientists learn more about cancer and the genes involved, it should be possible to design new approaches to curing this disease. For example, if a cancer is produced because a gene that should be inactive suddenly switches back on, it may be possible to design a way to shut that gene off again, and halt the tumorous growth. Thus the study of genes and how they work may one day lead to a cure for cancer.

STRUCTURE OF GLYCOGEN

links between sugars

glucose units

units called **sugars**. The most common sugar used in cells is **glucose**, a ringed structure of six carbons, six oxygens, and twelve hydrogen atoms. Glucose units are hooked into long branching chains to form a macromolecule known as **glycogen**. Sugars serve as a source of chemical energy. Cells break down these molecules, thereby releasing energy for chemical reactions. When there are extra glucose molecules that are not needed immediately, enzymes link them together into glycogen chains that are then stored for future use.

Shorter chains of sugars are hooked onto certain proteins in the cell. Thus sugars also serve a structural role, forming parts of other macromolecules. Proteins with attached sugars are known as glycoproteins, and are usually part of cell membranes. Sugars can also be attached to lipids, which are members of the final group of macromolecules, the fatty acids.

Fatty Acids The fourth kind of macromolecules within the cell are the fatty acids. These are long chains of carbon atoms with hydrogens attached. Some fatty acids are linked to a glycerol molecule to form triglycerides, which serve as an important source of energy for the body. When energy is required and other food sources are unavailable, triglycerides can be broken down to release energy used by the cell to carry out its functions.

Fatty acids can also have a phosphate group attached to form phospholipids, which are the main part of plasma membranes, the outer covering of the cell. In addition, fatty acids are the building blocks of several other important compounds found within cells.

Together then, macromolecules form the key structures within cells. DNA is the cell's blueprint, providing information in the form of genes. These genes direct the creation of proteins, which carry out all cellular functions. Some proteins are structural, such as crystallin, which forms the eye lens, while others are transporters, such as hemoglobin, which carries oxygen. Still others are enzymes, directing thousands of different chemical reactions within the living cell. The two other types of macromolecules, carbohydrates and fatty acids, provide energy resources and also form structural components of cell membranes and other organelles.

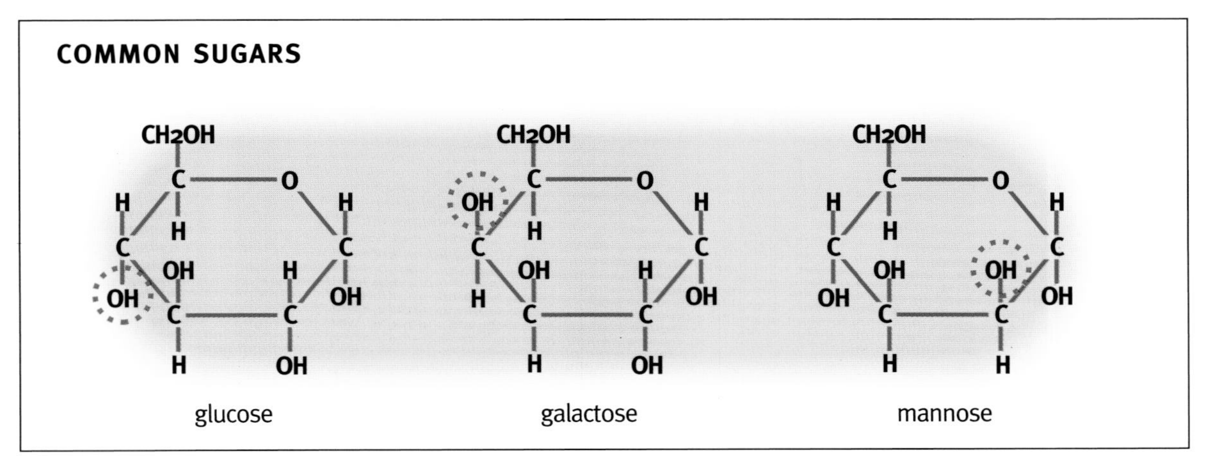

CELL DIVISION

Cells reproduce themselves through a process called **mitosis**. Every human being starts out as a single cell—a fertilized egg—that divides into two cells, which grow and then split into four, then eight, sixteen, and so on to eventually form the mature human body containing trillions of cells. Mitosis is also important once we are fully grown, because certain tissues, such as skin, must be constantly renewed and also replaced after a scrape or cut.

Since every new cell must receive a complete set of instructions on how to operate, the first order of business is to copy the DNA. This event, known as DNA replication, is performed by a polymerase enzyme. First, the double-stranded DNA molecule unwinds, and then polymerases read along both fibers, building new strands with complementary bases. The end result is two identical copies of all the genes in the cell. DNA replication is incredibly accurate: polymerases make a mistake only about once every one billion bases. Even when mistakes in DNA replication do occur, they are usually detected and repaired by another type of enzyme that constantly scans the double helix for abnormalities. This system is not perfect, however; permanent changes in DNA sequences, known as **mutations**, can accumulate over time and alter the function of important genes. This can lead, in some cases, to diseases such as cancer (see sidebar on page 14).

Once the genes are all replicated, the cell is ready to divide. In the first step of mitosis, the DNA is coiled up tightly into dense bodies called **chromosomes**. The cell now contains two complete sets of chromosomes, which will be equally distributed to the two new cells. The second step occurs when the chromosomes line up in the middle of the cell, and strings called microtubules attach to each one. Then one copy of each pair of identical chromosomes is pulled to opposite sides of the cell. When this is finished, a furrow pinches the cell in half to produce two new cells, each with a full set of genes and ready to carry out its assigned task in the body.

COMMON FATTY ACIDS

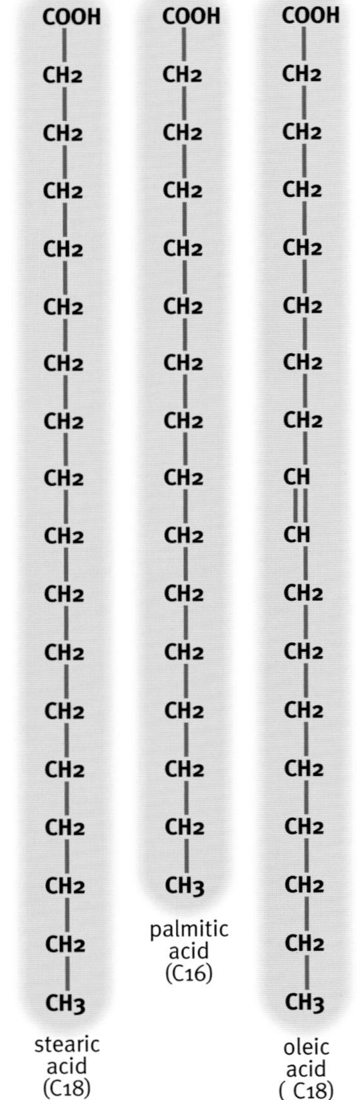

phospholipid

triglyceride

glycerol

CELL DIFFERENTIATION

So far we have considered the basic features common to all types of cells. But the body contains a large variety of different kinds of cells—blood cells, skin cells, bone cells—all very specialized in appearance and function. What makes these cell types, which all came from one original fertilized egg, so different from each other?

We have already seen that a particular cell type expresses only some of its genes,

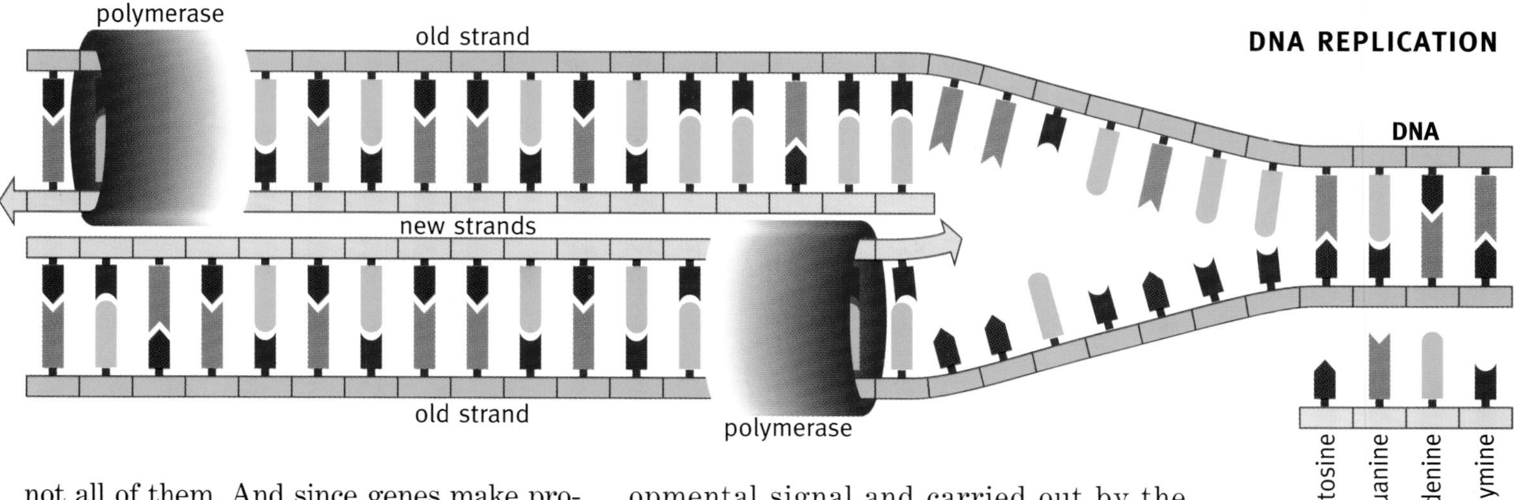

not all of them. And since genes make proteins, and proteins determine all cellular features, it follows that cell types are different from one another because they express different groups of genes.

There are many factors that signal a group of cells to activate certain genes and develop into a specific cell type. These signals are most important at the beginning of human development, when the fertilized egg divides and forms a rapidly dividing group of cells called an embryo. Some signals come from the environment inside the mother's uterus. There is also cell-to-cell communication, which influences genes to turn on or off. Also, the position of a cell within the growing embryo has an effect on which genes are active.

Once a set of genes is activated, a cell follows a program that leads to a specific cell type. For example, if a cell in the embryo receives a signal to become a blood cell, it then begins developing into a blood cell and gradually loses the capacity to become anything else. This programming then, started by a developmental signal and carried out by the expression of certain genes, is responsible for creating the many different cell types that make up the human body.

With this basic understanding of cells we are now ready to examine the major systems of the body. As we do, it is important to keep in mind that at the root of these larger, complex structures lies the standard unit of the human body, the individual cell.

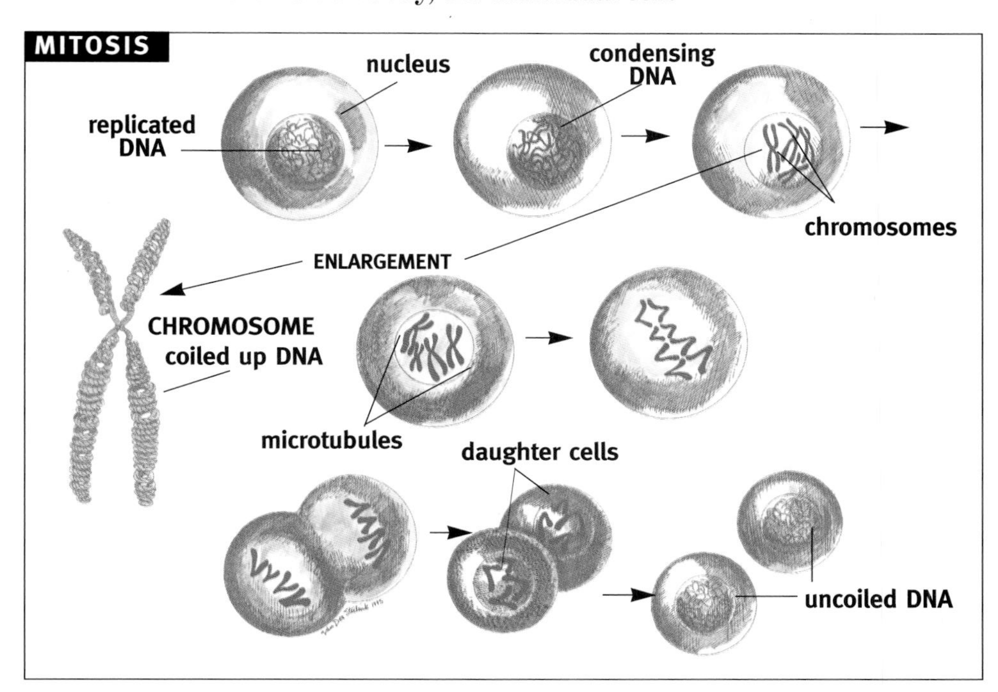

GENE THERAPY

Today scientists have a very powerful system to study genes called recombinant DNA technology. They have been able to isolate individual human genes and figure out their exact base sequence. This has revealed that some diseases are the result of mutations in DNA. An illness known as muscular dystrophy, which causes loss of muscle control and deterioration of muscle tissue, is caused by a defective gene. Cystic fibrosis, which causes fluid buildup in the lungs, among other problems, is also the result of a mutation in a single gene. Another disease, sickle-cell anemia, is the result of a base change in the hemoglobin gene, which then makes a defective protein that bends the red blood cells out of shape so they get stuck in small blood vessels.

One way to cure such diseases, in theory, is to put a correct copy of the defective gene into the body of the person suffering from the disease. If this new gene finds its way into the cell's DNA and works correctly, it will make a protein that functions properly and the problem should be fixed. Scientists have designed ways to introduce new genes into cells, and have in fact begun a few actual experiments to see if it works. If this strategy is successful, it will offer a cure for many diseases that have until now resisted treatment.

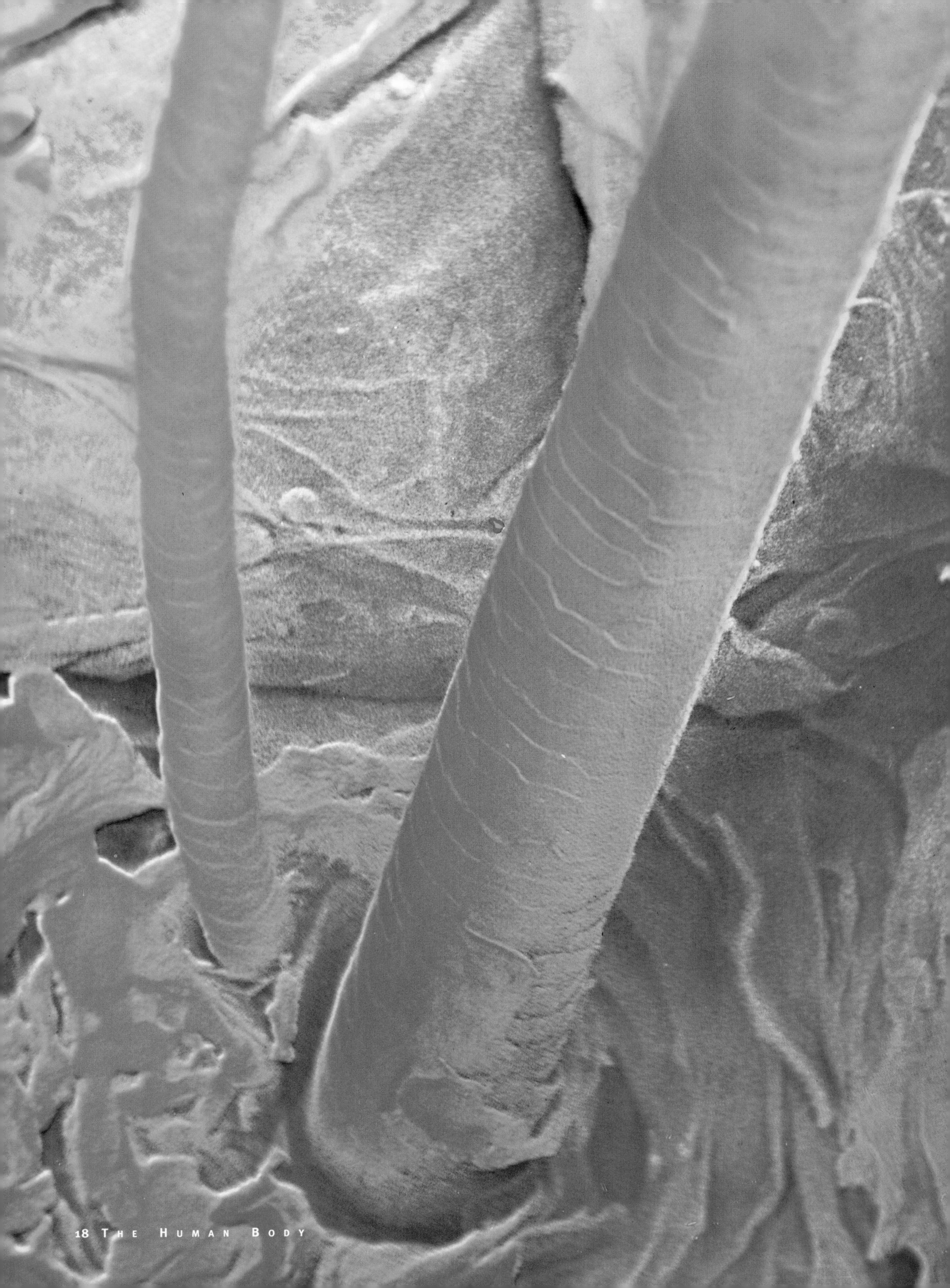

Chapter 2

THE INTEGUMENTARY SYSTEM

The outer covering of the human body, the skin, is a vital organ that performs several important functions. Skin is one of the body's largest organs, covering about 3,000 square inches (19,500 sq cm) in the average adult. The skin is composed of three layers. The outermost sheet of cells is called the **epidermis**. Underneath this layer is the **dermis**, which is thicker and composed of several kinds of cells and tissues. Between the dermis and underlying bones, organs, and muscles is the **subcutaneous** layer. These tissues coordinate to form the important system known as the integument.

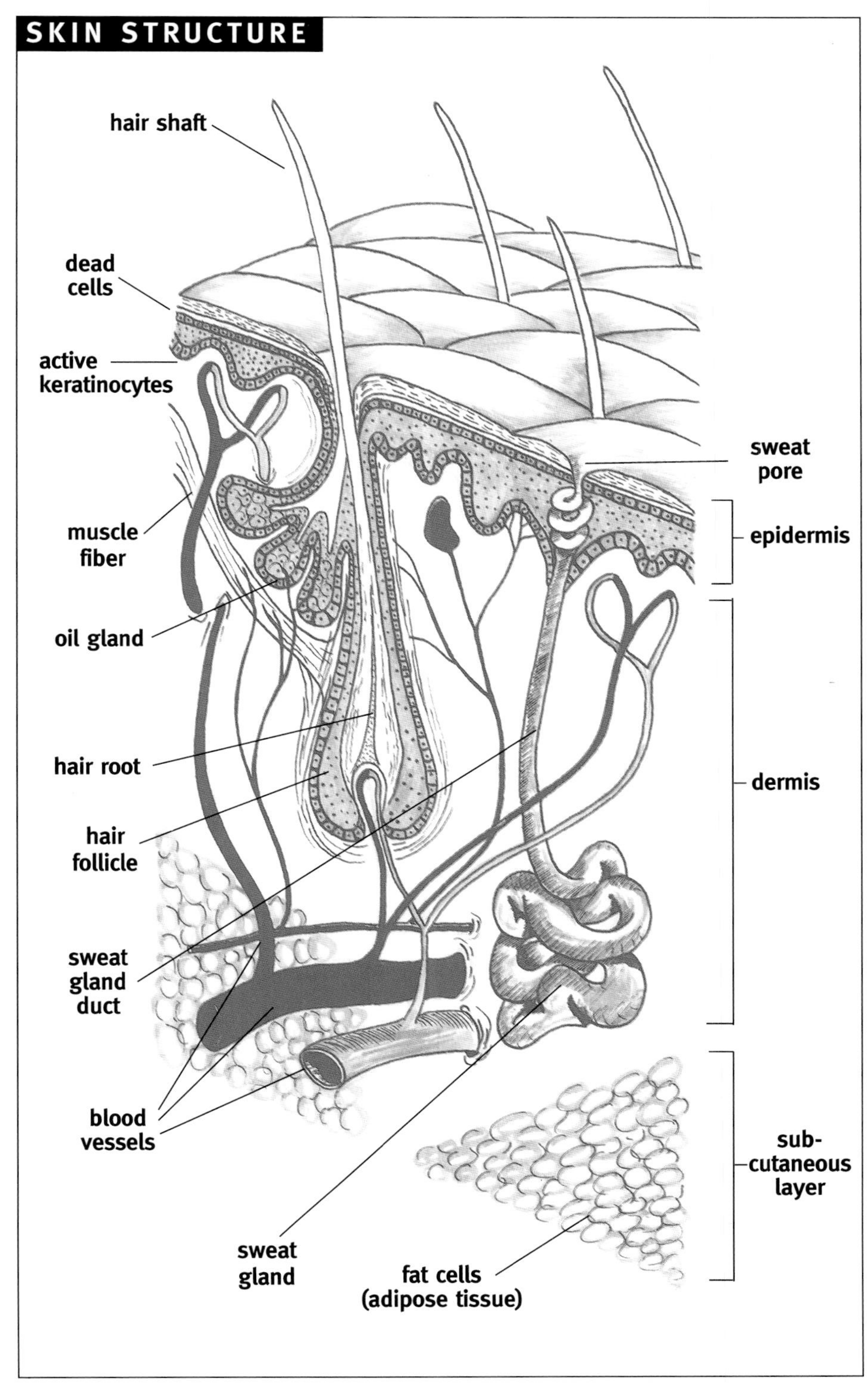

SKIN STRUCTURE

EPIDERMIS The outermost layer of skin is made up of several kinds of **epithelial cells**, which are cells that form on the skin's surface. The main cells in this layer are the **keratinocytes**, so named because they produce **keratin**, a protein that assembles into strong fibers. The bottom layer of the epidermis contains active keratinocytes that constantly grow and divide, pushing new cells toward the surface. As cells move up, they undergo a hardening process and transform into a tough sheet that is strengthened by a large number of connected keratin fibers. These cells eventually die, but remain at the top of the epidermis, where they form a barrier against the outside world.

This constant regeneration of the skin's outer surface is necessary because the dead layer of cells is worn off in our day-to-day activities. Whenever you bathe, wash your face, brush against a tree or the ground, or even just scratch an itch, some

PAGE 18: Hair shafts Electron micrograph showing two strands of hair emerging from follicles in the skin. The cuticle, a layer of thin overlapping cells, is visible on the outer surface of the strands. Body hairs like these help protect the skin from damage.

MELANOCYTE

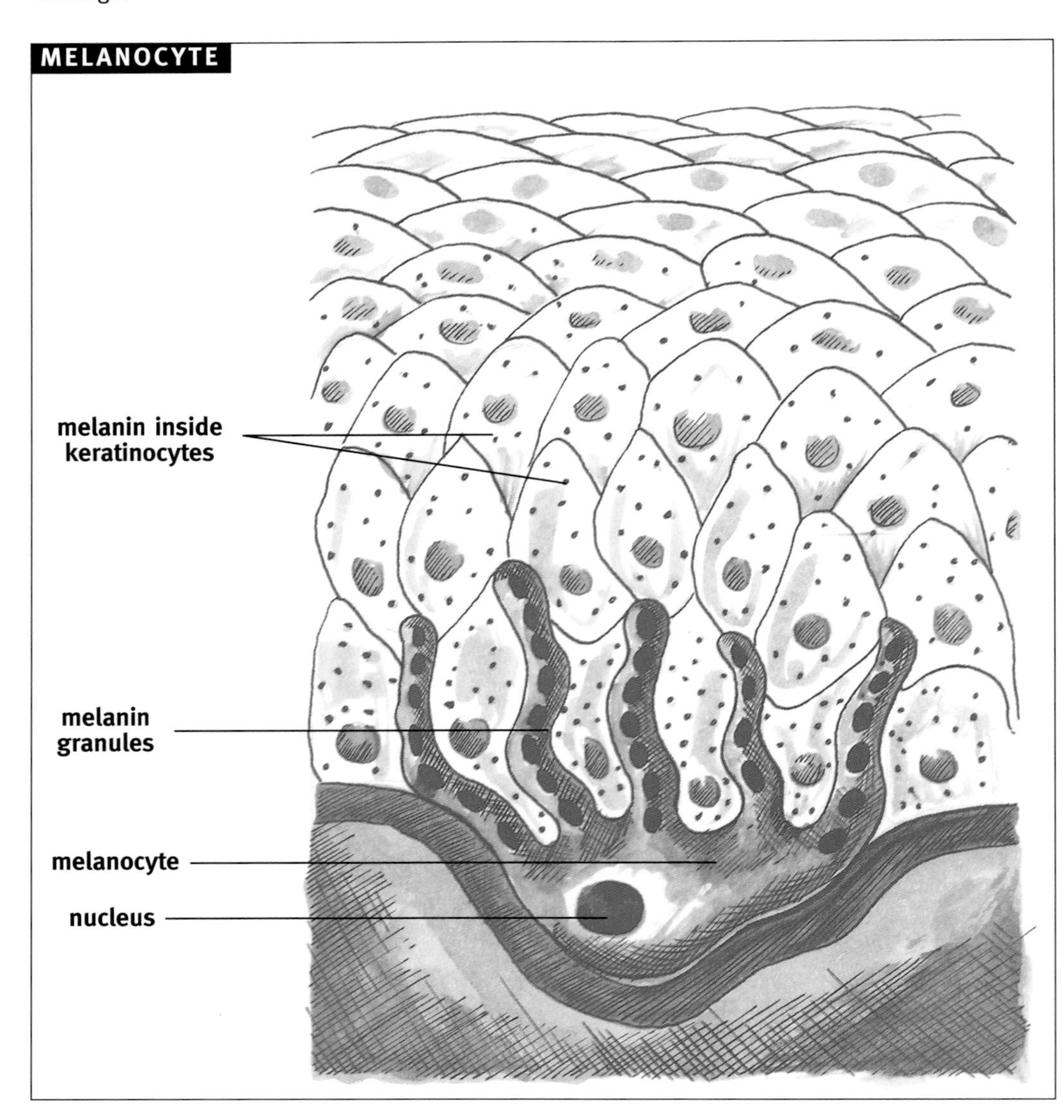

of this keratin layer is rubbed off. Without new cells to replace the old, our skin would be worn and ragged in just a matter of days. But the constant renewal process keeps the skin healthy and whole. In fact, the active keratinocytes divide at a constant pace, completely replacing the epidermis about every two weeks.

Another type of cell found in the epidermis is the **melanocyte.** These are spaced among the keratinocytes and have long fingerlike projections that contact surrounding cells. Melanocytes make a protein called **melanin**, which they pass on to nearby cells. Because melanin has a dark color, it gives the skin a brownish tone at the spot where it is deposited. In some people melanin tends to be laid down in patches rather than evenly over the entire skin. This spotted pattern is what we call freckles.

There are differences in skin color among the different races because the amount of melanin in the epidermis varies. For example,

WHAT CAUSES A SUNTAN?

Whenever you spend time outdoors, you learn firsthand that exposure to sunlight causes the skin to gradually darken. This process, called tanning, is the result of the pigment melanin building up in the skin. Tanning is carried out by cells within the epidermis called melanocytes.

Sunlight contains a type of energy known as ultraviolet (uv) radiation. When melanocytes are exposed to uv light, an enzyme called tyrosinase is activated to produce melanin. This enzyme makes large amounts of melanin that build up in the cytoplasm. Once the melanin is made, it collects into granules and is transported into the long projections of the cell that reach into surrounding tissue. One melanocyte makes contact with about ten other cells.

The next step is the release of melanin granules that are then taken up by nearby skin cells. As the epidermal layer takes up more and more melanin it becomes darker. An increase in melanin helps protect the skin from further exposure to the sun because this protein filters out uv light. In some people, melanin granules are laid down in patches, forming freckles. If sunlight is avoided for several weeks your tan will gradually fade and disappear. This is because the melanin granules slowly break down and dissolve.

A sunburn is not the same thing as a suntan. If skin cells are exposed to a heavy dose of uv radiation they will be killed—actually burned up. The painful red skin that is caused by a sunburn is the result of damaged cells breaking apart and irritating nerve endings in the skin. Sunburn is harmful and can lead to the development of long-term diseases, including skin cancer. Even a small amount of sun exposure causes permanent damage to the skin, so it is very important to wear sunscreen of SPF 15 or higher whenever you are exposed to sunlight, and to avoid long-term exposure altogether.

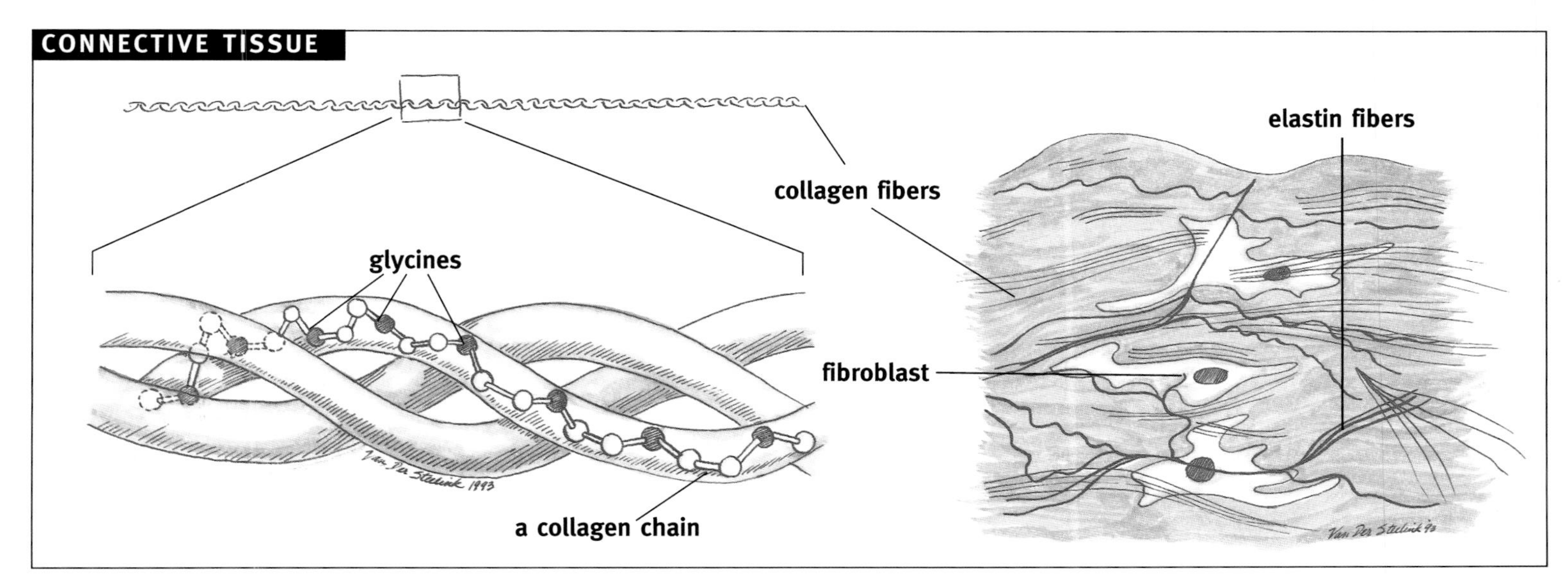

very dark-skinned people have a large amount of melanin; medium-skinned people have a medium amount; and light-skinned people have only a little. The pinkish tone in the skin of fair-complexioned people is due to blood vessels that carry red blood cells lying just under the skin. These vessels give off a faint reflection. The pink color apparent in pale skin is hidden by the higher melanin content in darker skin. Oriental people have a yellowish tone in their skin because it contains small amounts of another pigment, **carotene**.

A few people are born with no color in their skin at all. This is caused by a condition that blocks the production of melanin. Such people are called albinos, and have very white skin, white hair, and pink eyes, which are caused by a lack of pigmentation in the iris. Albinism occurs in all races, and also in animals. People with this condition are very sensitive to sunlight, and must be careful not to get overexposed. Albinism is very rare, occuring in about 1 of every 35,000 people.

On the tips of the fingers, the epidermis is pulled into curved ridges that form fingerprints. The pattern of these ridges is different in every person, which means your fingerprints are different from those of any other human being. These ridges help the fingers grip things: the grooves allow the skin to cling to surfaces better. The bottoms of the toes also have epidermal ridges that serve a similar function.

When the epidermis in a certain spot is constantly rubbed or pressed, it will respond by building an extra-thick layer of dead cells. Patches of this added protec-

MOLES

A mole, or *nevus*, is a small, elevated mass of dark-colored tissue on the skin's surface. About fifteen moles are present on the average human body, found primarily on the head, neck, and trunk, although they can occur anywhere on the body.

Moles consist of melanocytes that have grouped together and, for reasons not yet known, proliferated into a mass of cells that protrudes about the surrounding skin. Their dark appearance results from synthesis and storage of melanin granules within individual cells.

For the most part, moles are benign and do not pose a health concern. Doctors recommend surgical removal of moles that lie on areas that experience friction, such as the palms of the hands and soles of the feet. Moles are also removed for cosmetic purposes.

In very rare cases—about one in one million is the estimate—a mole can become cancerous. This is important because although the incidence of this phenomenon is extremely low, the type of disease that develops, melano-carcinoma, is one of the most rapidly progressing and fatal cancers known. When detected early, though, this type of cancer can be treated effectively. Moles that are becoming malignant usually signal this occurrence by a rapid increase in size, changes in shape or color, or spontaneous bleeding. Health professionals recommend periodic examination of all the moles on your body, and immediate reporting of any changes or abnormalities to a physician.

tive layer are called calluses, and are commonly found on the palms, fingers, and feet, where constant friction signals a buildup of keratin-rich cells.

Dermis The main cell type in the dermis is the **fibroblast.** These cells make an important structural protein called **collagen,** a chain of amino acids that forms a stiff, straight line. Collagen is an example of a secreted protein—it is made inside the cell and then pushed out through the plasma membrane into the surrounding space. Once outside the cell, collagen molecules wrap together into long ropes to form a sturdy layer of **connective tissue**, which is the foundation of the dermis.

Fibroblasts also make a protein called **elastin**, which forms elastic fibers in the dermis that allow the skin to stretch and bend. You can imagine how difficult it would be to move around if your skin was stiff and did not give and slide over your muscles and bones.

On the soles of the feet and palms of the hands, the dermis is extra thick. This provides a cushion on these surfaces, which is useful because a lot of pressure is put on these areas when we walk or pick up heavy objects.

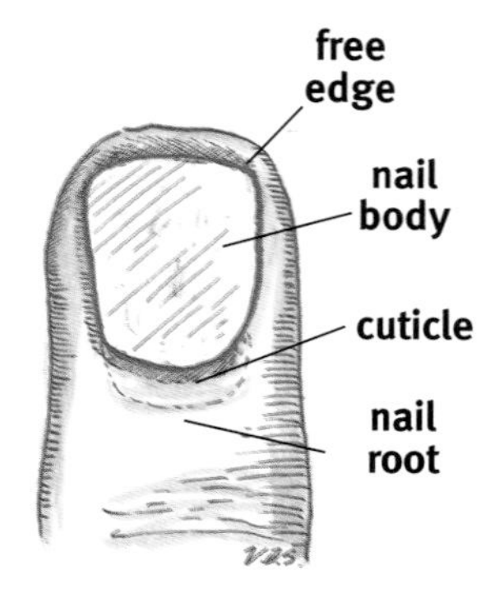

Subcutaneous Layer This layer of loose tissue, which lies under the dermis, is composed of connective tissue and another material called **adipose tissue**. Adipose, or fat, cells contain fatty acids, molecules that can be used for energy. Sandwiched between the dermis and underlying bone or muscle, the subcutaneous layer is soft and spongy. This helps cushion the skin and prevent damage from hard contact. The subcutaneous layer has a rich blood supply, as does the dermis. The epidermis does not contain any blood vessels, because most of the cells in this hardened outer covering are dead and thus do not require oxygen or nutrients.

SPECIAL STRUCTURES

The skin has some other interesting features—hair, nails, and oil and sweat glands.

Hair Within the dermis are many **hair follicles**, which are pouches of specialized cells that produce hair. Each hair is a collection of dead cells that are hardened into a thin shaft and pushed upward out of the follicle. Contrary to what you may have heard, cutting your hair does not make it grow faster: hair is produced at a steady rate whether it is long or short.

Hair follicles actually lie at an angle within the skin. If you look at the hairs on your arm, you can see that they do not come straight out, but are slanted. As a result, they lie down to form a thin mat that helps protect the skin. Each follicle has a small muscle attached to it. When your skin is cold, this muscle responds by contracting (tightening up), which pulls the follicle into an upright position under

NAIL STRUCTURE

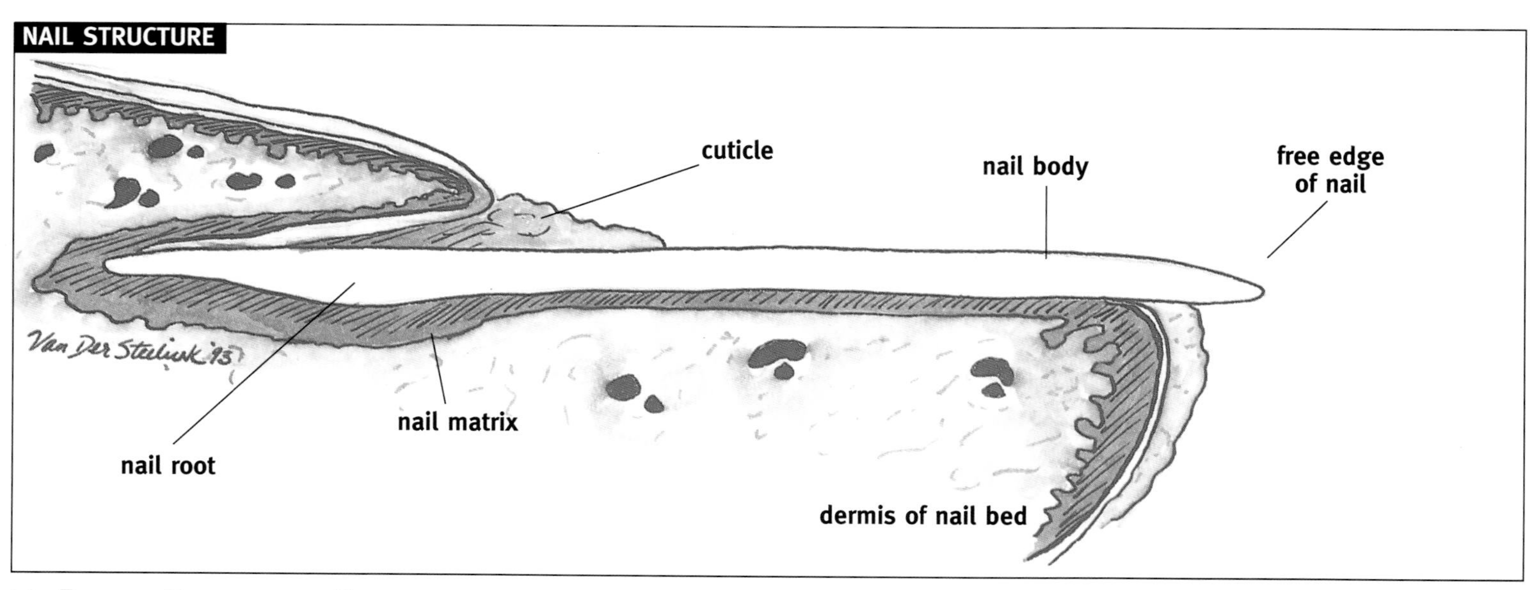

the skin, causing "goose bumps." In animals that have thick hair or fur, this response forms an air space between the skin and hair that insulates the body, but in humans the body hair is too thin to provide much warmth.

While the hair covering most of the body is too thin and short to be of much use, on the scalp it is thick enough to give some protection, especially from sunlight. The eyebrows help keep dirt and water out of the sensitive eyes, and tiny hairs in the nose and ears help prevent dirt and germs from getting inside the body.

Oil Glands Inside the hair follicles are small pockets of cells that produce **sebum**, an oily mixture of fats and proteins. This oil is produced within the cells, secreted into the follicle and pushed upward and out onto the hair and skin. Sebum spreads over the skin and keeps it moist and soft. Without this oily coat the skin would dry out, crack, and peel. Another benefit of sebum is that it seals the skin and prevents too much water from escaping the body. In addition, this oily substance contains chemicals that help prevent infection by inhibiting the growth of microbes (microorganisms).

Oil glands are found over most of the body, and are numerous and large on the face, neck, back, and chest. The palms of the hands

WOUND HEALING

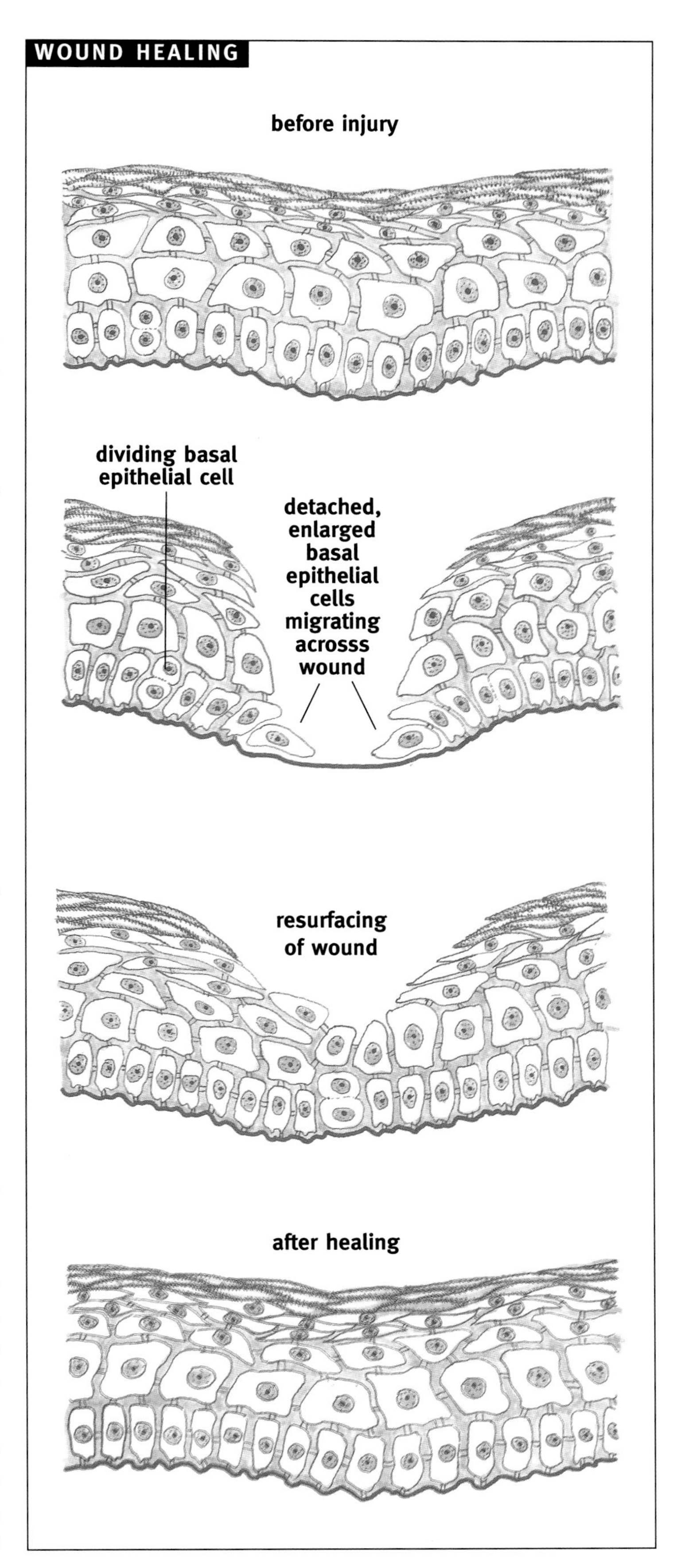

WOUND HEALING

The skin has a remarkable capacity to repair itself. When the skin is damaged, epithelial cells at the ends of the wound begin dividing rapidly. The new cells move into the damaged area and cover the opening. The cells then pile up and restore the skin to its proper thickness, forming a smooth surface that usually is exactly like the original skin.

Very large or deep cuts that extend through the skin are more difficult to heal. The deeper tissues do not have the ability to regenerate as well as the surface of the skin. The body rebuilds such deep wounds by sending fibroblasts into the area to cover the opening and repair the damage. But this usually leaves rough uneven tissue that forms a scar instead of smooth skin. Fortunately, scars often fade with the passage of time.

do not have any oil glands, which is why they often are drier and flakier than other regions of the body, and why many people use hand lotion to soften the skin in this area.

Sweat Glands A different type of gland found in the skin produces a watery substance called perspiration, or sweat. These sweat glands do not connect to follicles, but open directly onto the surface of the skin. They are found all over the body, and are very numerous in the palms, where there are about 3,000 of them per square inch (about 500 per sq cm). This is why a person's palms palms sometimes get very moist.

Perspiration is mostly water, but it also contains salt, lactic acid, urea, and several other chemicals. Because some of these substances are waste products that the body must eliminate, they collect in the sweat glands, and are expelled through the skin along with water. Thus, sweating is one way of expelling waste products.

The main function of sweat glands, however, is to keep the body from overheating. When you go outside on a hot day or exercise heavily, your internal organs and muscles begin to heat up. If they get too hot damage can occur, particularly to the brain. The sweat glands respond to this situation by pushing drops of sweat out onto the skin. Indeed, when you are extremely hot, your entire body becomes soaked in a layer of moisture.

Once perspiration is on the skin, contact with the outside air causes the water to evaporate. In this process water molecules change from a liquid state into a gaseous one. As the water molecules change states, escaping into the air, they absorb energy, which means they pull heat away from the body, cooling it down. Evaporation is sped up by the movement of air, which is why a breeze against your moist skin feels so cool.

Nails Fingernails and toenails are tough coverings made of keratinocytes that have become extremely hard. Live cells just under the back of the nail in an area called the nail matrix grow, divide, and push new nail material outward. The fingernails grow at a rate of about four-hundredths of an inch (0.1 cm) per week, while the toenails grow a little more slowly.

ACNE

With the onset of puberty, the level of hormones in the body elevates drastically. The increase in one of these hormones, androgen, stimulates sebaceous (oil) glands to enlarge and produce more sebum, and the fatty substances in this fluid provide a rich environment for bacterial growth. As microbes invade a sebaceous gland and multiply, swelling and inflammation set in. This reaction can block the pore completely and prevent secretion from the gland, resulting in the formation of pimples. The condition of multiple, large pimples is called acne. Severe acne can produce serious infections and leave permanent scarring. The skin of the face, neck, and trunk are most commonly affected, but pimples can occur anywhere on the body's surface.

Washing the skin regularly helps prevent acne by stripping away materials that block the pores, and by killing bacteria that inhabit sebaceous glands. Topical medicines are also effective at destroying bacteria that cause acne. Regular exercise is also beneficial to the skin because it increases blood flow to skin cells, providing them with nutrients and oxygen for maximum efficiency. Increased circulation also generally stimulates secretion, helping the sebaceous glands eliminate excess fluid.

Diet is another important factor. Foods with high fat content tend to promote acne, since fatty substances are in part eliminated through the skin. Fat-rich and greasy foods thus add to the load that sebaceous glands must process and secrete. Junk foods and sugary sodas, which contain high levels of chemicals the body must eliminate, can also overburden the skin's capacity to extrude waste materials.

For some people, genetic factors play a major role in acne and exercise, a healthy diet, and good hygiene are not enough. To combat the most severe cases of acne, doctors prescribe antibiotics or chemicals that alter the concentration of circulating hormones. As the body matures through puberty and hormones in the blood level out, the activity of sebaceous glands declines and, for most people, pimples arise infrequently thereafter.

WRINKLES

The skin is a loose, elastic sheet that slides and adjusts as our muscles and bones move beneath it. If you look closely at the skin on your arm, you will see a pattern of wrinkles crisscrossing the skin; these tiny folds are what allows the skin to stretch and bend as we move.

As the integumentary system ages, it loses much of the fatty tissue in lower layers. The elastic quality of the outer skin also deteriorates with time, due to the breakdown of elastin, a protein component of skin tissue. Both of these factors cause wrinkles to deepen and appear more prominent, resulting in the characteristic appearance we associate with old age.

The compound tretinoin, also known by the brand name Retin-A, is currently used to prevent and diminish wrinkles. This drug induces outer layers of the skin to slough off more rapidly, uncovering newer layers that are more pliable and less wrinkled. Retin-A was originally used to treat acne, and has only recently been found to be effective on wrinkles. It has no effect on very deep wrinkles, however, which can be eliminated only through plastic surgery.

Nails give added protection to the ends of fingers and toes. These areas are especially sensitive and at risk of being damaged because we use our hands and feet almost constantly. In addition, fingernails help us pick up and work with small objects that are otherwise difficult to handle.

FUNCTIONS OF THE SKIN

Some of the functions of the skin have already been mentioned. Because it wraps the entire body in a tough, stretchy covering, the skin is the main physical barrier that protects the body from the outside world. It prevents microbes, chemicals, water, and even ultraviolet radiation from getting into the softer tissues within.

Special features of the skin such as hair and nails also serve to protect the body from damage. Oil glands lubricate and soften the skin, keeping it smooth and preventing cracks and flaking. Chemicals within the oily coat stop the growth of microbes, and there are also special cells within the skin that fight infection.

The skin also prevents too much water from being lost by the body. This is important because the chemistry of our internal organs requires a large amount of water. Sometimes, though, the skin actually secretes water in the form of sweat. This is the main way that our body temperature is kept from getting too high. Besides cooling off the body, sweat also carries waste products out through the skin.

Another important activity of skin is the synthesis of vitamin D, a chemical that regulates the deposition of calcium in the bones. Vitamin D can also be absorbed from various foods, but in the absence of dietary sources, the skin plays a role in producing this important molecule. Through a series of reactions, skin cells convert cholesterol into **cholecalciferol**, which is then processed into the active form of vitamin D in the liver and kidney. Most of the intermediate steps in this pathway are catalyzed by enzymes, but one step is actually carried out in the skin by ultraviolet radiation, a component of sunlight. Vitamin D deficiency causes a disease in children known as rickets (from the Old English word *wrickken*, meaning "to twist"), in which the bones are not fully calcified and remain soft and flexible. This affliction was common in England long ago, when diets routinely lacked essential nutrients such as vitamin D, and gloomy weather blocked out sunlight for much of the year.

Because the skin is an important system of the body, it is important to take care of it. This includes bathing regularly to clean off dirt and microbes, keeping nails trimmed and smooth, and eating healthy foods to provide good nutrition. It is also important to avoid exposure to extreme cold and heat, and excessive sunlight, all of which can damage the skin and lead to serious medical problems.

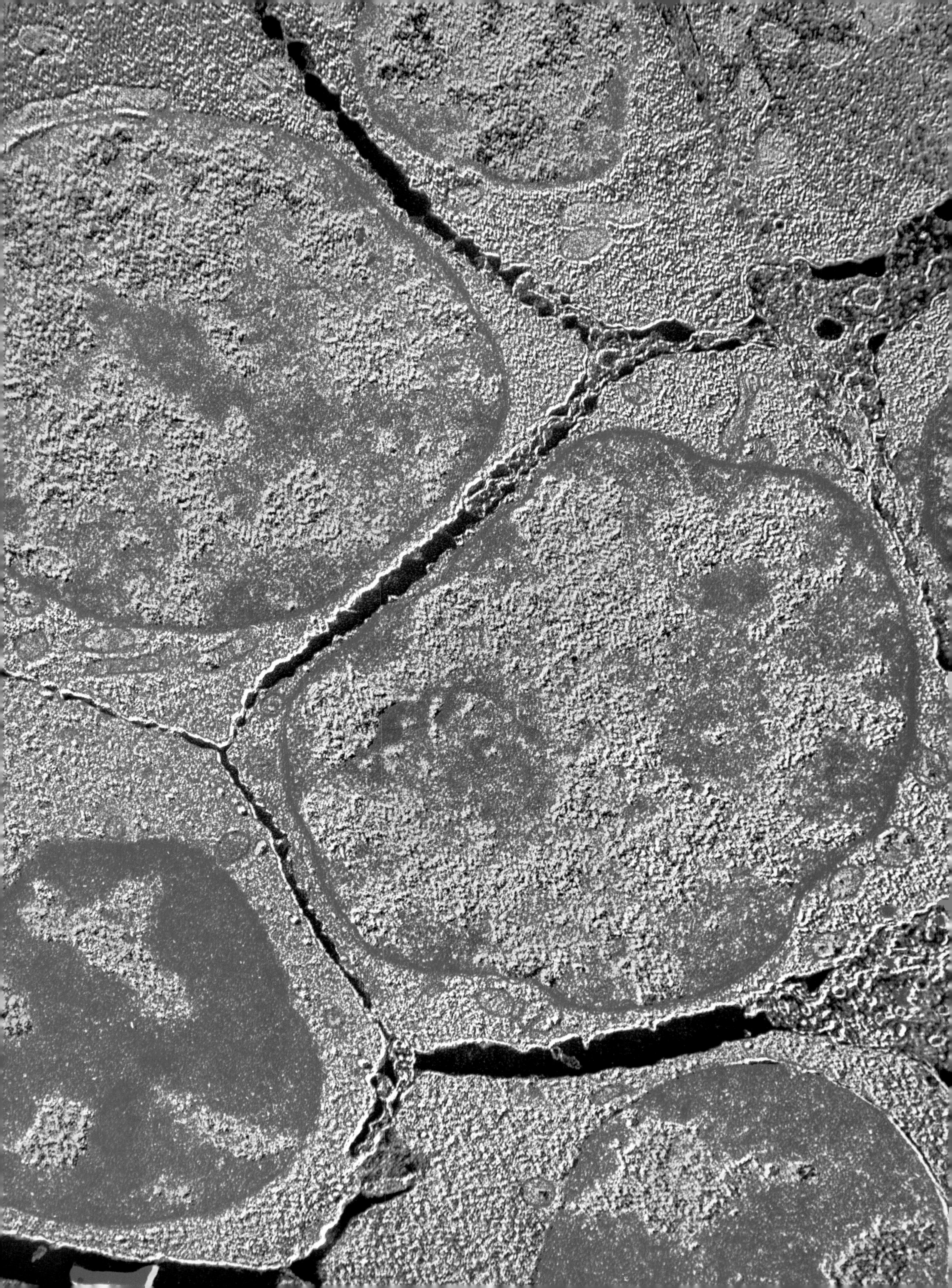

Chapter 3

THE SKELETAL SYSTEM

The human skeleton is made up of 206 separate bones that come in many different sizes and shapes. Together the bones form a framework that supports the rest of the body and protects fragile internal organs. Let's begin with an examination of bone tissue—the cells and other materials that make up the solid part of bones. Then we will survey how the bones are classified and named, and consider how everything fits together. Finally we will take up the various functions of the skeletal network.

BONE TISSUE

Many people are surprised to learn that bones contain living cells. While it is true that bones are made up mostly of hardened, nonliving matter, there are also many cells that live in tiny pockets within the hard matrix of the bone. Also, some bones in the body are hollow in the middle. These inner cavities are filled with **bone marrow**, a mixture of cells that form new blood cells. Let's now examine the three types of cells commonly found in bone tissue: **osteoblasts**, **osteocytes**, and **osteoclasts**.

OSTEOBLASTS The bone-forming cells of the body are called osteoblasts. This cell type makes the protein collagen, which is also a structural component of connective tissue in the skin. Along with collagen, osteoblasts make another protein known as osteonectin. As osteoblasts make these proteins and secrete them, a material called osteoid builds up. Calcium, a mineral, then combines with these proteins and the mixture hardens into bone matrix.

OSTEOCYTES As the matrix is laid down, some of the osteoblasts are surrounded and end up embedded in a hard casing of newly formed bone. These cells no longer produce much collagen or other secreted proteins, and they take up residence within the bone itself. Known now as osteocytes, they form a network of living tissue that operates within the hard bones.

Even though osteocytes are encased in solid bone, they are not completely isolated from one another. Tiny canals known as canaliculi run between neighboring cells, allowing the osteocytes to contact each other. It is not clear what signals pass between the osteocytes, but there is some evidence that they control the activity of the other types of bone cells.

OPPOSITE PAGE: Stem cells Electron micrograph of cells in the bone marrow that divide and produce new cells that will become erythrocytes (red blood cells). The large dark structures inside these cells are the nuclei, and the surrounding pink material is the cytoplasm.

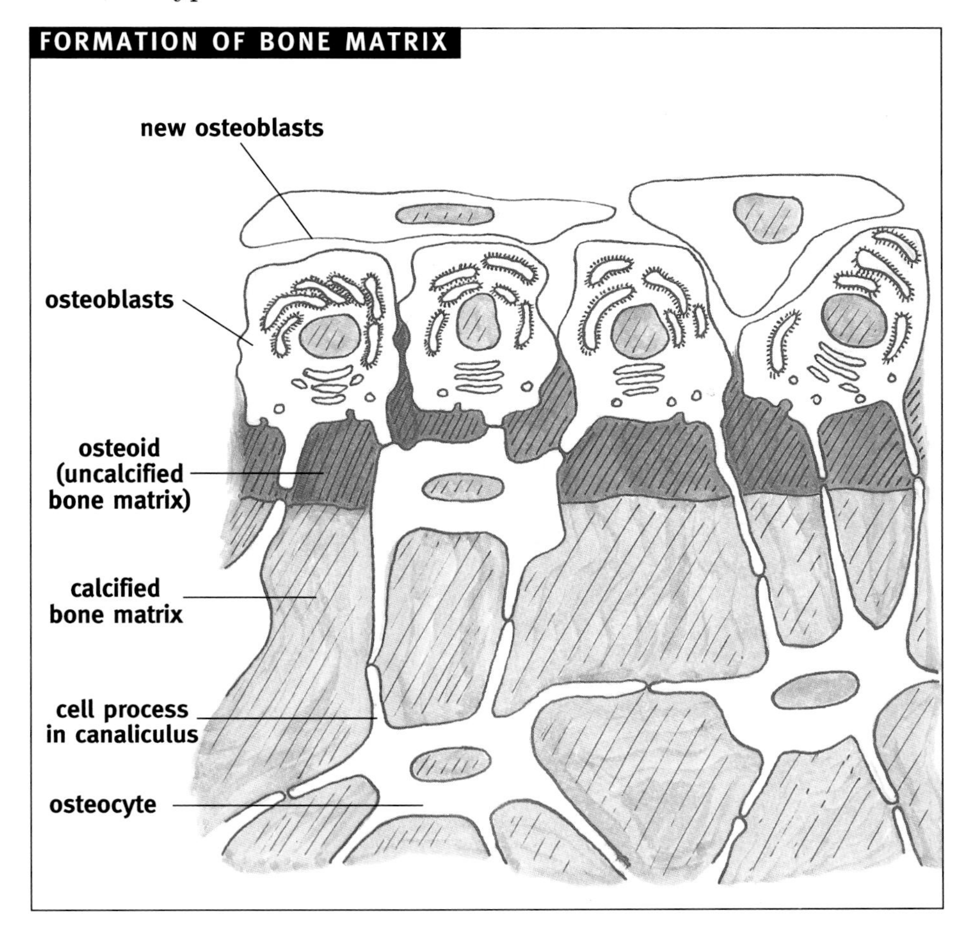

Osteoclasts The third cell type of the skeletal system does exactly the opposite of what the osteoblasts do. Osteoclasts actually dissolve bony material. They dig their way into bone, carving out tunnels by dissolving the proteins within the solidified matrix. Why this happens is the topic we will address next.

BONE REMODELING

It might be a little unsettling to learn that your bones, the sturdy framework of your body, are constantly being torn down and rebuilt. But this is exactly what happens. Every year about seven percent of the bony material in your body is broken down and replaced with new matrix. It begins with osteoclasts digging channels through old bone. As a channel deepens, blood vessels grow into the new opening, supplying nutrients and oxygen to cells in the area. Over time the new opening is gradually filled in by osteoblasts that lay down new bone matrix.

Exactly why this remodeling process goes on is not yet known. It may be the skeleton's way of adapting to the tremendous stress and pressure it must withstand. When the osteocytes in a particular region die, that section is immediately dissolved and rebuilt, complete with new living cells. Thus, osteocytes may act as guards that initiate the remodeling process when damage occurs.

Remodeling is responsible for repairing bones after they are fractured. Osteoclasts become very active at the edges between broken bones and eventually tunnel out and replace the whole area. This mends the break and restores the original firm structure.

Several factors control bone growth, development, and remodeling. Some hormones—chemical signals that influence the activity of cells—have strong effects on bone tissue. The levels of calcium and that of vitamin D are also important factors.

SKELETAL STRUCTURE

Now we are ready to examine the skeleton and the individual bones within it. Bones come in four shapes. Long bones are column-shaped bones, long and narrow; the arm and leg bones are good examples. Short bones are cube-shaped; wrists and ankles are the two places where short bones are found. Flat bones are broad and flat; the ribs are a good example of this bone type. The large bones of the skull also fit in this category. Irregular bones are those with complex shapes that don't fit

THE FUNNY BONE

Almost everyone has experienced the strange sensation of banging their elbow against a hard object and feeling a sharp tingle run down the arm and fingers. It doesn't even take hard contact to cause this reaction—sometimes just a light bump in exactly the right spot sets it off. The sensation is not quite painful, but it is rather uncomfortable and not like anything else you usually feel in your body.

When this happens people say that you have "hit your funny bone." Although this is the common name used to describe this phenomenon and will probably not be changed, it is wrong in both ways. First, when you bang your elbow and experience flashes of heat and numbness shooting through your arm, it is not very funny. Second, there is not a part of the skeleton called the "funny" bone, including the elbow.

In fact, it is not the bony elbow that reacts when you bang it against something. Bone tissue contains few or no pain sensors that could produce this kind of tingling sensation. But there is a large nerve bundle called the ulnar nerve that lies along the back of the arm. This nerve runs through a notch where the two arm bones join to form the elbow. You can easily feel this notch and the large nerve itself when your arm is straight. Because of this positioning, the sensitive ulnar nerve is exposed and easily pinched when the elbow is bumped.

Pressure on the ulnar nerve causes it to temporarily short-circuit, sending vibrations down the arm that your body senses as tingling or burning. Fortunately, the effect doesn't last long. Within about thirty seconds the nerve regains normal control and the "funny bone" episode is over.

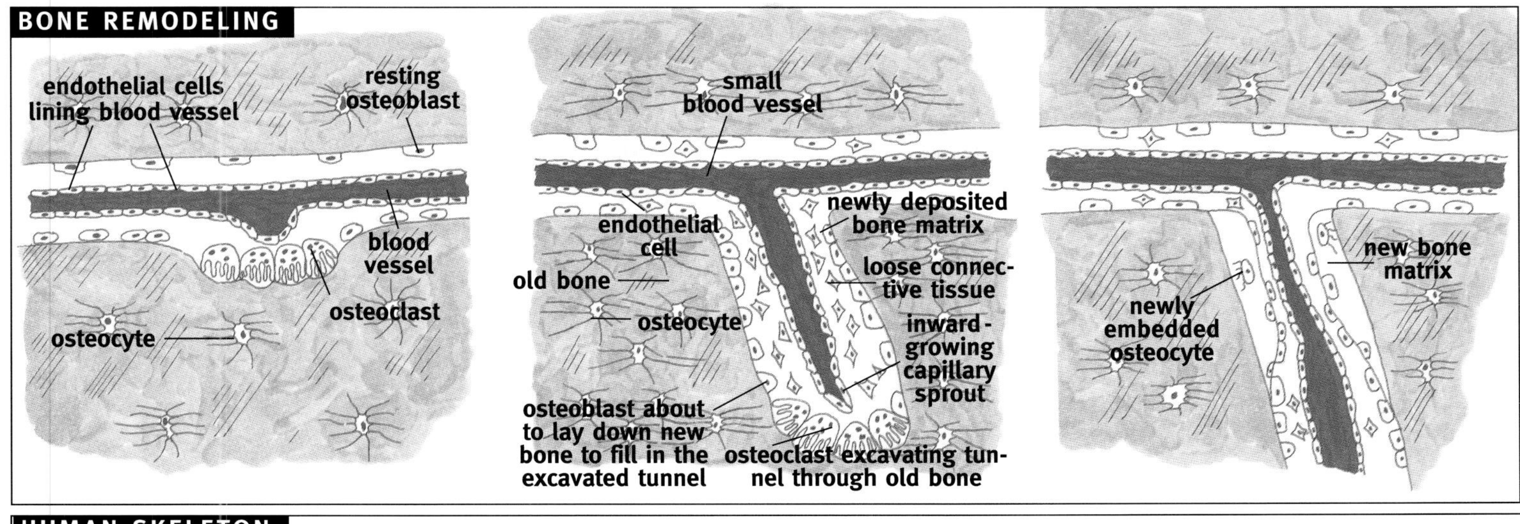
BONE REMODELING
endothelial cells
lining blood vessel
resting
osteoblast
blood
vessel
osteoclast
osteocyte
small
blood vessel
endothelial
cell
old bone
osteocyte
newly deposited
bone matrix
loose connec-
tive tissue
inward-
growing
capillary
sprout
osteoblast about
to lay down new
bone to fill in the
excavated tunnel
osteoclast excavating tunnel through old bone
new bone
matrix
newly
embedded
osteocyte

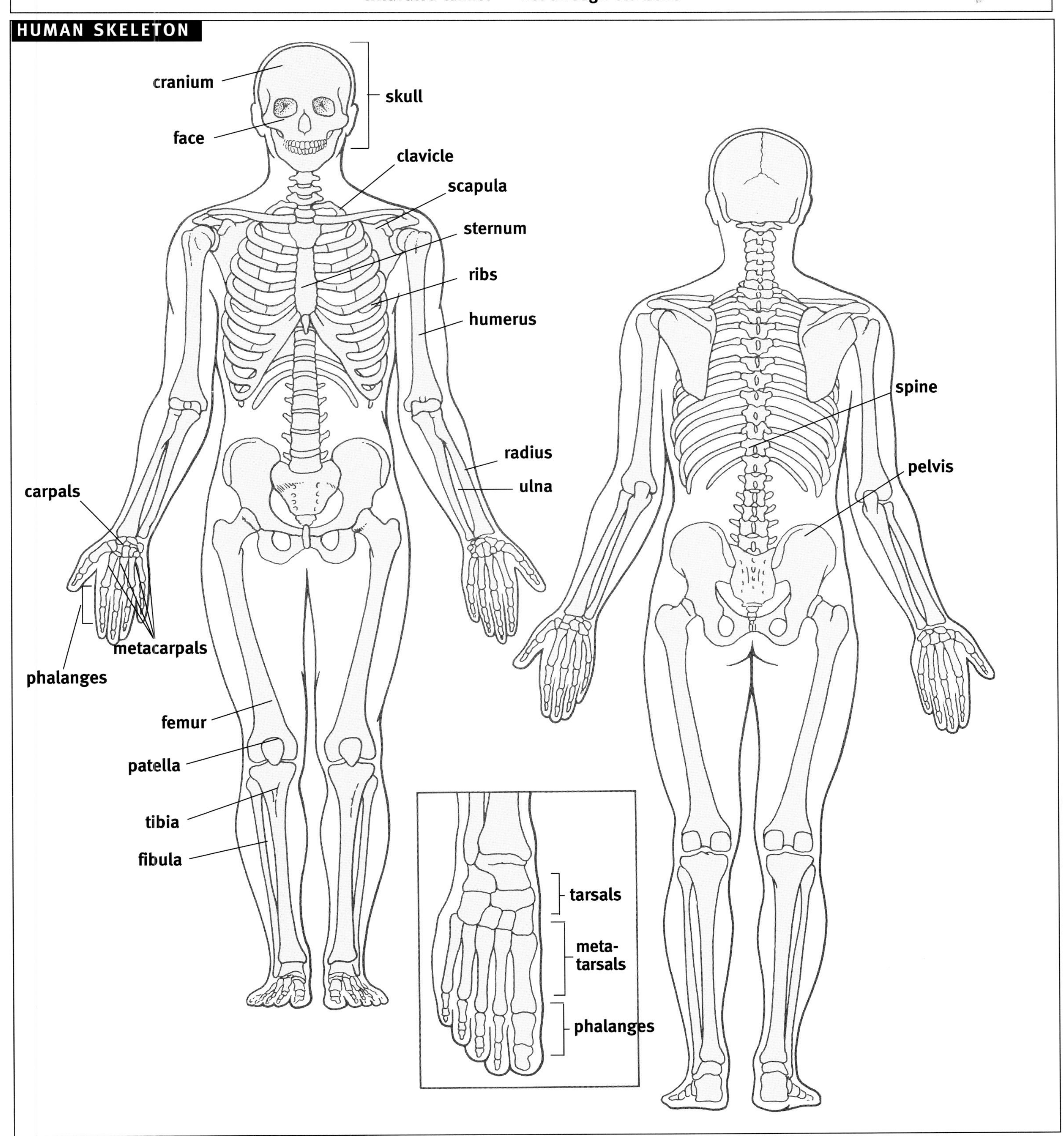
HUMAN SKELETON
cranium
skull
face
clavicle
scapula
sternum
ribs
humerus
radius
ulna
carpals
metacarpals
phalanges
femur
patella
tibia
fibula
spine
pelvis
tarsals
meta-
tarsals
phalanges

into the other groups. Examples are the spinal vertebrae and the facial bones. The skeleton can be divided into the following sections:

Section	Bones
Skull	29
Spine	26
Rib cage	25
Upper appendages	64
Lower appendages	62

SKULL The main part of the skull, called the **cranium**, is made up of eight flat bones, which form a closed, rounded structure that holds the brain. Fifteen bones form the face, which is composed mostly of irregular-shaped bones such as the **mandible**, or jawbone. Several bones of the skull are paired. For example, the two parietal bones cover the top and sides of the head. As we consider the rest of the skeleton, it will be seen that paired bones are a common theme in skeletal structure. This is because the human frame is symmetrical, which means that the two halves match.

SPINE A series of special bones called **vertebrae** fit closely together in a row to form the spine, also known as the spinal column or backbone. Each vertebra has a thick, rounded body at the front that stacks between neighboring vertebrae, as well as a back part that surrounds the fragile spinal cord.

The top seven bones are known as **cervical** vertebrae. They are designed to allow maximum movement while still protecting the spinal cord. This is why your neck is quite flexible. These top vertebrae have a relatively small body, since they support just the head—a light weight compared to the load carried by the bones lower in the spine.

Next in line are the twelve **thoracic** vertebrae, which support most of the upper body. There are two "arms" on the sides of these bones where ribs attach and are held in place to form the chest. These bones lock closely together and allow only limited movement.

Almost at the bottom of the spine are five large vertebrae called the **lumbars**. They each have a very large body that supports the weight of all the bones above as well as the entire upper trunk. The lumbars fit together tightly and allow

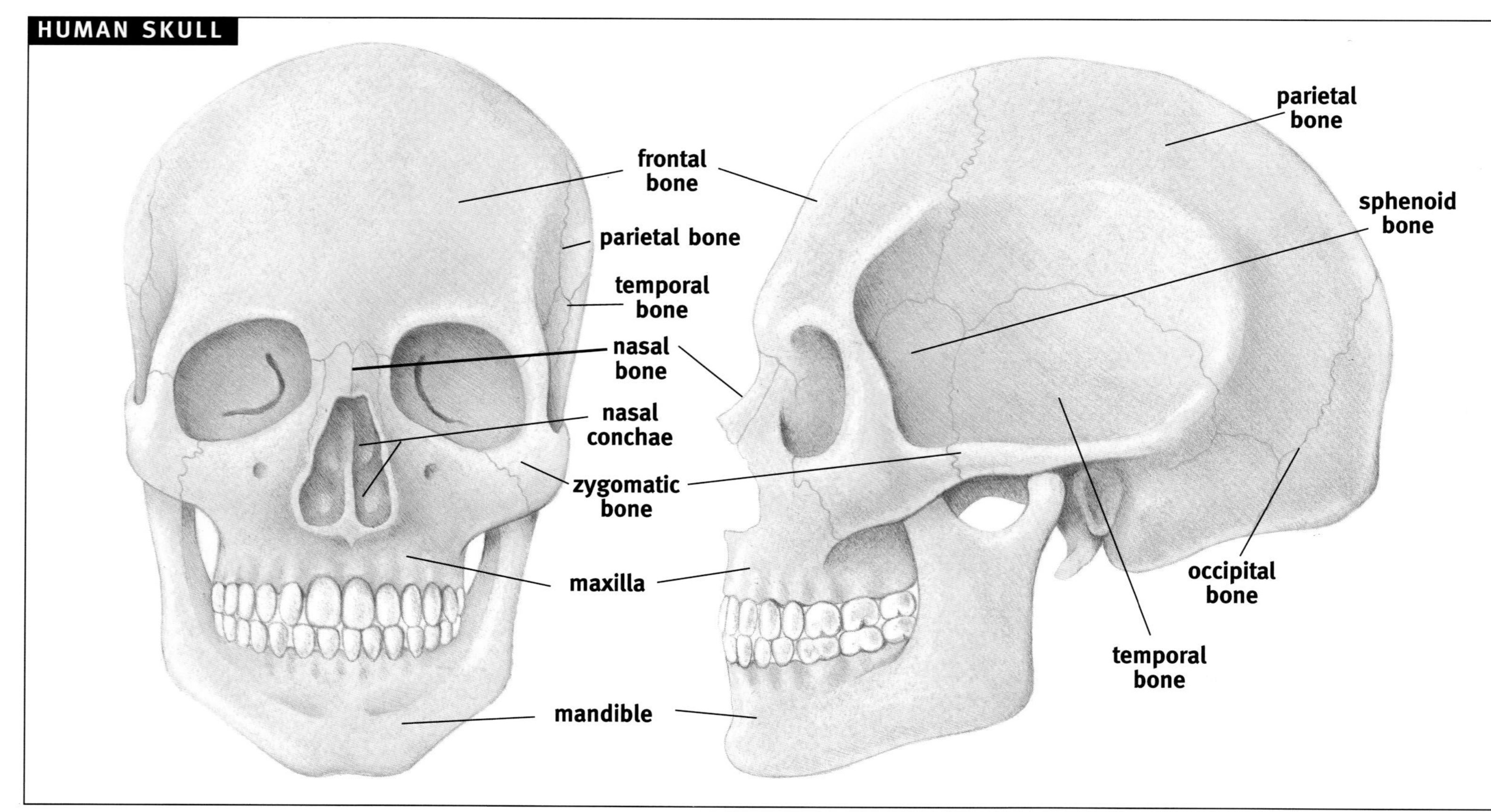

almost no movement at all. In fact, in some older people, two or more lumbars fuse together to become one solid structure.

After the last lumbar come the **sacrum** and **coccyx**. These two bones form the back of the pelvis, which supports the lower part of the abdomen.

The spinal column is not straight: it bends into a series of gentle curves. This makes the spine somewhat springy, increasing the maximum load that can be supported and absorbing the impact of walking and lifting heavy objects. If the vertebrae were lined up perfectly straight, the spine could not yield under force and would be easily damaged.

Rib Cage The ribs curve from the **sternum**, or breastbone, in the front of the chest around to the spine, where they hook into the thoracic vertebrae. This creates a large hollow cavity that holds and protects the heart, lungs, and several of the abdominal organs. The part of the rib that connects to the sternum is actually not bone; it is a softer material known as **cartilage**. This tissue is not as strong as bone, but it is more flexible, which allows the rib cage to bend under pressure.

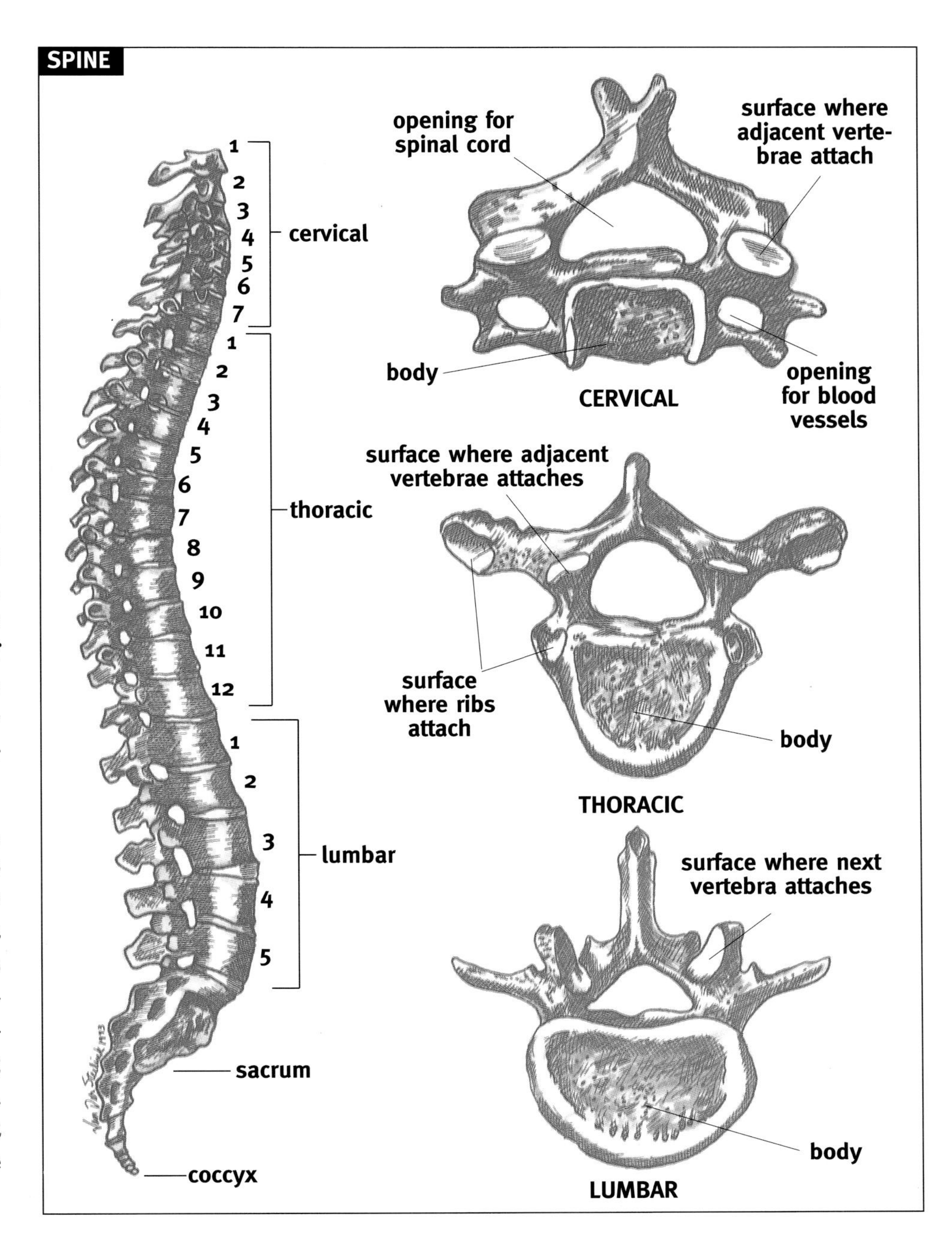

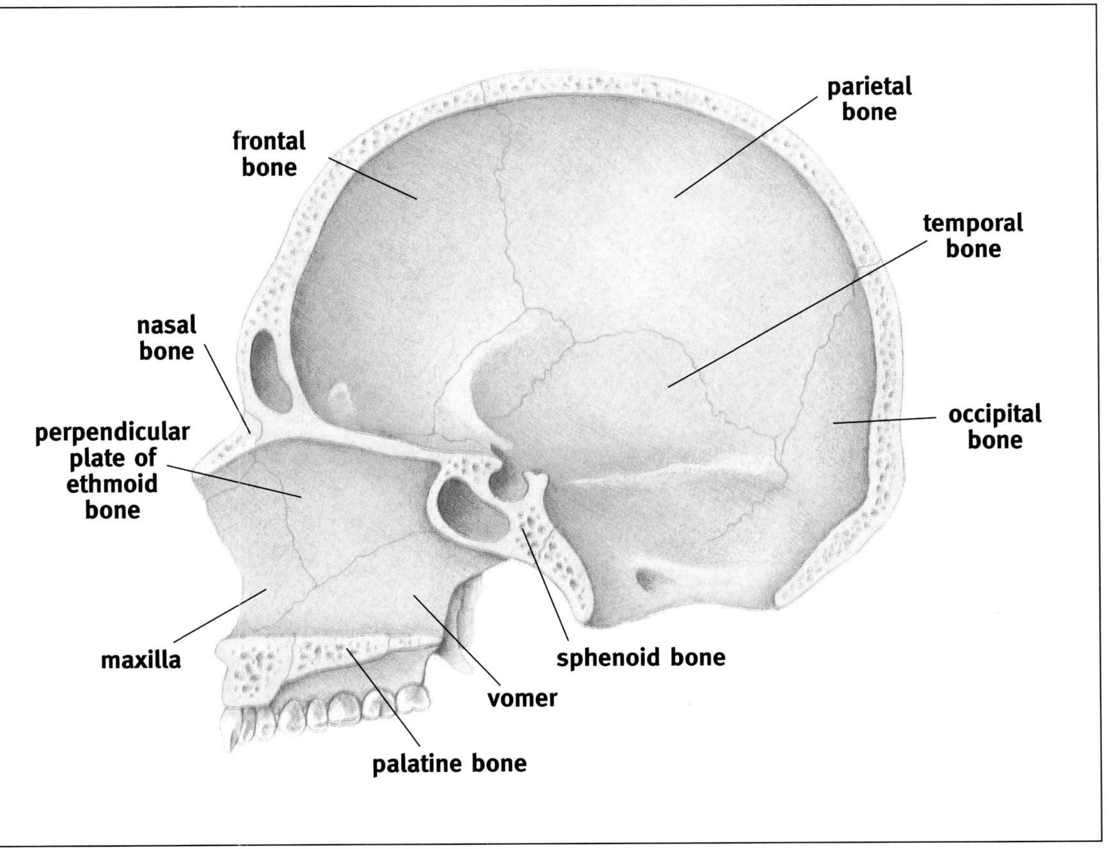

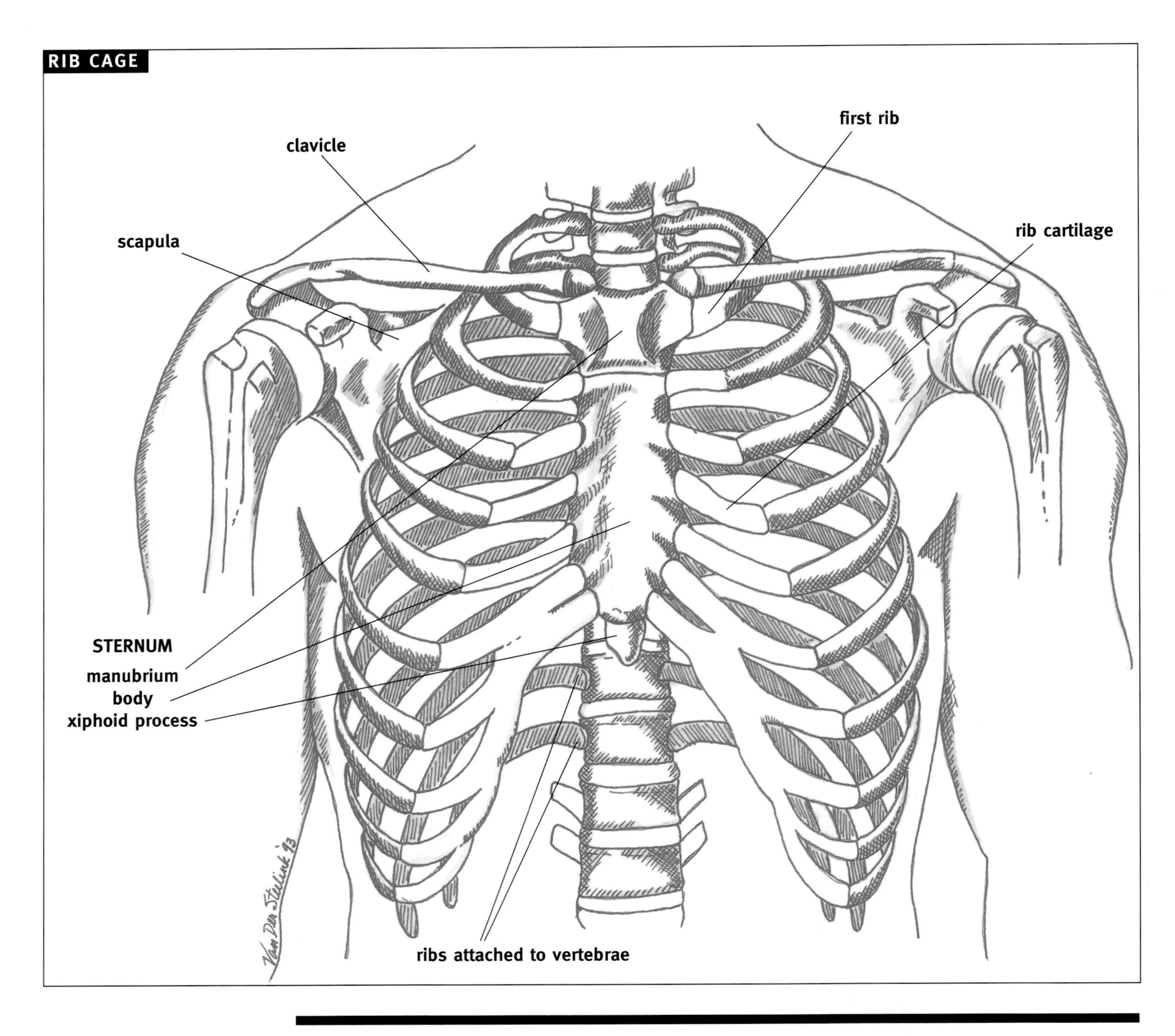

ARTHRITIS

Any disorder that produces swelling and inflammation of the joints is classified as arthritis. Mild and temporary episodes of arthritis, characterized by pain and stiffness in the joints, affect almost everyone over the age of fifty. As the body's articulations age and accumulate wear and tear, it is common for occasional pain, inflammation, and edema to occur.

Rheumatoid arthritis is a severe form of this disease that afflicts millions of people all over the world. It begins with fluid buildup in the synovial membranes, causing swelling and inflammation, and produces extreme pain due to pressure on surrounding nerves. In some cases this condition disappears rapidly, but in others, the joints remain swollen for long periods of time and destruction of articulating surfaces begins. In its later stages, rheumatoid arthritis causes permanent disfigurement, particularly in the joints of the hands, and also leads to fusion and complete immobilization of articular surfaces.

The cause of rheumatoid arthritis is not yet known, but current investigation suggests that this malady has several features of autoimmune disease. This means that the body's own immune system is activated against tissues in the joint region and mounts a destructive response that destroys cells in the articulations and synovial membranes. What triggers this response is not yet understood, but knowing that the immune system is involved has led to the development of new therapies that are now being tested for effectiveness against this crippling disease.

Appendages This group includes the bones of the shoulders, arms, and hands. The **clavicle**, or collarbone, connects the sternum to the shoulder area, while the **scapula** covers the upper back and forms the shoulder socket. The **humerus** is the large bone in the upper arm, and the forearm contains two bones, the **ulna** and **radius**.

There are a large number of separate bones in the hand: eight wrist bones called **carpals**, five in the palm area known as **metacarpals**, and a total of fourteen bones in the **phalanges**, or fingers.

Lower Appendages The thighbone, or **femur**, which connects to the hip, is the longest bone in the body. Below it is the **patella**, or kneecap, and the two bones of the lower leg, the **tibia** and **fibula**. All of the leg bones are thick and strong, allowing them to support the weight of the body when we stand, walk, or run.

The ankles and feet contain many bones. Seven **tarsals** make up the ankle, followed by five **metatarsals** in the arch area of the foot. These attach to the fourteen **phalanges**, which form the toes.

UPPER APPENDAGES

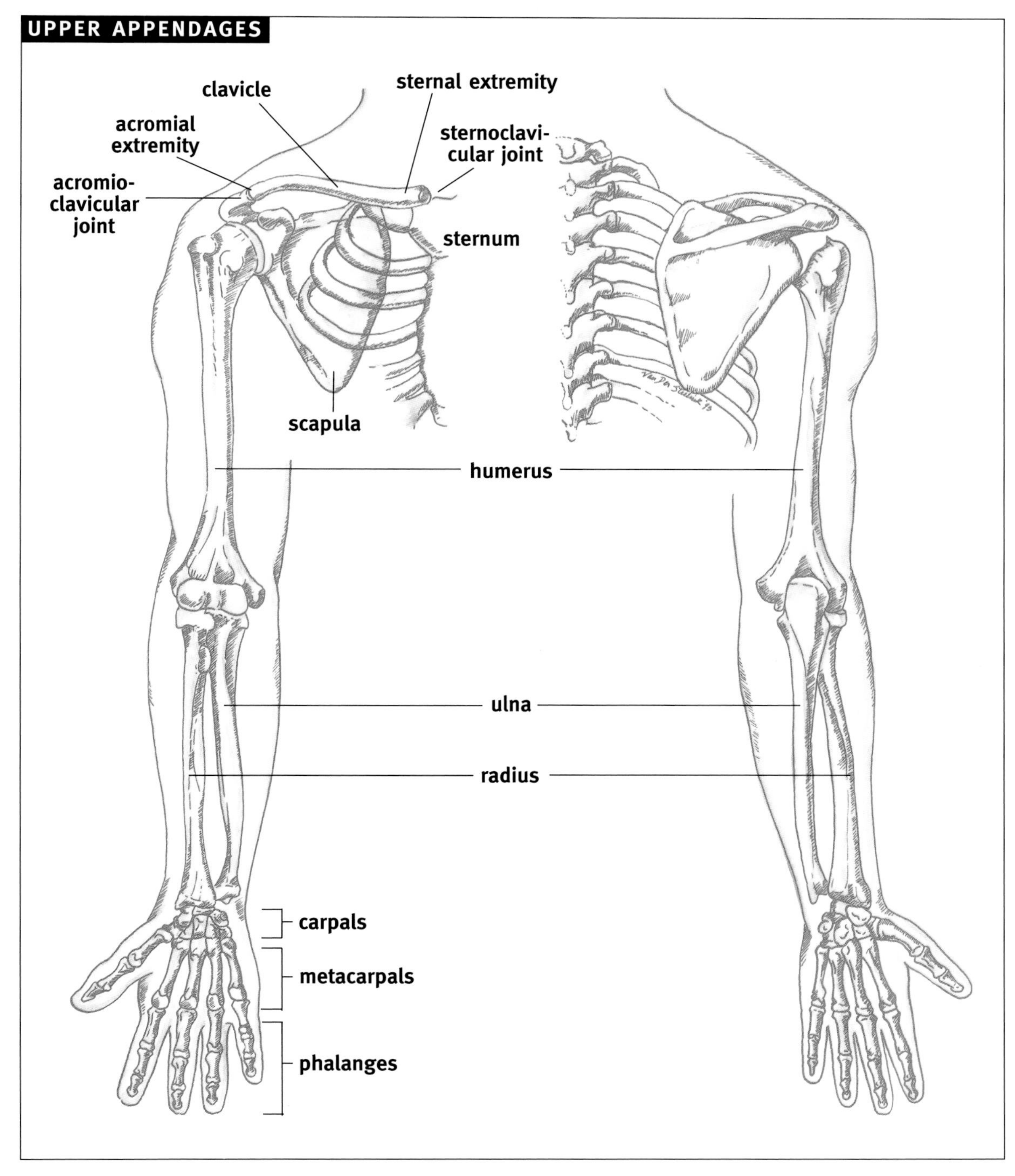

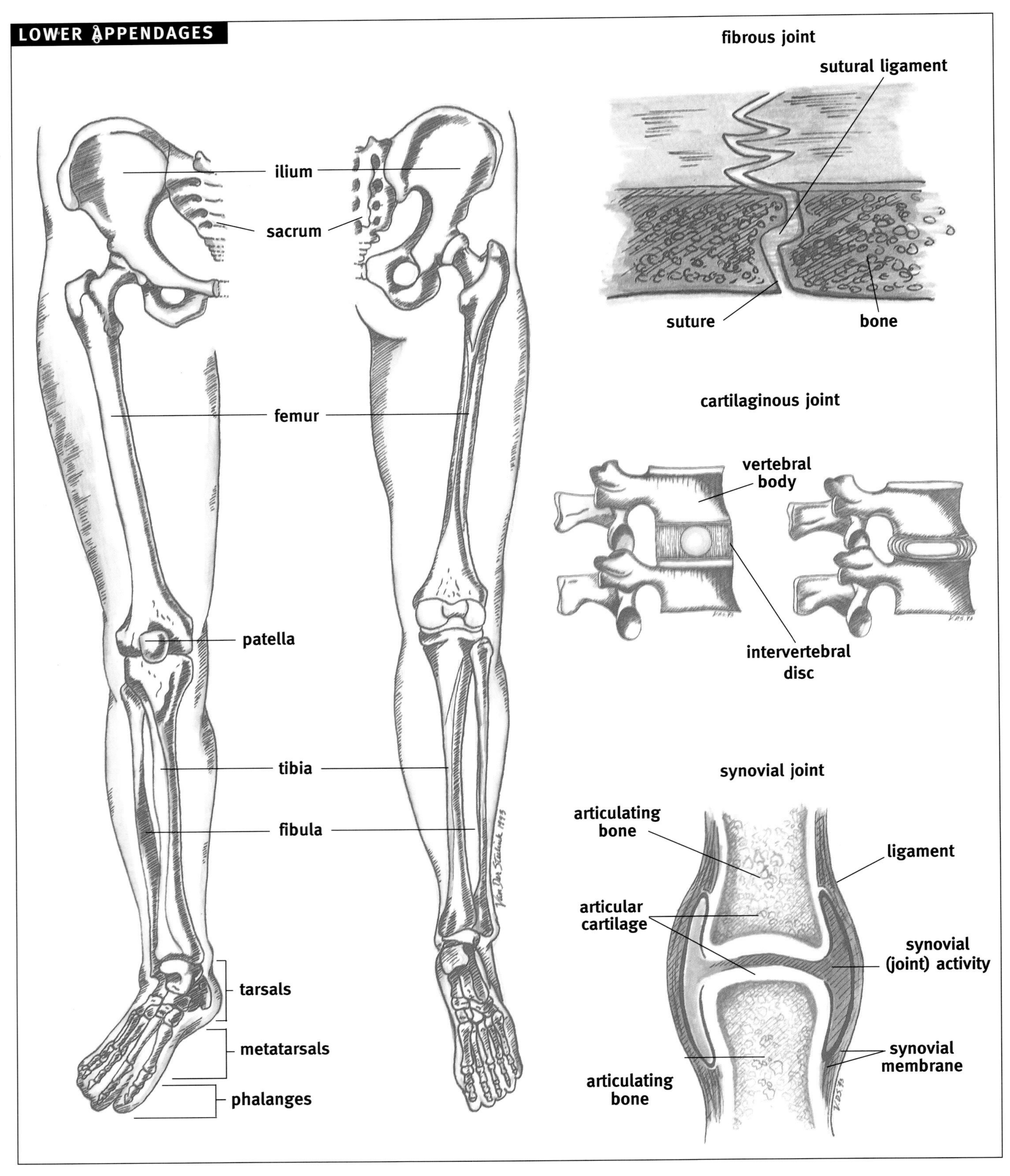

The two hipbones, or **ilia**, combine with the **sacrum** and **coccyx** to create the pelvis. This structure is located in the middle of the body and forms a sturdy base for the trunk above and the legs below.

JOINTS (ARTICULATIONS)

In the human skeleton there are many points where bones contact each other. These connections are called joints, or articulations. There are three basic types of joints.

Fibrous Joints Some bones fit together very tightly. The result is a fibrous joint that allows no movement at all. Bones of the skull are joined in this way. These joints, also called sutures, fuse in adults so that the skull bones are no longer separate but form one solid structure.

Cartilaginous Joints These joints contain cartilage that holds the two bones together and also supplies cushioning. An example is the articulations between adjacent vertebrae. These joints contain special structures called intervertebral discs. When force is applied to the spine, these discs compress like shock absorbers, easing the pressure and preventing damage. The joint at the front of the pelvis, the symphysis pubis, is also a cartilaginous joint.

Synovial Joints All of the movable joints in the body are in this category. The adjoining bones are covered with cartilage and separated by a thin sack filled with synovial fluid, which reduces friction between the moving surfaces.

Synovial joints are divided into three groups. Gliding or sliding joints have limited movement and are wrapped tightly in strong connective tissue. The knuckles are a good example. Hinge joints are more flexible but can move in only one direction. The bones in the fingers are connected by hinge joints. The knees and elbows are other examples. Pivot joints allow rotation. The top two bones in the neck have this kind of joint, which allows the head to turn sideways. Ball and sockets are the most freely movable joints in the body, allowing motion in more than one direction. The hip is an example, as is the shoulder, which is the most mobile joint in the body.

Freedom of movement also makes the shoulders and hips more prone to injury. Perhaps you know someone who has suffered a dislocated shoulder. This happens when the upper arm or shoulder is hit or pulled at a certain angle, popping the humerus out of its socket. Most of the time it can be manipulated back into place, but extreme cases require surgery.

FUNCTIONS OF THE SKELETAL SYSTEM

As a whole the skeleton gives shape and support to the body, as well as protection to fragile internal organs. Because many of the bones in the body are connected by movable joints, the skeletal frame also serves to make the body flexible and allow it a great deal of movement. Not only can we walk, run, jump, lift, and throw, but our agile hands and fingers can perform complex jobs requiring very delicate maneuvers.

Some bones contain marrow, a tissue that produces the cells of the blood. This process, known as **hematopoiesis**, creates a constant supply of new oxygen-carrying cells to replenish old, worn-out blood cells.

The bones also act as a storehouse for calcium, an important mineral that is used in many ways by various organs. When calcium is needed in other areas such as the muscles, bone calcium can be released and moved to this tissue.

DOUBLE-JOINTED?

The most flexible articulations in the body, the synovial joints, are held in place by tough, stretchy fibers called **ligaments**. The ligaments keep the two joining bone surfaces pressed together and prevent them from moving so far that they dislocate, or slip out of place.

Some people have unusually loose ligaments surrounding certain joints. These people are said to be "double-jointed," because some of their joints are extremely flexible. Perhaps you know someone who has double-jointed thumbs. Such an individual can bend his or her thumb downward so far that it actually touches the wrist. It is a little gruesome to watch but is not painful or damaging. Almost any synovial joint in the body can be double-jointed, but it occurs most commonly in the thumbs, fingers, and jaw.

The name for this condition is not really accurate—there is not an extra joint that permits increased flexibility. It is simply that slacker ligaments allow a greater range of motion than normal. The term "double-jointed" probably arose because in extreme cases the two bones actually pop out of place, giving the sensation of a second articulation. This popping is the result of the bone surfaces separating when the joint is forced past the normal range of motion.

Joints that are too flexible can be a problem. The loose ligaments around these articulations sometimes don't hold the bones together tightly enough, and they dislocate or move out of alignment easily. In extreme cases surgery may be performed to shorten the ligaments, tightening up the joint so that the bones stay in place.

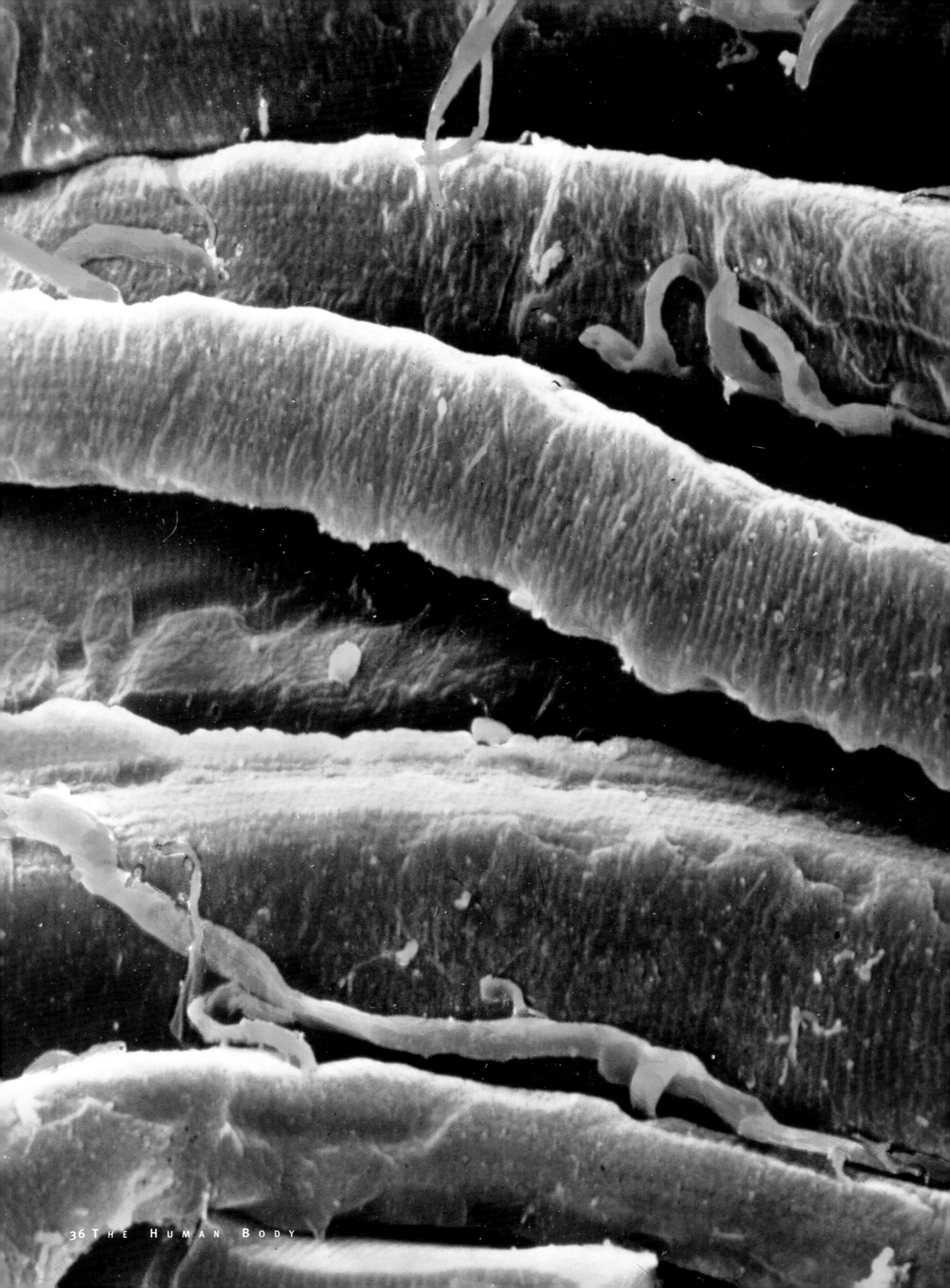

Chapter 4

The Muscular System

In the last chapter we saw how the skeletal system provides a framework for the body, complete with joints that allow movement of various kinds. But the bones cannot move by themselves. Another kind of tissue is required to set the body in motion: muscle.

There are over 600 separate muscles in the human body. In fact, muscle is the most common type of tissue, taking up about 45 percent of our total weight. The reason that so much of the body is devoted to muscle tissue is because various types of movement play key roles in maintaining health, as well as getting us around our environment.

Let's first consider the different types of muscle cells and their structure and function. Then we will examine the ability of muscle tissue to contract. After that we will explore how muscles cooperate with the skeletal system to produce movement.

TYPES OF MUSCLE

There are four different kinds of muscle cells in the human anatomy.

Myoepithelial Cells Special muscle cells found only in the body's surface layers, or epithelium, such as the skin, myoepithelial cells are the cells that contract to push fluid out of sweat glands and onto the skin. Myoepithelial cells are also found in the iris of the eye, where they constrict the pupil to shield the sensitive inner eye when it is exposed to bright light.

Heart Muscle Cells Also called cardiac muscle, heart muscle cells are found only in the heart. The constant beating of the heart is a strenuous, demanding job that requires cardiac muscle to be exceptionally strong and durable. Heart muscle cells are specially designed for this task, which will be considered fully in chapter 6.

Smooth Muscle Cells The tiny muscle fibers attached to hair in the skin that cause goose bumps are made of smooth muscle. Another example is the muscle layer in the intestines, which pushes food along. Smooth muscle contracts rather slowly compared to other types, and is designed for special jobs in softer tissues.

These three types of muscle are under involuntary control, which means that they work without you thinking about it.

OPPOSITE PAGE: Muscle fibers Electron micrograph of individual fibers (red) in a bundle of skeletal muscle. Each fiber is encased in a thin sheet of connective tissue that protects the filaments within. Blood vessels (blue) that supply muscle with oxygen and nutrients are also visible.

MUSCLE CELLS

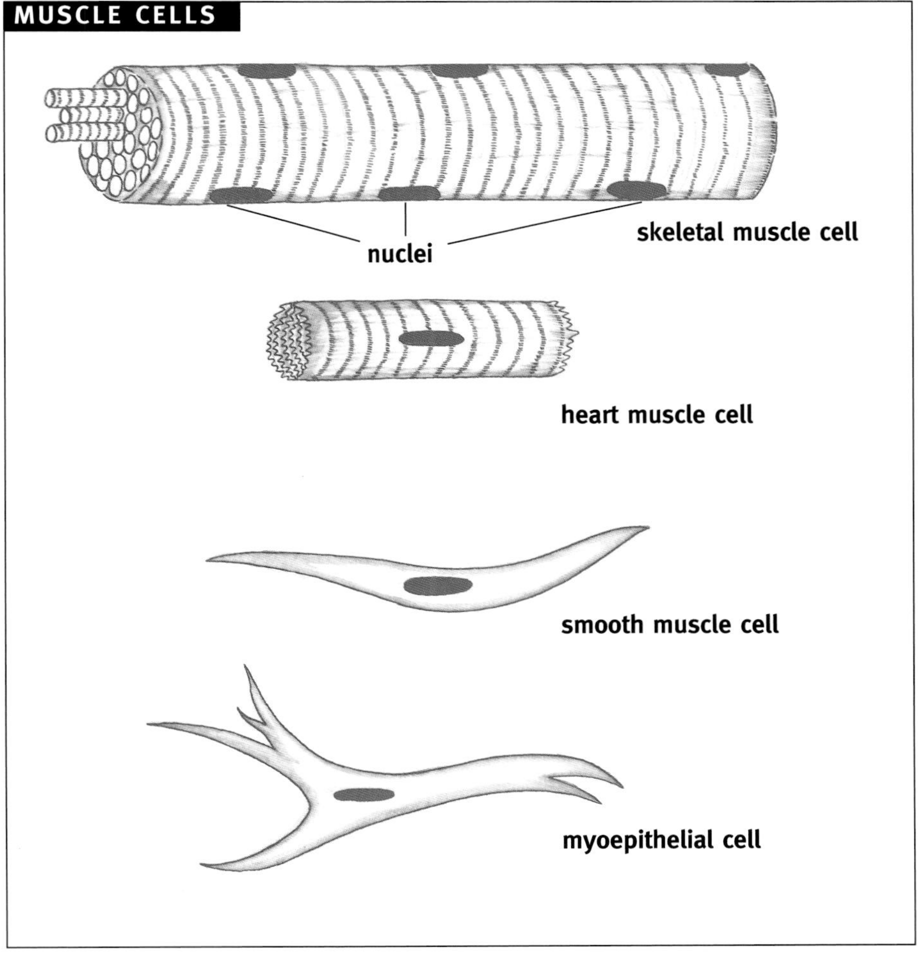

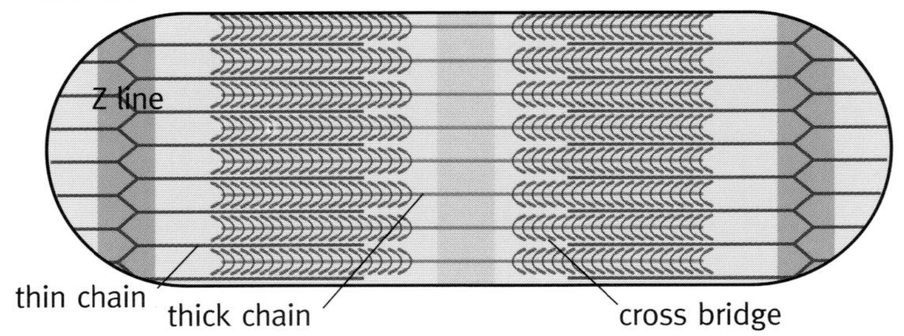

You do not have to consciously think about making your heart beat—it automatically contracts and relaxes on its own. Likewise, you do not pay attention to food moving through your digestive system, or intentionally make your skin form goose bumps. All of these processes occur on their own.

Skeletal Muscle Cells The main kind of muscle in the body, skeletal muscle cells form all of the major muscle groups that control skeletal movement. The name comes from its attachment to various bones of the skeleton, which are pulled to create motion. Skeletal muscle is under voluntary control. This means that you consciously determine whether these muscles work or not. For example, if you need to lift your arm to pick up a book, you must think about it, and send messages from your brain to your arm muscles directing them to move in certain ways.

MYOBLASTS

Muscle tissue forms from cells known as myoblasts. Skeletal muscle is created when many separate myoblasts join together and fuse into specialized fibers.

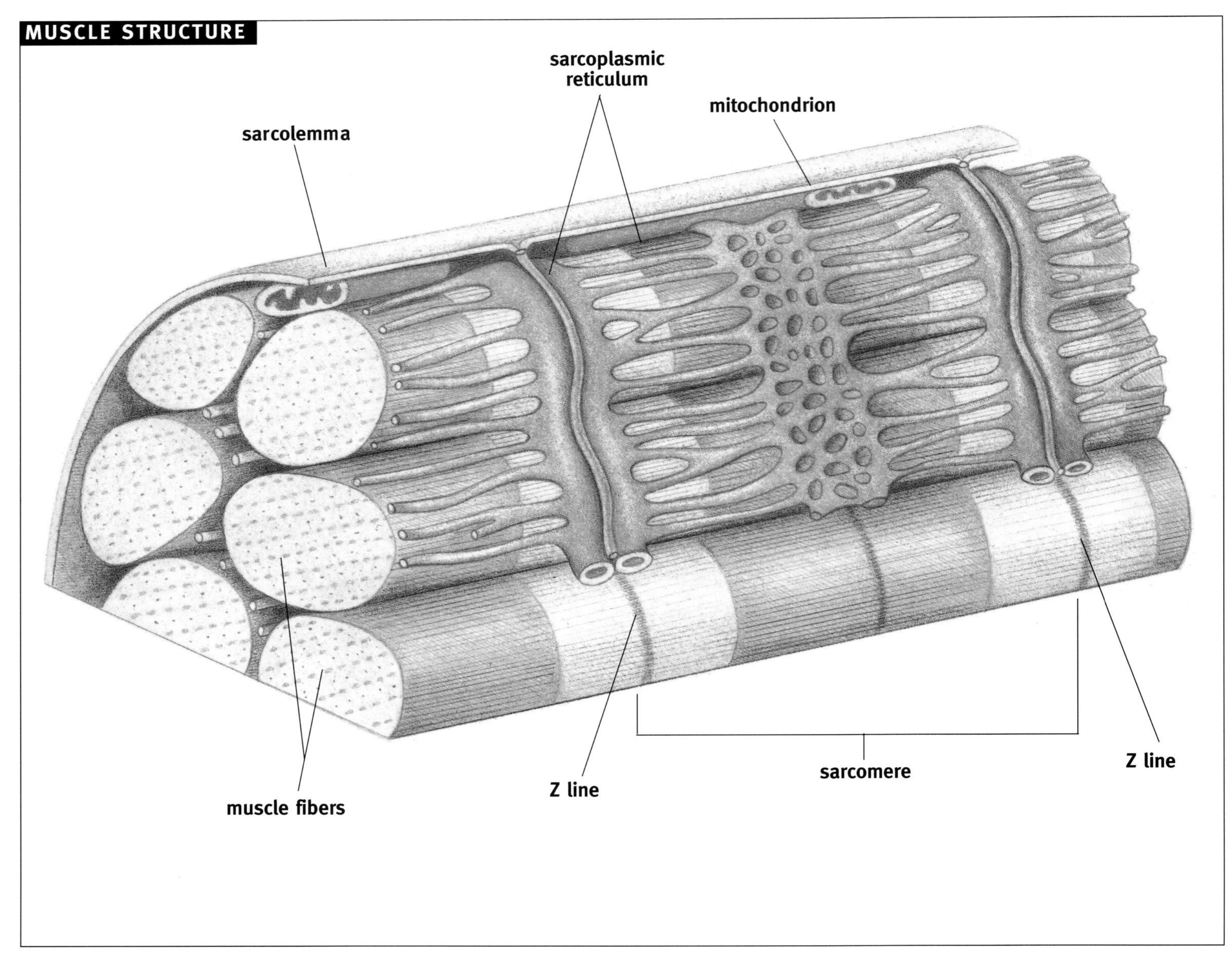

This creates a very large muscle cell—up to 18 inches (45 cm) long in some cases—that works as a single unit. Thus, a mature skeletal muscle cell does not look much like the typical body cell described in chapter 1. It is still a cell, with nuclei and mitochondria and other organelles, but it has become highly specialized in order to perform its job in the body. As we go on to other cell types in the next chapters, we will find that almost all cells are designed for specific tasks and take on unique shapes and structures suited to their functions.

The first three muscle types—myoepithelial, cardiac, and smooth—remain as individual cells, though cardiac cells take on the appearance of skeletal muscle. This is because cardiac and skeletal muscles have a highly organized system of fibers that produce a lined pattern. The fine structure of this lined pattern in skeletal muscle is our next topic.

MOTOR END PLATE

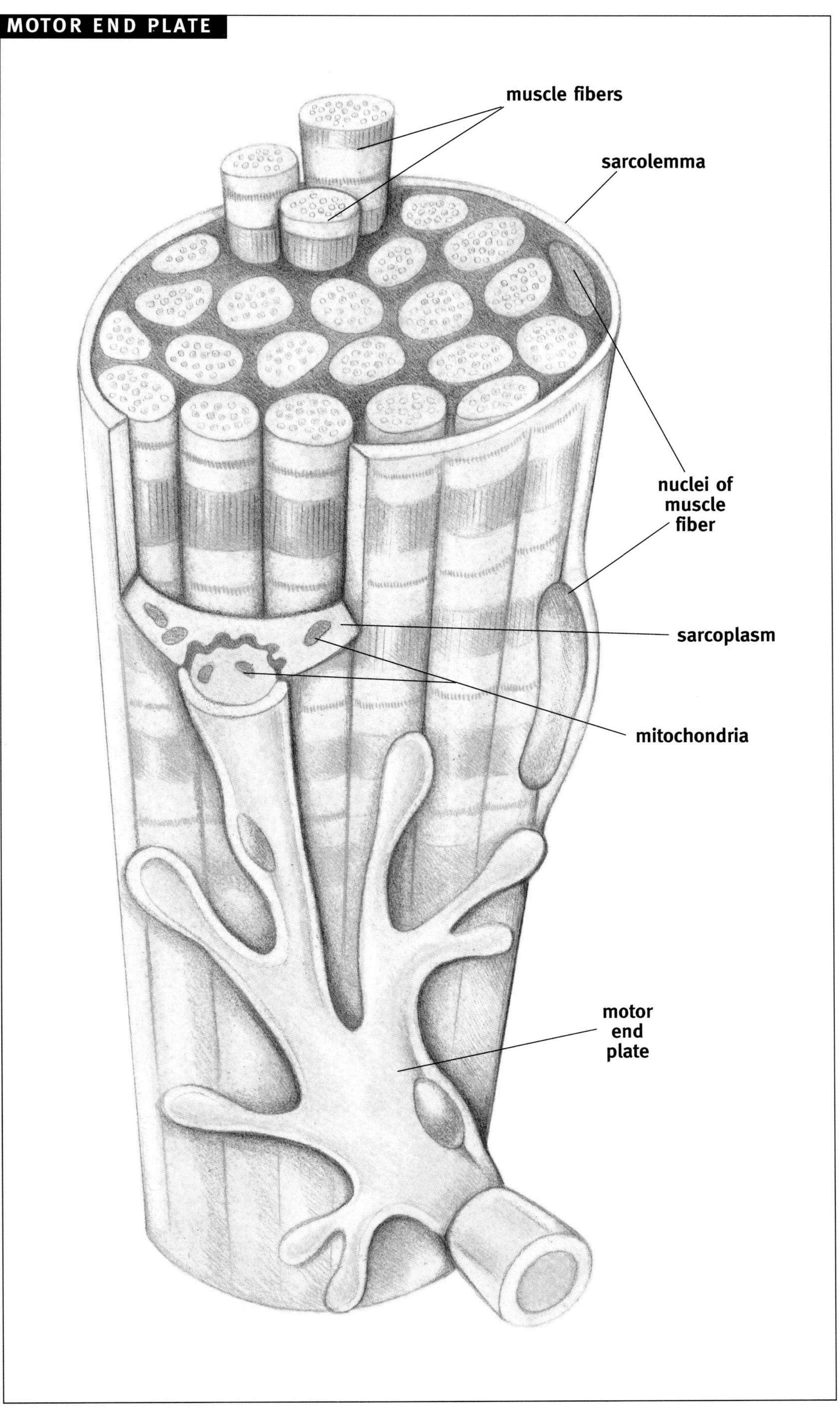

MUSCLE FIBERS

Under the microscope, skeletal muscle tissue has a distinct pattern of overlapping lines. The repeating sets of lines are always parallel to the direction the muscle pulls, which gives a clue about their function: the overlapping lines are special proteins that are responsible for muscle movement.

When myoblasts begin to gather into muscle fibers, they make huge amounts of two proteins: **myosin** and **actin**. Molecules of myosin are assembled into a thick chain with one end of each myosin sticking out to form a paddlelike structure called a cross-bridge. Actin gathers into a thin, straight chain of repeating units.

In the muscle fiber, thick chains and thin chains are lined up next to each other so that they overlap, forming the highly organized pattern of muscle tissue. Both thick and thin chains are anchored to a plate called the **Z line**. The region between two Z lines is called a **sarcomere**. It is the sarcomere that acts as the basic unit of muscle tissue. An individual muscle fiber contains many thousands of sarcomeres, and one

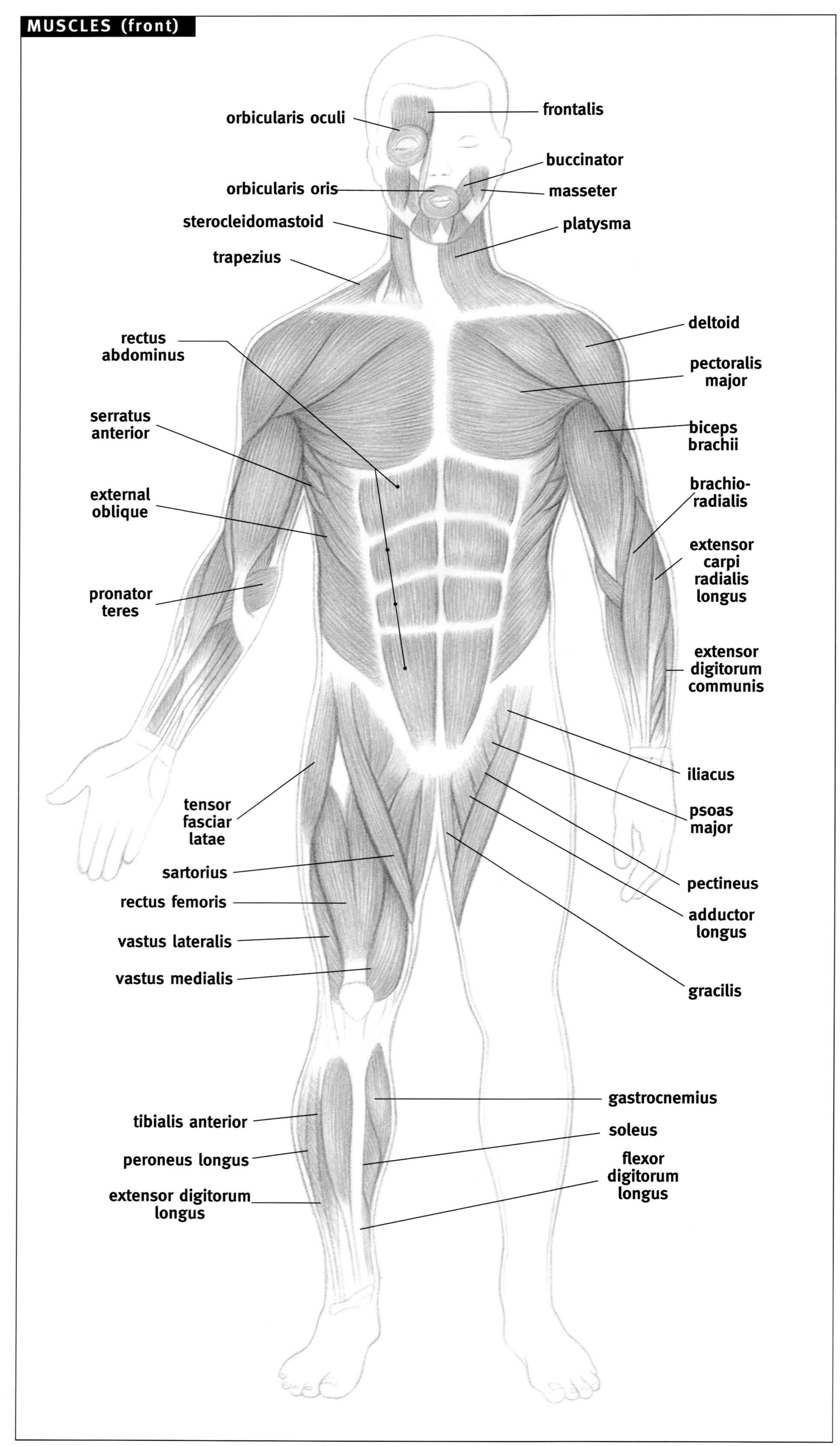
MUSCLES (front)
frontalis
orbicularis oculi
buccinator
orbicularis oris
masseter
sterocleidomastoid
platysma
trapezius
deltoid
rectus abdominus
pectoralis major
serratus anterior
biceps brachii
brachio-radialis
external oblique
extensor carpi radialis longus
pronator teres
extensor digitorum communis
iliacus
tensor fasciar latae
psoas major
sartorius
pectineus
rectus femoris
adductor longus
vastus lateralis
vastus medialis
gracilis
gastrocnemius
tibialis anterior
soleus
peroneus longus
flexor digitorum longus
extensor digitorum longus

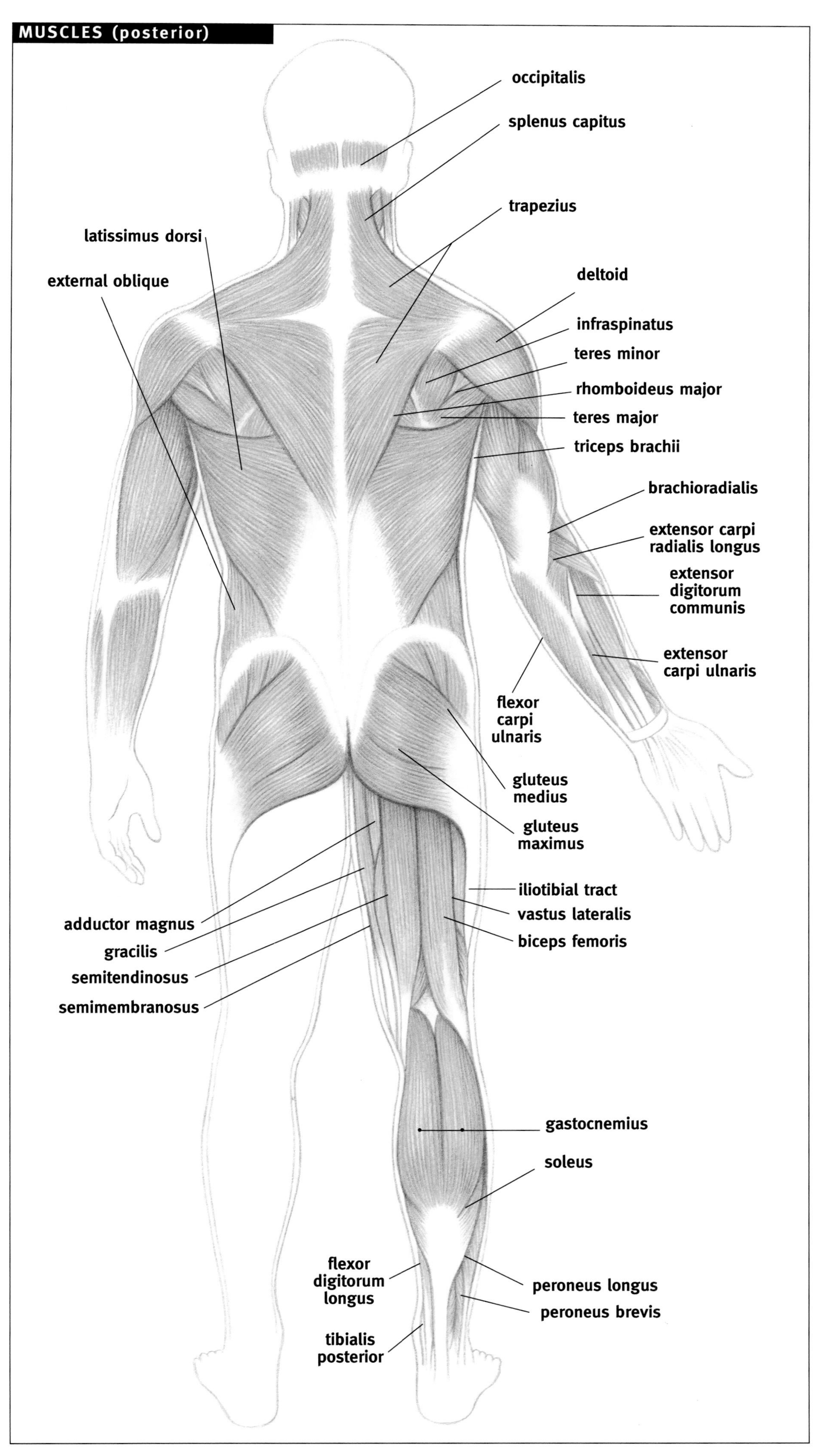
MUSCLES (posterior)
occipitalis
splenus capitus
trapezius
latissimus dorsi
external oblique
deltoid
infraspinatus
teres minor
rhomboideus major
teres major
triceps brachii
brachioradialis
extensor carpi radialis longus
extensor digitorum communis
extensor carpi ulnaris
flexor carpi ulnaris
gluteus medius
gluteus maximus
iliotibial tract
vastus lateralis
biceps femoris
adductor magnus
gracilis
semitendinosus
semimembranosus
gastocnemius
soleus
flexor digitorum longus
peroneus longus
peroneus brevis
tibialis posterior

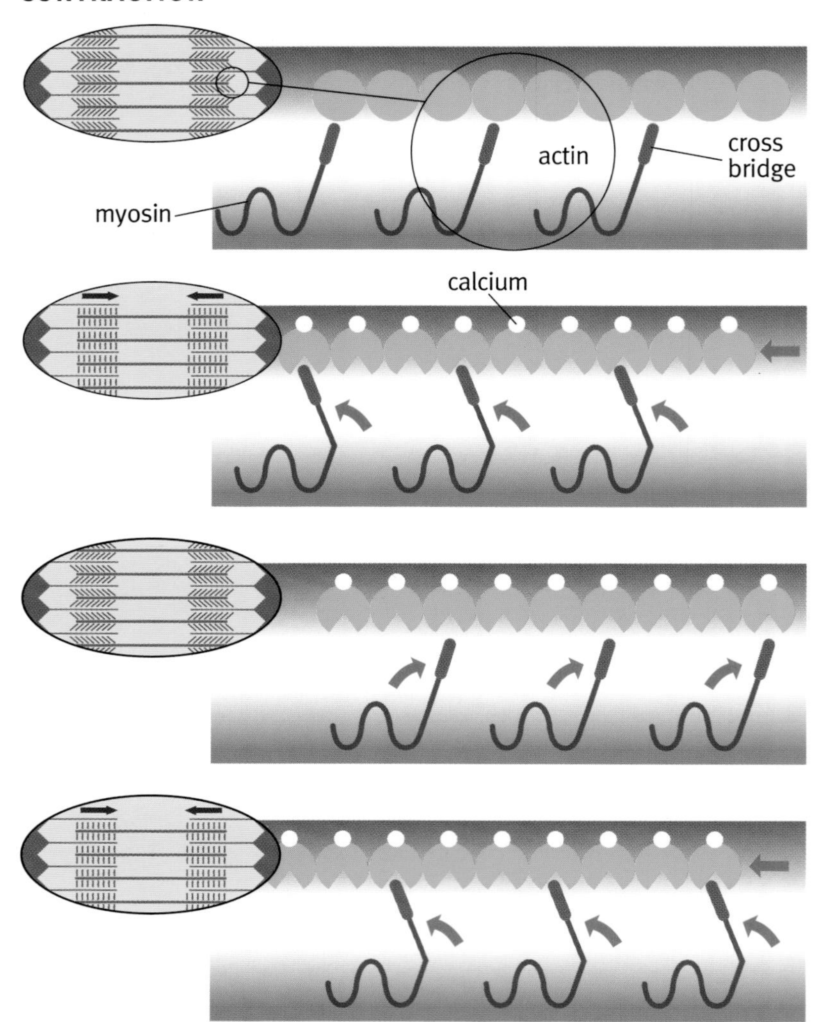

muscle contains hundreds of separate fibers.

Though most of the space in a muscle fiber is taken up by columns of sarcomeres, there are also other important structures. Mitochondria, which produce an energy-rich molecule called **adenosine triphosphate**, or ATP, lie between bundles of fibers. Surrounding the muscle fiber is a membrane called the **sarcolemma**, and inside of this outer coat is the **sarcoplasm**, a network of tubules and sacs that contains calcium.

Attached to each muscle fiber is a nerve known as a **motor neuron**. The end of this nerve fits tightly against the outside of the sarcolemma to form a structure called the **motor end plate**. It is the motor neuron, activating sarcomeres through the motor end plate, that signals the muscle to contract.

Here is how a muscle contraction happens: When you decide to pick up a book, your brain sends a signal through the proper motor neurons out to the muscles in your arms and hands. When the signal reaches the motor end plate, the impulse is transferred to the sarcoplasm—the network of tubes full of calcium. The calcium is then released into the muscle fiber.

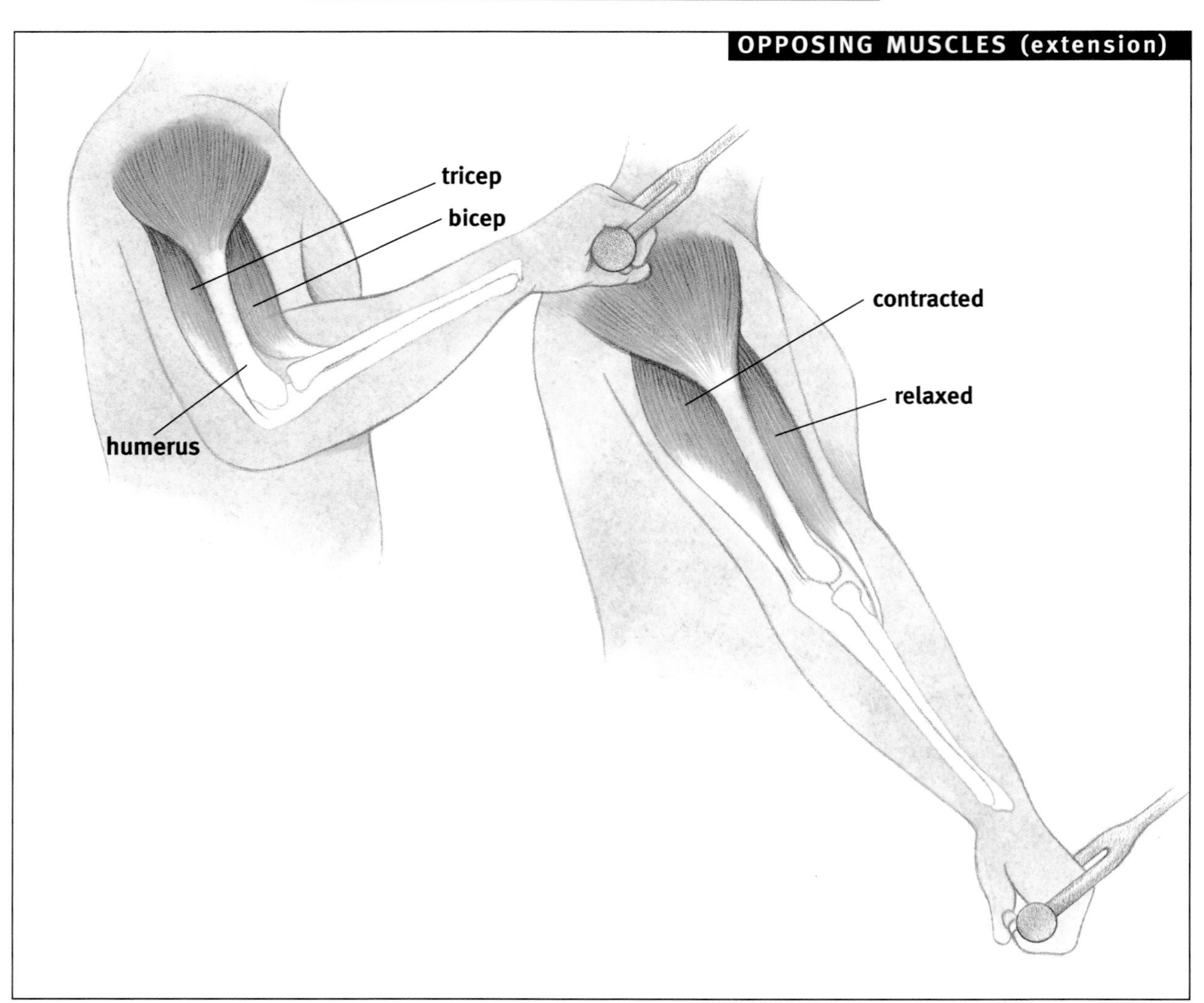

When calcium floods into the muscle, it binds to actin molecules in the thin chains of the sarcomere. This binding changes the shape of the actin molecules, opening up a place for the paddle-shaped cross-bridges of

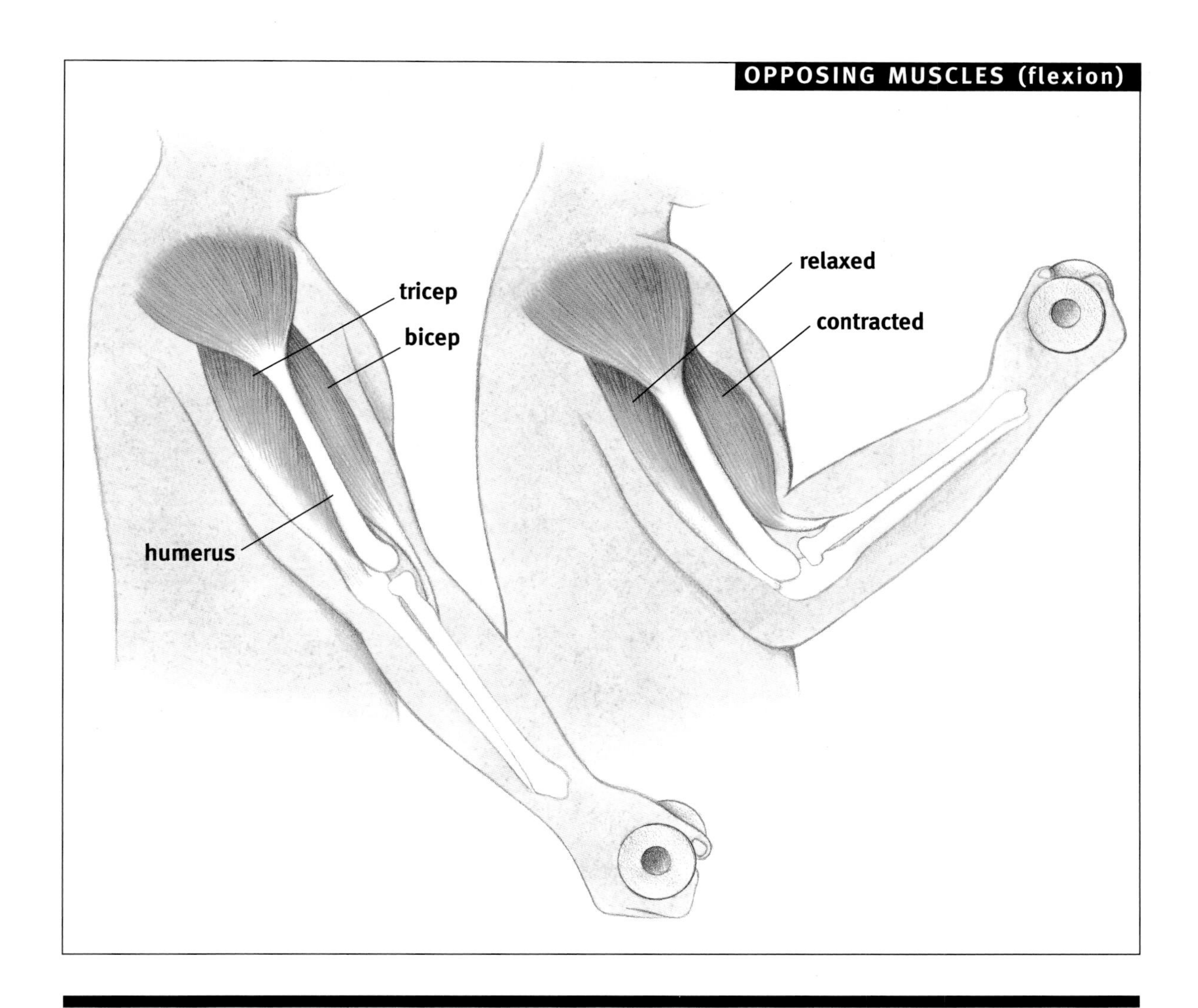

STRENGTH TRAINING

One way to increase the strength and size of muscles is through a program of strength training. You may be familiar with barbells and other exercise equipment designed to strengthen and tone the body's muscles. A program of weight training is a series of exercises designed to isolate and fatigue each muscle group individually. This is done by repeating a certain motion over and over until a specific muscle or group of muscles is exhausted. These exercises may be performed with or without weights, as long as the muscles are fatigued. Muscle tissue responds to a regime of regular, controlled stress by increasing in size and strength. Blood flow to individual muscle cells increases, and the fibers and bundles acquire higher capacity for work. In addition, the overall tone of muscle becomes firmer and remains more rigid with regular exercise, producing a firm, healthy physique.

An important aspect of strength training includes proper stretching of muscles, tendons, and ligaments. Unless muscle fibers are fully extended from time to time, they tend to bunch up and develop a limited range of motion. When tight muscles are subjected to sudden, maximum exertion, tearing of muscle fiber and tendons can result, producing serious injury. Careful flexion and extension before and after exercise keeps muscles loose and flexible.

Strengthening the body's muscles includes side benefits for other tissues and organs, too. Firming up the muscle fibers connected to spinal vertebrae promotes correct alignment and flexibility of the spine, and reduces the chance of back injury. Exercise also stresses bone tissue and stimulates repair and replacement, helping prevent osteoporosis and other skeletal disorders. Working muscle requires lots of energy, which can be obtained from fat stores in the body. Thus exercise can help reduce weight and prevent obesity.

Strengthening skeletal muscle also has a positive effect on the heart. Since working muscle requires high levels of oxygen, blood flow must increase, which means the heart must pump harder. The natural consequence is the strengthening of the heart muscle, which makes it more efficient and decreases the risk of cardiac failure. Strength training also releases mental stress, relaxing the mind as it builds the body.

For all these reasons, many people choose strength training as a regular component of their week, knowing that regular exercise is an important part of a healthy life-style.

myosin to attach. The cross-bridges lock into the light chain, linking the light chain from one Z band to the heavy chains from another Z band.

The next step requires energy in the form of ATP. This molecule is produced by the mitochondria of the muscle cells, and is abundant in the sarcomeres. Using the energy from ATP, the cross-bridges pull against the light chain, just like the oars of a rowboat pulling against water. As a result, the thin and thick chains move past each other, shortening the sarcomere.

Once the cross-bridges have completed a stroke, they are released from the light chain, and spring back to their starting position. They can then attach to actin molecules farther up the light chain and use ATP to take another stroke. This squeezes the sarcomere together even more, shortening the muscle fiber. In this way, all of the sarcomeres working together cause the muscle to contract. And as the muscle shortens it pulls the bones attached to it, creating movement.

A single muscle fiber by itself can pull only a small load, but thousands of fibers working together create a very strong force. As a result, your finger muscles contract your hand around the book, and your arm muscles lift, picking it up.

When you are ready to put the book back down, the signal at the motor end plate stops. Calcium is quickly pumped back into the sarcoplasm, ending the contraction, and your hand releases the object. This all happens very quickly. Most muscles can contract and relax many times a second—watching an accomplished piano player work skilled fingers over the keyboard shows just how quickly muscles can respond.

The process of contraction requires a large amount of energy. When you run, lift, or perform heavy work, your muscles use up a lot of ATP, making you tired. As you rest, your body has a chance to make more ATP and store up energy for the next time you need it.

If you continue working your muscles after ATP stores are exhausted, they switch to another source of energy, which is less efficient but allows you to keep going. When this happens, large amounts of a chemical called lactic acid are produced as a by-product. The acid builds up in your muscles and irritates nerves in the area. This is what makes your muscles sore after hard work or strenuous exercise. The lactic acid is eventually eliminated from the muscles, but it can take a few days.

MUSCLE STRUCTURE AND FUNCTION

The names of muscles come from Latin words and sometimes give a clue about the movement a certain muscle produces.

Muscles are attached to bones by a very strong tissue called a **tendon**. Some ten-

BODY BUILDING

Some people push muscle building to the limit, working out four or five hours a day or even more. The result is that the muscles hypertrophy—they grow very large and form bulges under the skin when contracted. There are contests in which bodybuilders compete for prizes, flexing their firm muscles and showing just how developed the human body can become through heavy exercise. Because muscle contractions use up a lot of energy, serious weight lifting is a demanding and very tiring sport. The top lifters typically work out several hours at a time, sleep up to twelve hours a day, and eat huge amounts of food, all of which doesn't leave much time for anything else.

What happens to muscle tissue to cause hypertrophy? Mature skeletal muscle cells can no longer divide to create new myoblasts, because their chromosomes have lost the ability to replicate. This means that muscle growth is not a result of new cells being added to muscle tissue. What muscle cells do have is nuclei, which means they have DNA, and the genes to make more protein. Heavy exercise stimulates muscle cells to make more myosin and actin, which are assembled into new sarcomeres, creating more muscle fibers. With continuous exercise, individual muscle cells increase in size from added fibers, swelling the muscles to a larger size.

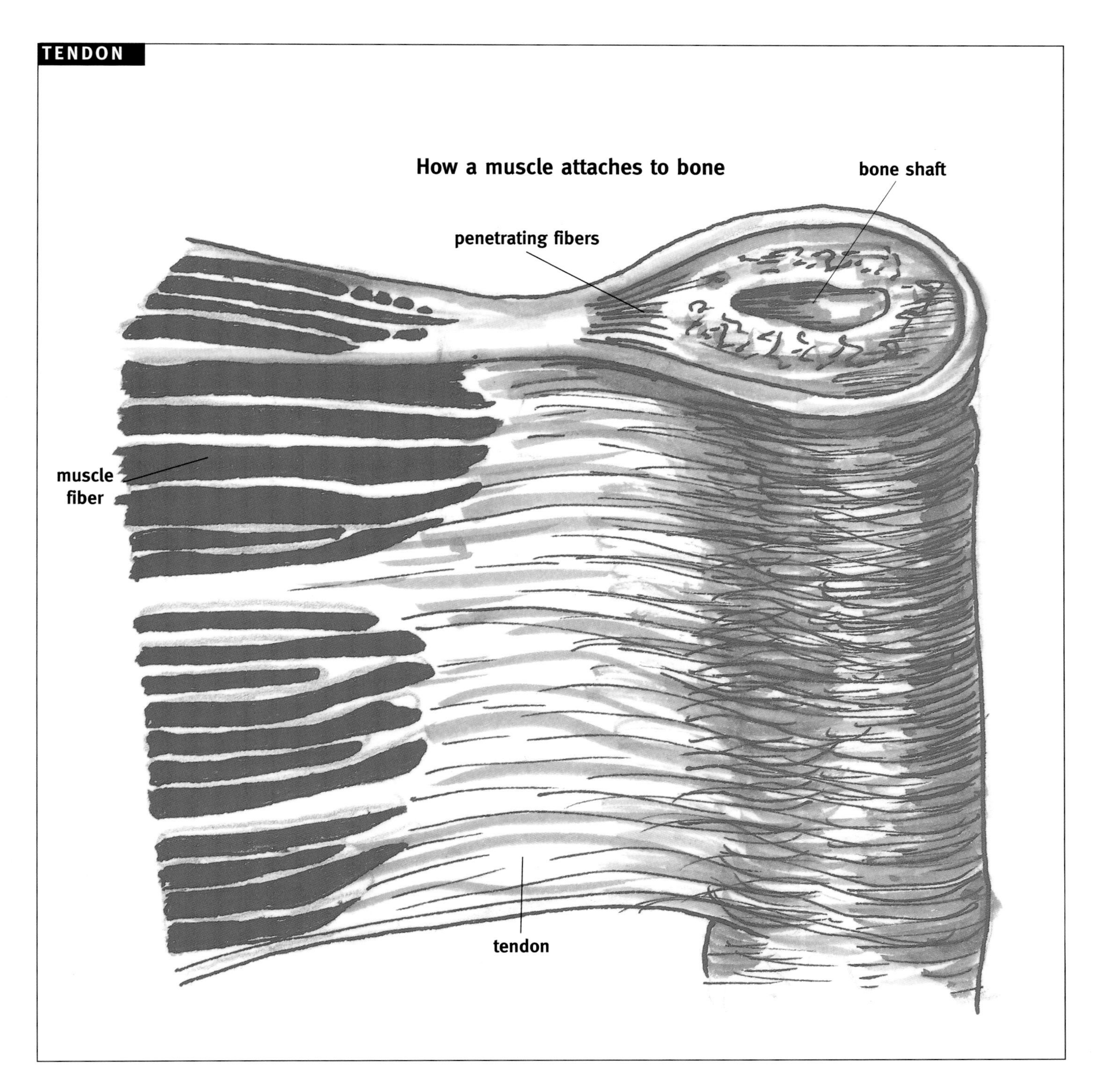

don fibers actually penetrate into the bone matrix, while others wrap around the bone on the outside. This creates a firm grip on the bone for the muscle to pull against.

Muscle groups are often arranged in pairs. An example is found in the the upper arm. The biceps muscle lies on the front side of the humerus, and the triceps muscle is in back. These two muscle groups move the forearm in opposite directions. When the biceps contracts, the forearm is flexed, or drawn in toward the upper arm. The triceps muscle is contracted to extend, or straighten, the lower arm. When one of these muscles contracts, the other automatically relaxes so that they are not pulling against each other.

This arrangement of opposing muscles around joints is a common pattern in the body. Practically any motion you can think of—standing, sitting, turning the head side to side, swinging the legs back and forth—are all produced by paired muscles that produce opposite movements.

The muscular system is capable of taking the human body through an incredible range of motion. Our muscles work so smoothly and efficiently most of the time that we take for granted our ability to get around. Frequent exercise and good nutrition are important to keep our muscles healthy, firm, and working properly; without these, muscles will atrophy.

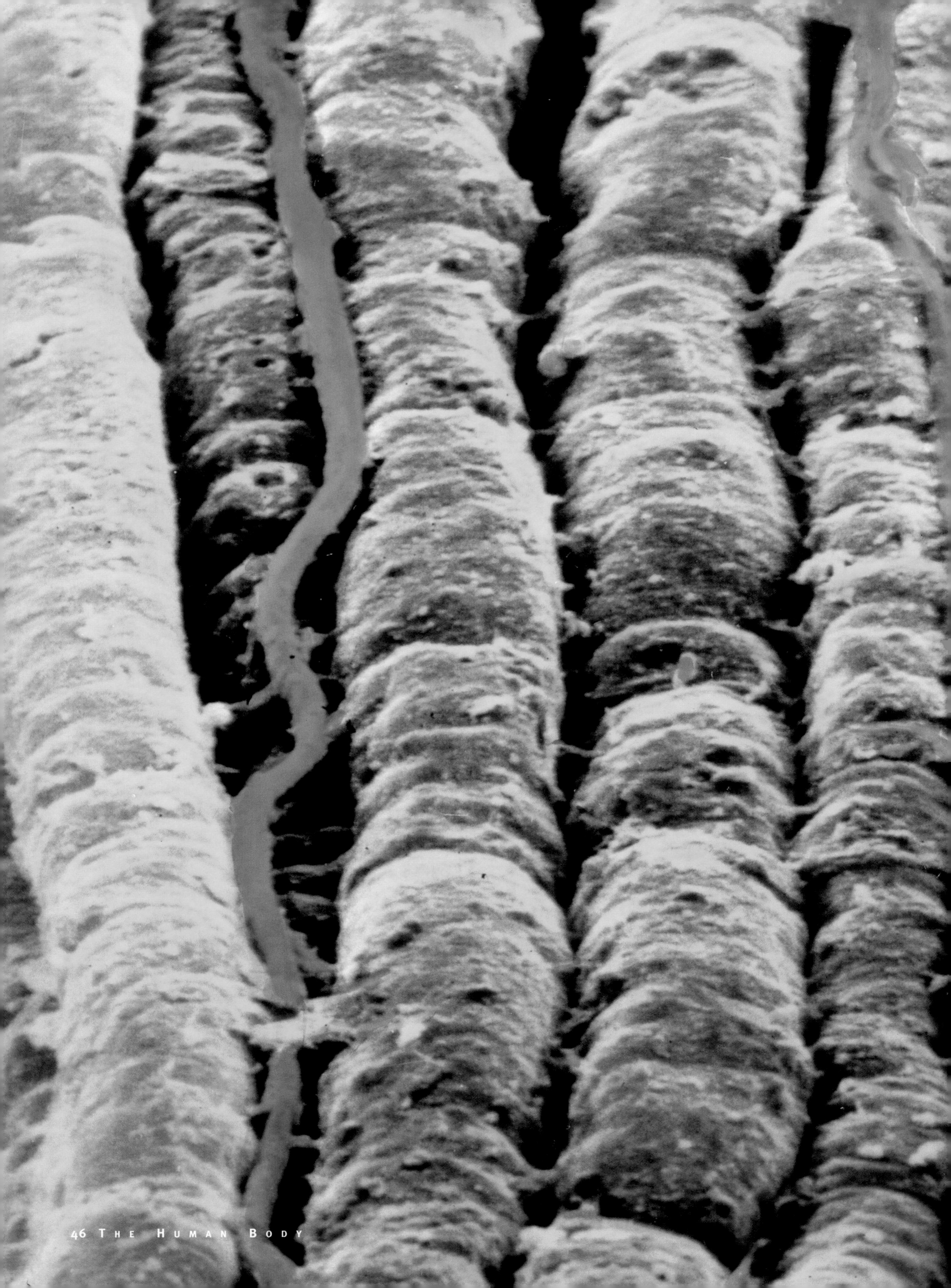

Chapter 5

THE NERVOUS SYSTEM

A common theme in the workings of the human body is specialization. From the topics covered so far we can see that cells, tissues, and organs are designed to carry out specific jobs that benefit the body as a whole. Just as a community is made up of teachers, police officers, bankers, and other people with different skills, so the body has specialized bone cells, muscle cells, and skin cells, each of which plays a vital part in our health and well-being. Working together, the cells of the body, like the members of a community, can accomplish much more than individuals working alone.

An important part of any complex system is communication. Imagine how confused your city or town would be without telephones, mail service, radio, television, or any other way to send and receive messages. Communication between cells is just as important. Even a simple task like walking across the street involves precise contraction and relaxation of thousands of muscle fibers at exactly the right time.

The nervous system is the body's communication network. It includes the brain, the control center of the entire body, which regulates the activities of all the other systems. Another part of the nervous system senses conditions in the environment around us and signals the right responses, such as jerking your foot upward when you accidentally step on a sharp object.

Let's begin with the cell types that make up the nervous system and detail how they function. Then, the general structure of this system, including the major divisions and functions of various nerves, will be considered. Finally, we will cover the special senses of smell, taste, hearing, and seeing, and briefly address the processes of higher thought.

OPPOSITE PAGE: Nerve fibers Electron micrograph of a nerve track containing several individual fibers. Layers of Schwann cells, which appear yellow in this photograph, are wrapped around the fibers, insulating them for optimal signal conduction. Blood vessels (small blue tubes), which feed and oxygenate nerve tissue, are also visible.

THE NEURON

STRUCTURE The basic unit of the nervous system is the nerve cell, or **neuron**. A neuron has a cell body containing the nucleus, several thin fibers on one side called **dendrites**, and one very long fiber on the other side called the **axon**. Neuron cell bodies are about the size of a typical cell, but the fibers, particularly the axon, can be extremely long; some extend from the lower spine down the entire length of the leg—about 36 inches (90cm) in an average adult.

Another cell type found in the nervous system is the **glial cell**. These support and

NEURON

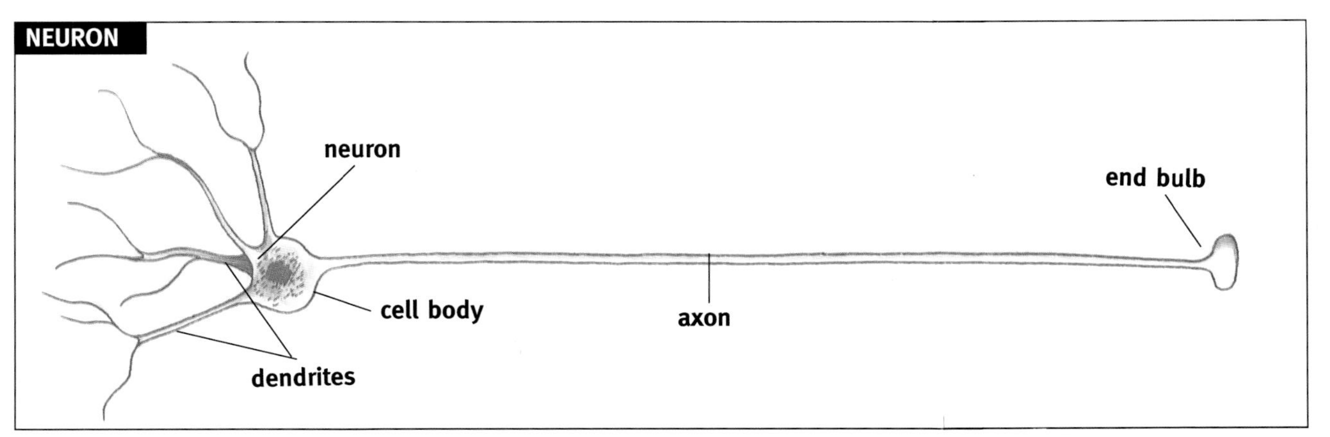

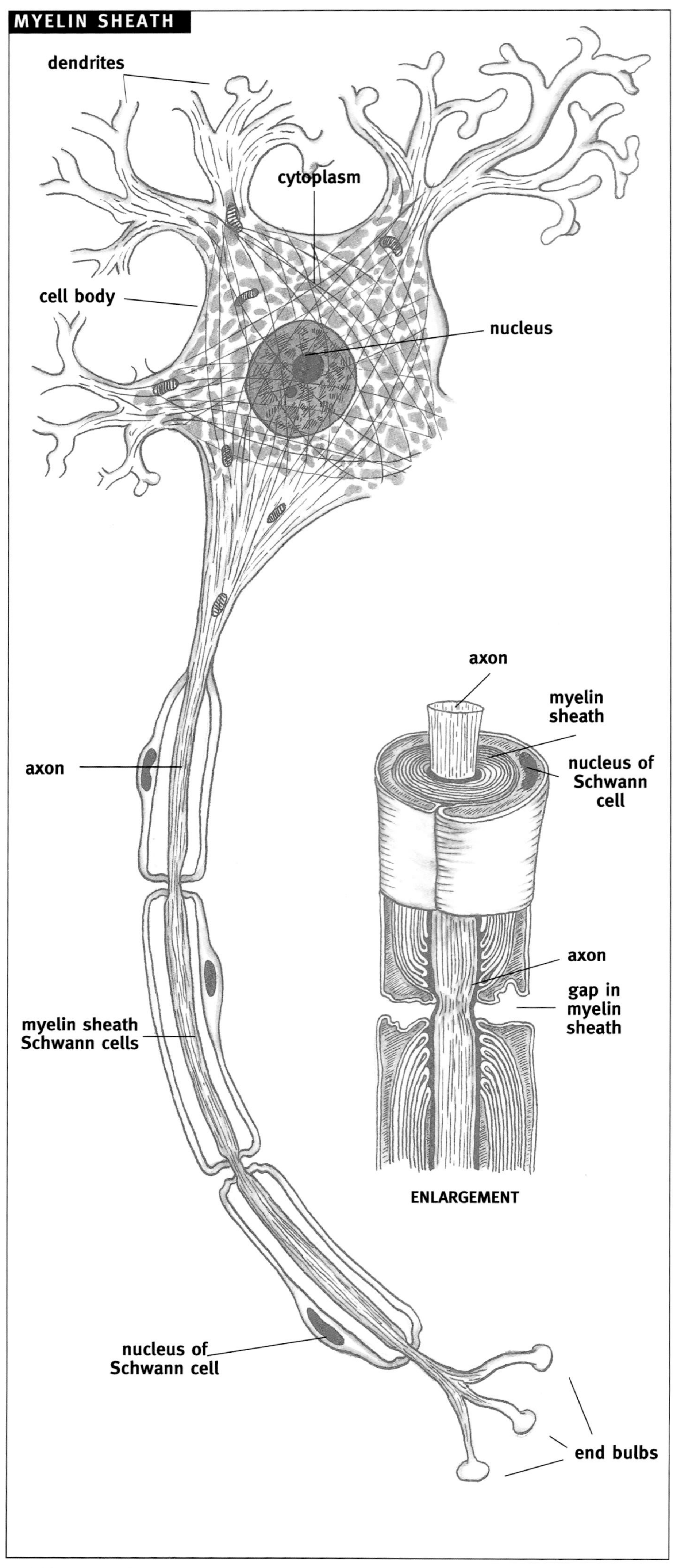

protect neurons and anchor them to neighboring cells or other structures. The axons of many neurons are covered by **Schwann cells**. These cells, which are rich in a substance called **myelin**, wrap around the axon to form a protective barrier known as a **myelin sheath**.

Schwann cells also aid in the repair of damaged axons, which can be restored even after complete separation. Nerve cell bodies, however, cannot regenerate. This is why nerve damage from accidents or disease is permanent—once the cell body of a neuron dies, the entire cell is destroyed. Since mature nerve cells cannot divide, more neurons cannot be produced to replace the damaged ones. This leaves the affected part of the body without nerve supply from then on.

Function Neurons are specially designed to carry signals from one place to another. They do this by conducting an electrical impulse along their dendrites and axon, much like a telephone wire conducts an electric current. Special features of neurons make them suited for this task.

The property that allows neurons to transmit an impulse is the ability to regulate certain charged chemicals. The important chemical in this system is the sodium ion, which carries a positive charge. Neurons have a **sodium pump**, which constantly pushes sodium out of the cell. As a result, a net positive charge builds up on the outside of the cell membrane. The inside of the cell builds up a net negative charge because of the many proteins and negative ions in the cytoplasm. Thus the cell membrane acts as a wall, separating the positive and negative charges. At this stage the cell membrane is polarized, which simply means the net charge on each side is different.

This separation of charges is the same principle that is at work in a battery, where positive and negative particles are grouped on opposite sides. The attraction of charged particles for each other creates a force, or a potential force, which is ready to go to work when wires are attached to the battery to create a current.

In a similar way, the nerve cell creates a membrane potential, a force that can actually be measured. When a nerve cell is stimulated to conduct a signal, holes form in the membrane. This forms a channel that allows a few sodium ions to rush in, reversing the charge across the membrane. The membrane is depolarized at that spot, creating an impulse. The impulse spreads down the membrane, triggering another channel to open, and carrying the signal along the nerve fiber. The channels are open only a fraction of a second, then slam shut once the impulse is past. This restores the membrane to a polarized state, ready for another signal. Nerve impulses always travel in one direction, beginning at the dendrites and moving along the axon.

By conducting impulses, then, neurons pass signals from one part of the body to another. But nerve pathways are made up of many neurons lined up in a chain. How is the impulse transferred from one neuron to another?

If you had to guess, you might think the axon of one neuron is attached to the dendrites of the next cell in line, so that the impulse simply travels from one cell membrane to the next. But this is not the case. Under the microscope, it can be seen that there is actually a space between the fibers of neurons in a pathway. This space is called a **synapse**, and makes a break in the pathway that the impulse cannot cross directly.

Since impulses cannot be transferred by direct physical contact, nerve cells use a different method; the electrical signal is changed into a chemical signal. At the end of the axon are tiny sacs, or vesicles, full of special chemicals called **neurotransmitters**. When an impulse reaches this point, the vesicles fuse to the cell membrane and dump

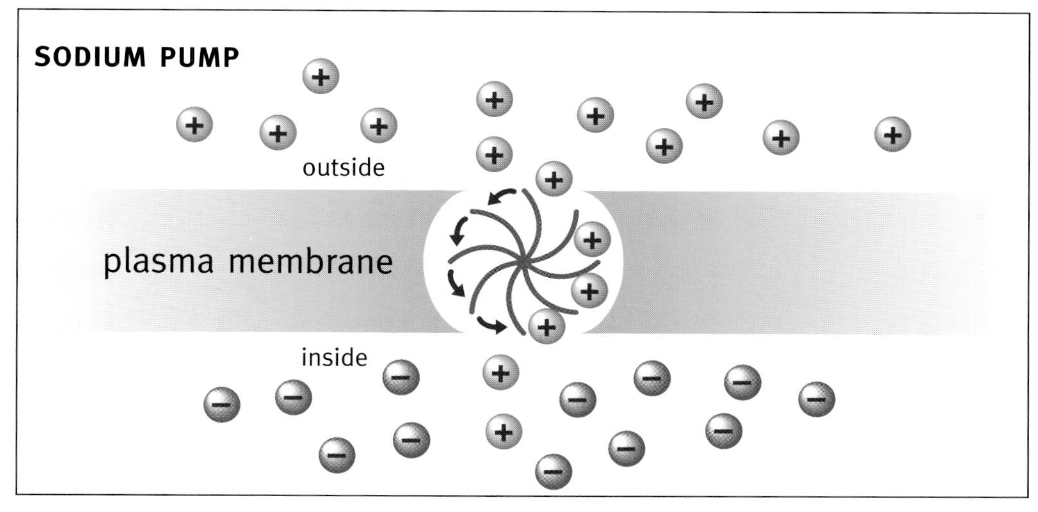

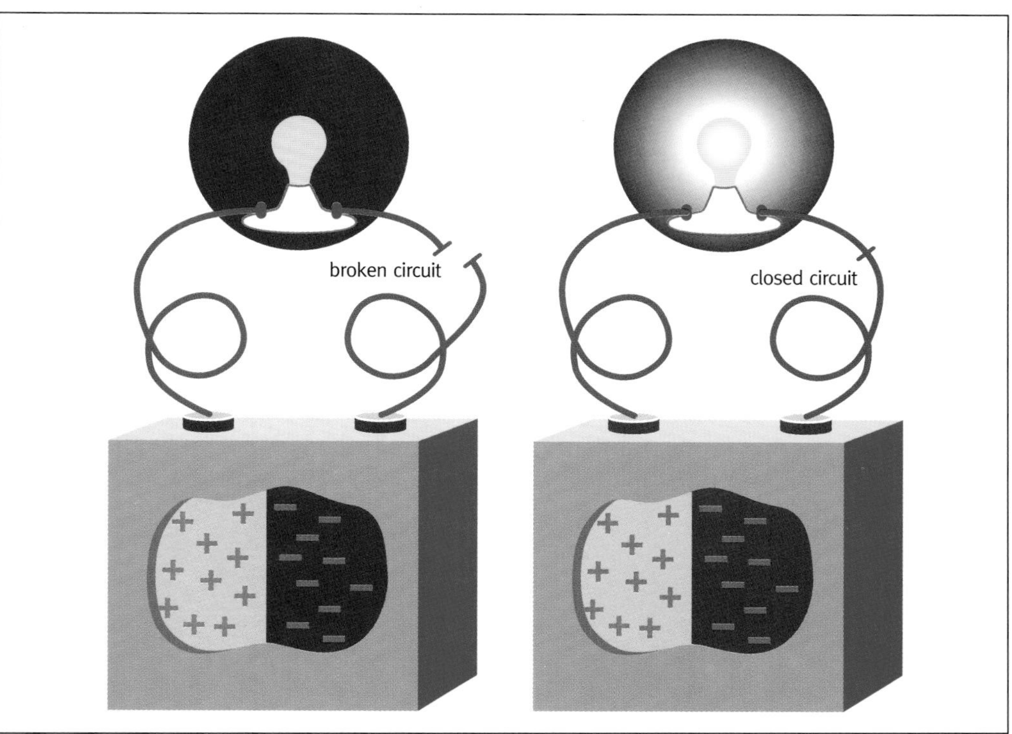

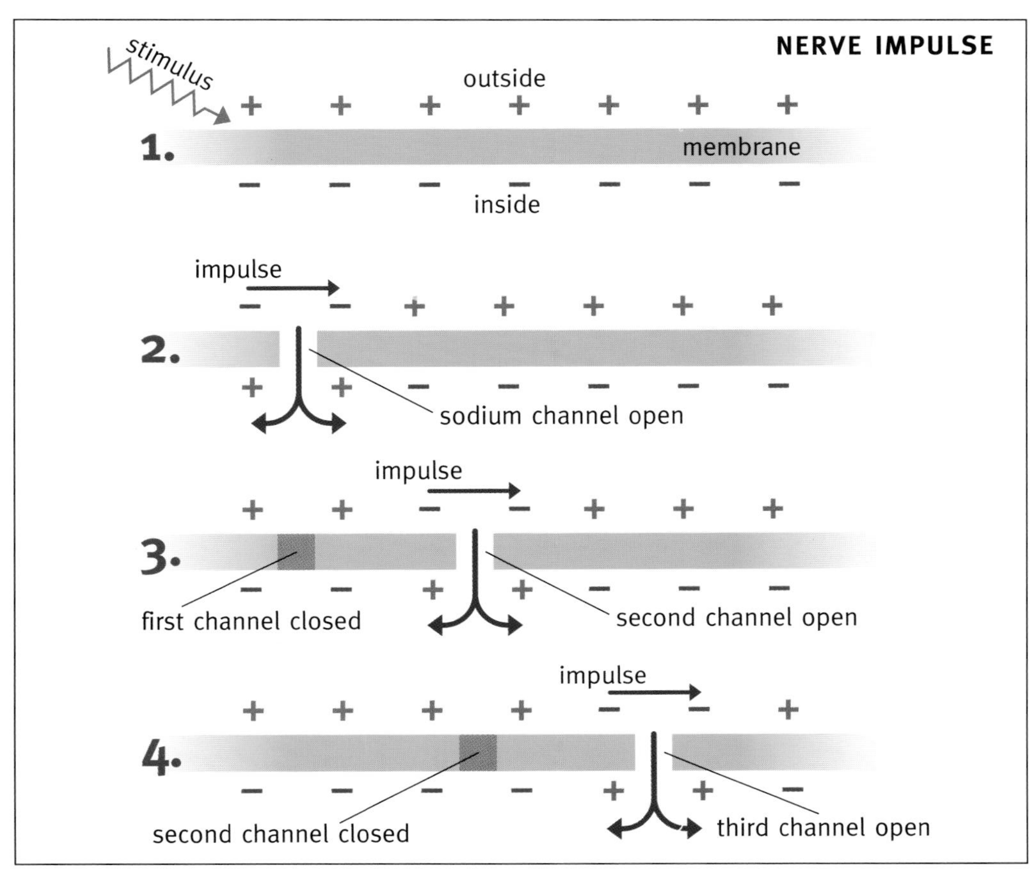

their load of neurotransmitters into the synaptic cleft, the space between axon and dendrite. The chemicals quickly travel to the surface of the dendrite, only a millionth of an inch away, and attach to the membrane. This depolarizes the dendrite, sending the impulse on its way.

Transmission of nerve impulses across a synapse occurs very quickly. In fact, the nervous system can carry signals through the body at incredible speed; it takes only one-fiftieth of a second to send a message from your brain through a chain of neurons, across synapses, and down to the muscles in your foot. That means impulses travel at an average rate of over 200 miles (360 km) per hour.

Now that we understand how individual nerve cells work, we are ready to examine how they are grouped and arranged to take in information and send out signals to control the body. Let's start with the two main divisions, the central and the peripheral nervous systems.

THE CENTRAL NERVOUS SYSTEM

The brain and spinal cord make up the central nervous system, a collection of billions of neurons connected to each other by dendrites and axons.

Brain More complex than the largest computer, the human brain receives information, processes it, and sends out messages to control all body functions. The adult brain, which weighs about three pounds (1.4 kg), is the one body organ that is so complicated that scientists have only recently begun to discover exactly how it works.

The **cerebrum**, where information processing occurs, is the largest division. The **cerebellum** is the structure that maintains your balance when you are standing

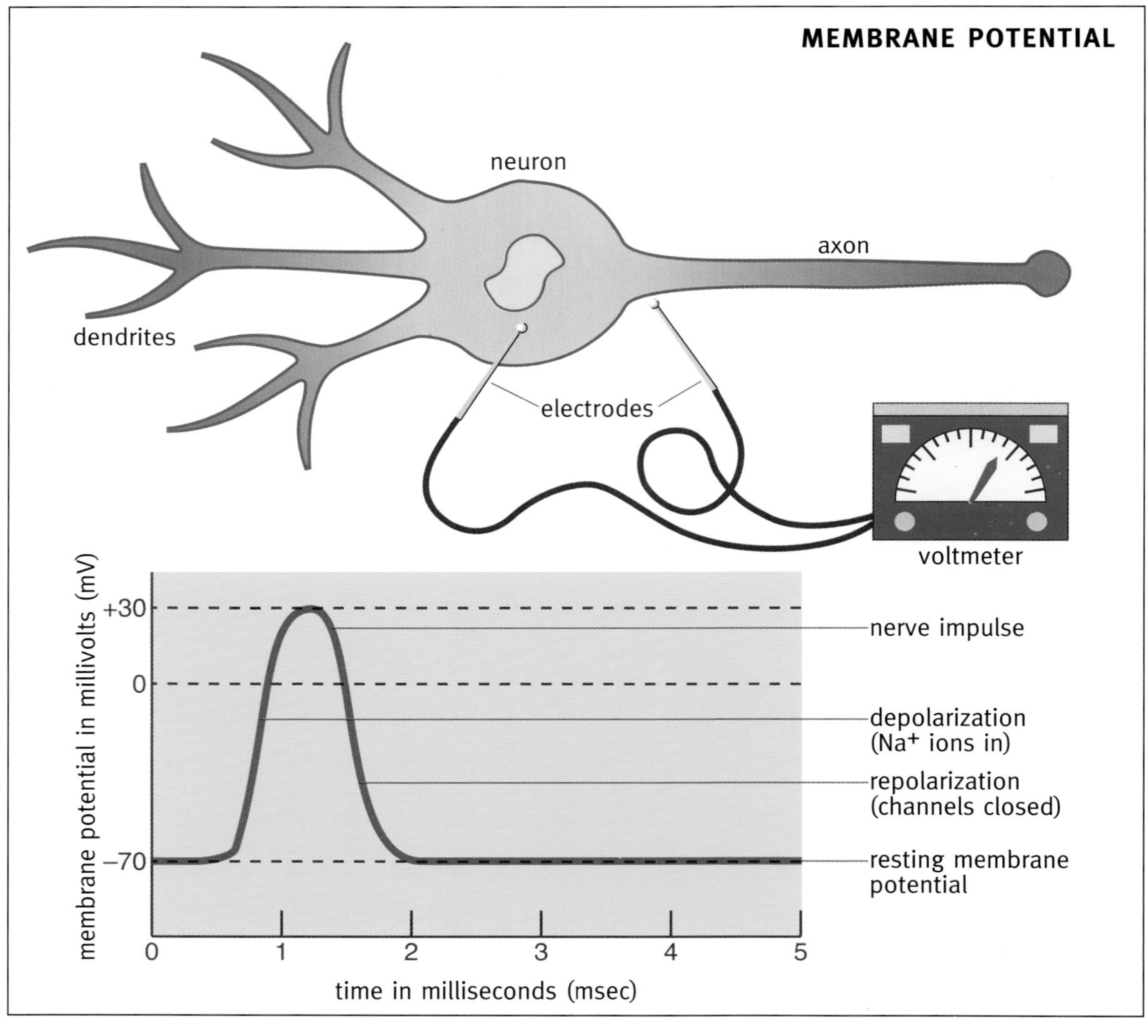

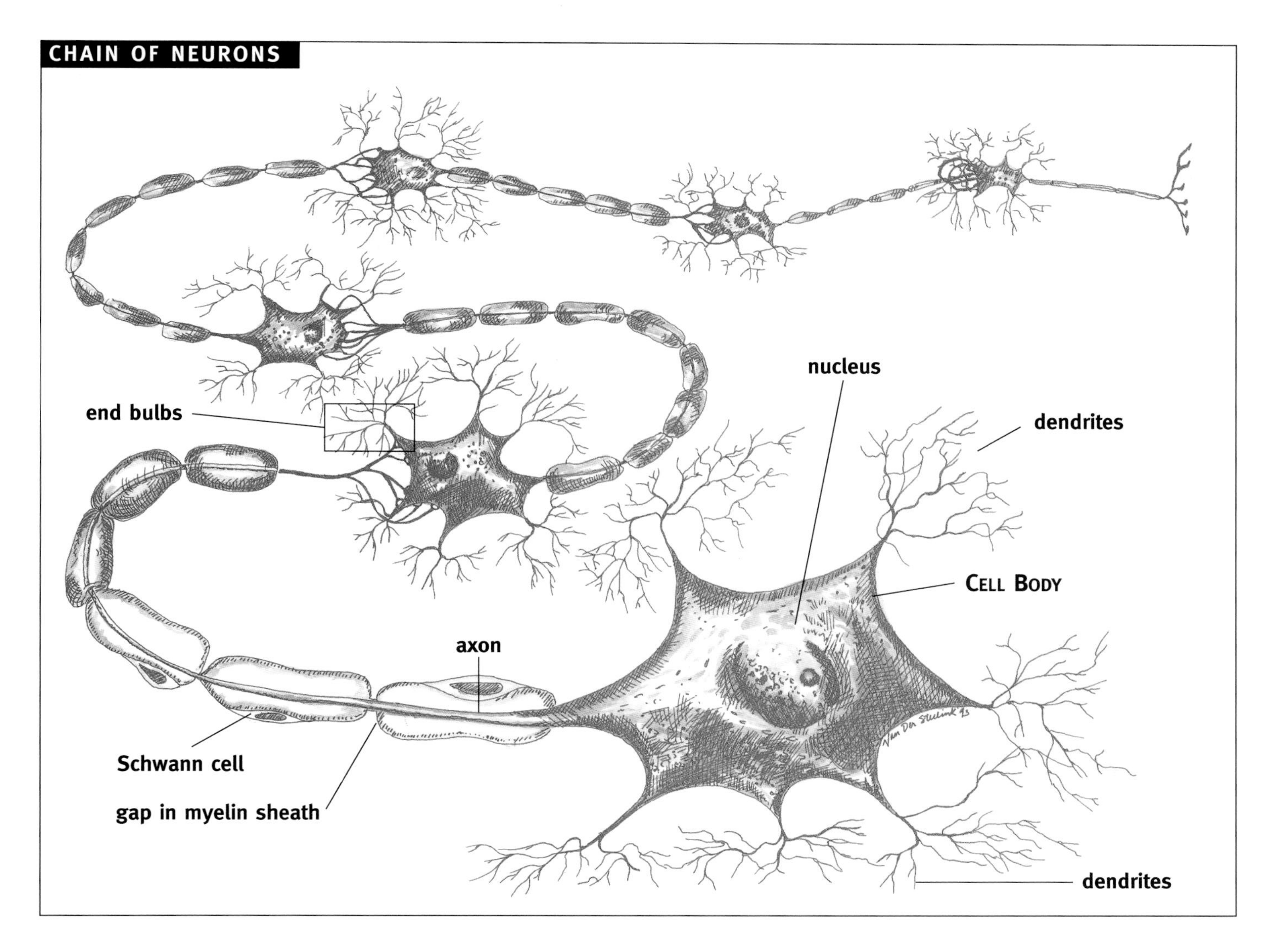

up, and the **diencephalon** contains structures that control the endocrine system, which will be covered in chapter 10. Below these regions is the **brain stem**, which connects the brain to the spinal cord.

Specific areas within the brain monitor and control different areas of the body. Many other body functions have yet to be connected to exact locations in the brain.

Surrounding the brain is a triple layer of thick membranes called the **meninges**. These tough membranes help protect the brain from invasion by microbes, and also cushion the soft neural tissues when you bump your head. The brain is also surrounded by a rich blood supply, as well as a special substance known as **cerebrospinal fluid**, which bathes the neurons in nutrients and other chemicals the brain needs to work properly.

Twelve major nerve bundles called the **cranial nerves** connect the brain directly to tissues and organs in the head regions. This connection provides direct control over the eyes, ears, muscles of the mouth, and other parts of the face and neck.

Spinal Cord Running down through the middle of the vertebrae is the spinal cord,

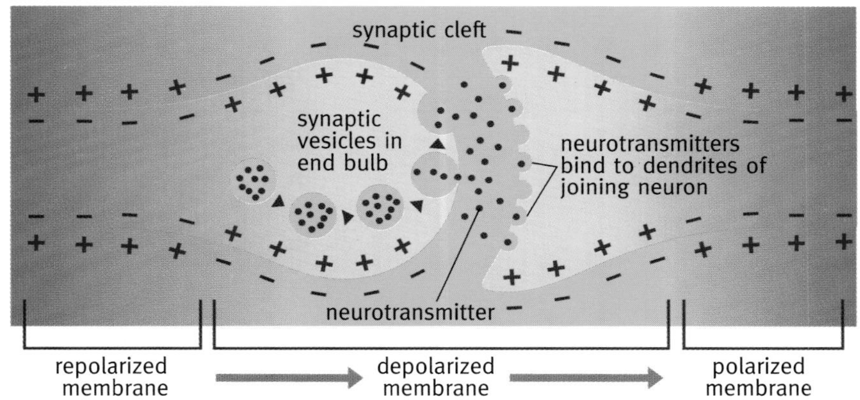

which contains billions of nerve fibers that carry signals in both directions. The cord is composed of two types of tissue: ascending tracts, which transmit signals from the rest of the body up to the brain, and descending tracts, which carry impulses from the brain out to muscles and other tissues.

Branching off from the spinal cord between vertebrae are the spinal nerves. These nerve trunks connect all of the body's organs and tissues below the head to the central nervous system.

Some of the nerves entering and exiting the spinal cord have connections to each

BRAIN STRUCTURE

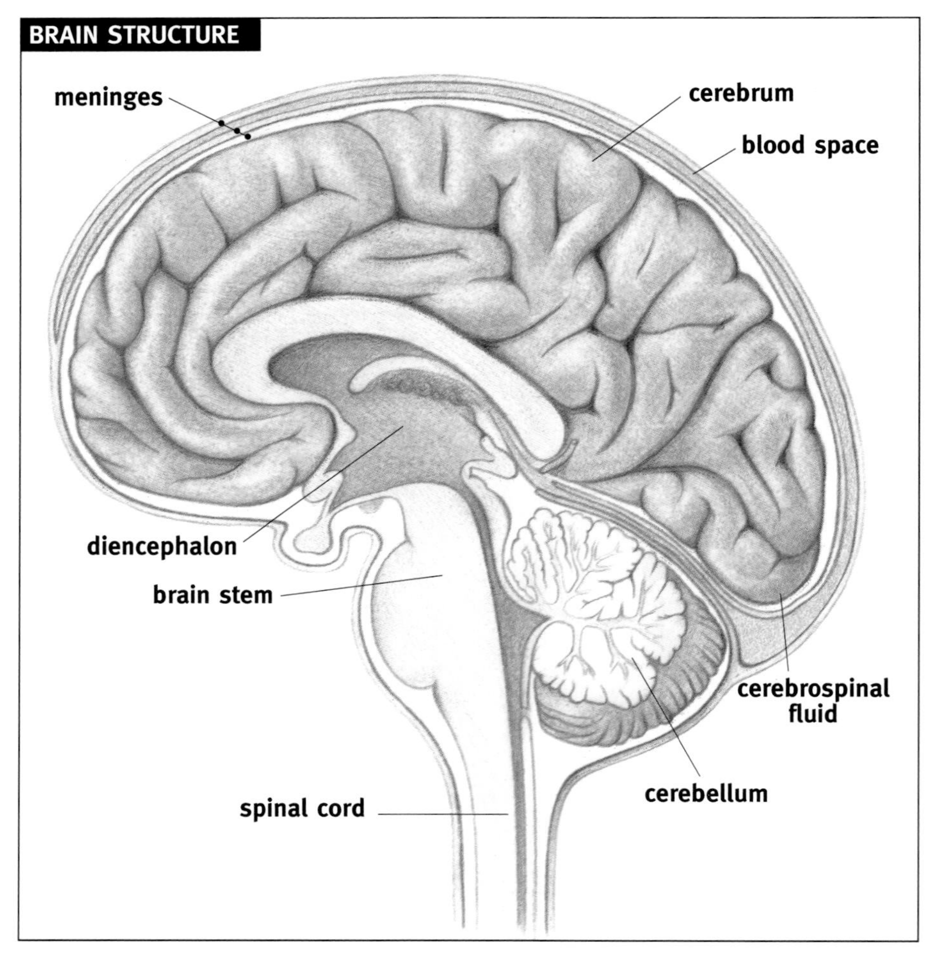

other as well as to pathways up to the brain. This arrangement forms a loop that does not depend on the brain for a response, allowing a faster and simpler reaction in critical situations. Such a neural pathway is called a **reflex arc** and provides rapid adjustments to outside conditions. When you accidentally touch a hot flame, for example, a reflex arc quickly jerks your finger away, minimizing damage to your skin. This reflex occurs without brain involvement, so that the response is already over before you even have time to think about it.

THE PERIPHERAL NERVOUS SYSTEM

All of the nerves outside the brain and spinal cord are part of the peripheral nervous system. These nerves can be grouped into three divisions: sensory, motor, and autonomic.

Sensory In order to control other organs and systems, the brain must receive informa-

BRAIN CONTROL AREAS

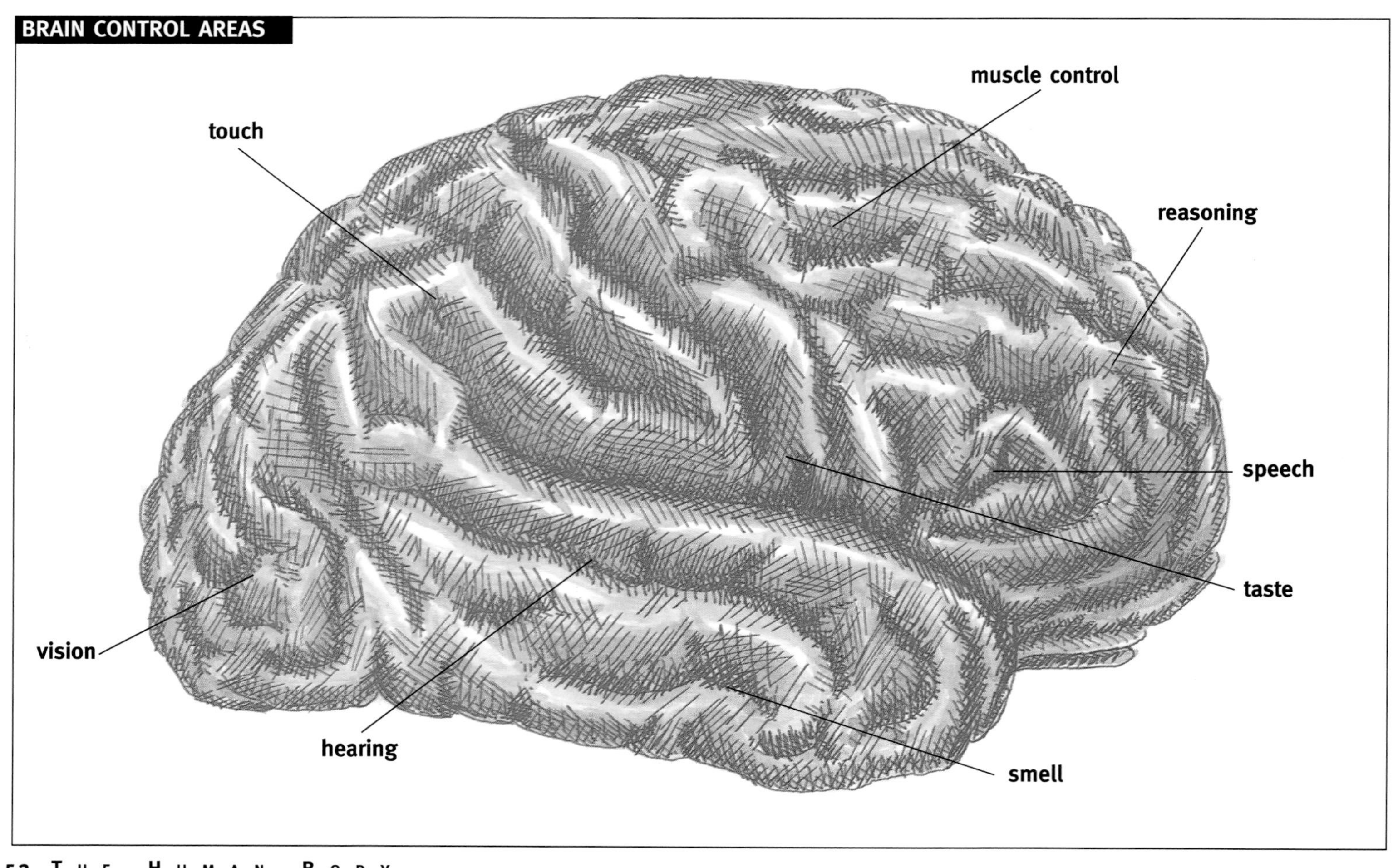

tion about conditions both inside and outside the body. This information is provided by **sensory neurons**, which send messages into the central nervous system. Sensory neurons are designed to detect specific types of stimulation.

Touch Meissner's corpuscles are nerve endings just under the epidermis that respond to something coming into contact with the skin. Anything that touches the skin changes the shape of these corpuscles slightly, causing them to send impulses toward the brain. There are also nerve fibers wrapped around hair follicles, which is why you can sense things brushing against the hair on your arms or legs without experiencing actual skin contact.

Pressure Sensors in the subcutaneous layer known as Pacinian corpuscles respond to deep pressure, such as your arm being squeezed.

Pain You may wish your body did not have any pain neurons, especially when you get hurt. But sensing pain is useful; it makes you aware that something is wrong and needs attention. Pain receptors are dendrites of certain neurons that respond to cell damage. When cells are stressed they release chemicals that trigger pain receptors to send impulses toward the brain. As most of us already know firsthand, pain receptors are found almost everywhere in the body.

Temperature The sensory neurons that signal hot and cold are not well understood. Whatever their design, they are activated in response to changes in the temperature around the body or the skin itself as it comes in contact with hot or cold surfaces.

Position Special neurons in muscles and joints make us aware of the position of various body parts. For example, with your eyes closed you can tell if your arms and legs are straight or bent. This provides the central nervous system with immediate information it can use to adjust the body's position when needed.

The number of sensory neurons is not the same throughout the body. For example, many more receptors for touch and other sensations are found in the hands than on the back or stomach.

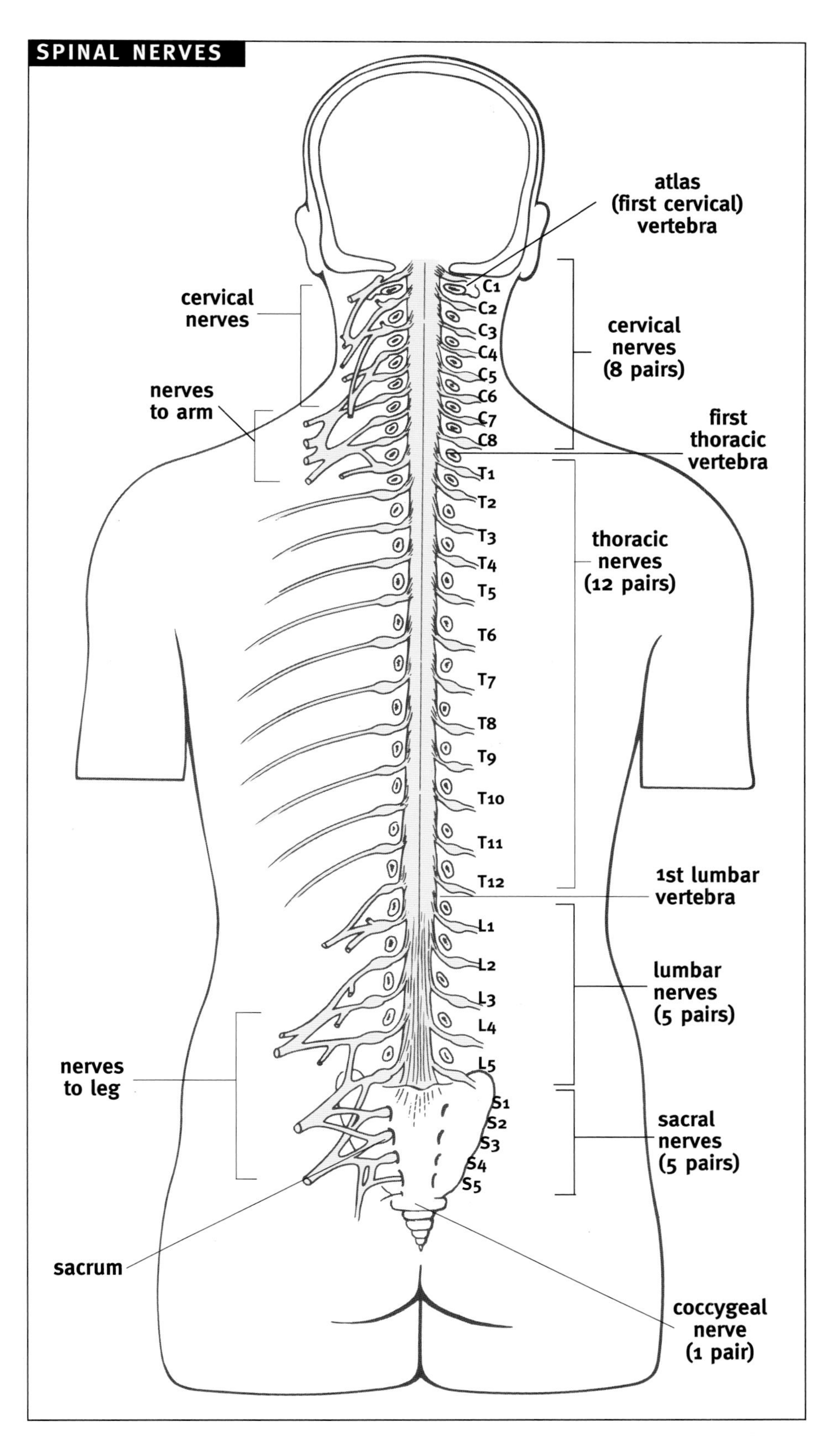

Motor A large part of the nervous system is devoted to connecting every muscle fiber in the body to the brain. Nerves connected to muscles are called **motor neurons**, since they control the body's motor functions or movements.

Motor neurons attach to muscles through the motor end plate, as described in chapter 4. Impulses that are sent from the brain through the motor neurons signal muscles

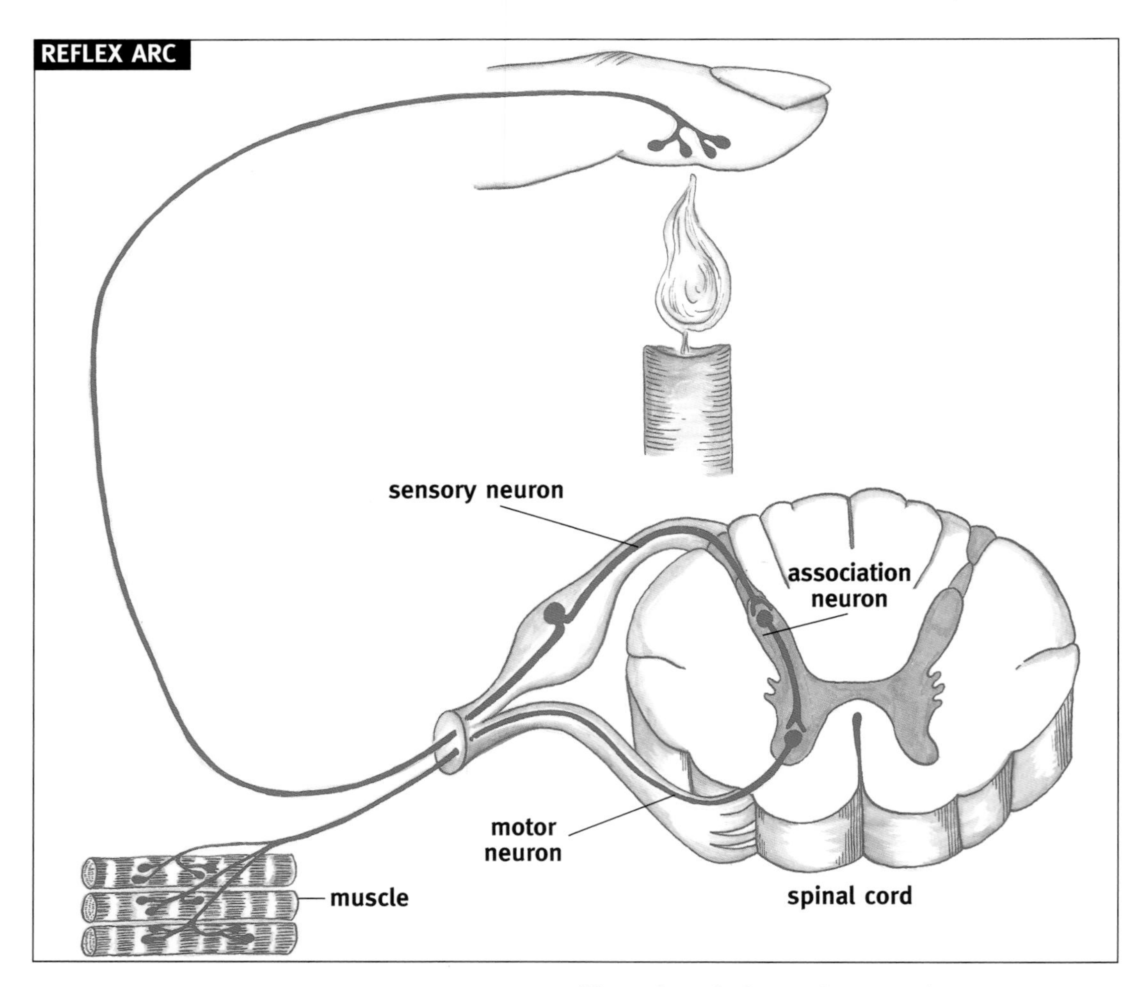

vides for the detailed movements that allow our hands to perform delicate and complicated tasks.

Except in a few cases, motor neurons are voluntary, that is, they are under conscious control. This means you must think about moving your legs to walk, your arms to climb, and other skeletal muscles to produce movement.

AUTONOMIC While skeletal muscle is under voluntary control, other muscle types usually are not. Smooth muscles in the skin and other organs are attached to nerves that send impulses without you knowing it. Together these neurons form the autonomic nervous system, which carries signals from the brain out to organs and tissues.

The autonomic system affects the activity of many of the internal organs. For example, contraction of intestinal muscles to push food along is regulated by this system. The heart, though it beats by itself, is also regulated autonomically.

There are two divisions of autonomic nerves, **sympathetic** and **parasympa-**

to contract, pulling the skeleton into various positions.

A large number of separate nerve fibers connect to muscles in the fingers and thumb. With many motor neurons per muscle, more control is possible. This pro-

SLEEPING LEGS

Have you ever sat in a cramped position for a long time and then stood up to discover that your legs are numb? When this strange, awkward feeling occurs we say our legs have "gone to sleep." Standing up straight or walking normally is difficult because the legs tingle and burn, and just won't work right. What causes this strange feeling?

Nerve cells are among the most chemically active in the whole body. This means they require a constant, heavy supply of blood to bring them oxygen and nutrients, which they use up at a very fast pace. The brain, for example, which is made up almost entirely of nerve cells, has an extremely rich blood supply. Although it makes up only 2 percent of a person's total body weight, the brain receives 10 percent of the body's entire blood supply.

Sitting in certain positions for a long time puts pressure on the legs. But it is actually not pressure on nerves in the legs that makes them go to sleep. It is possible to pressure nerves, but that takes more than just sitting—the leg nerves are too deep and protected to be easily pinched. There are, however, large blood vessels running down the legs that supply nerves. These vessels can be pinched, slowing down the delivery of oxygen and nutrients to nerves in the area.

With reduced blood supply, the nerves stop working correctly, resulting in numbness. Sometimes you don't notice this until you try to stand up—then you feel the tingling sensation running down your legs. As you rub them and move around, blood flow is restored and the nerves slowly regain feeling and motor functions.

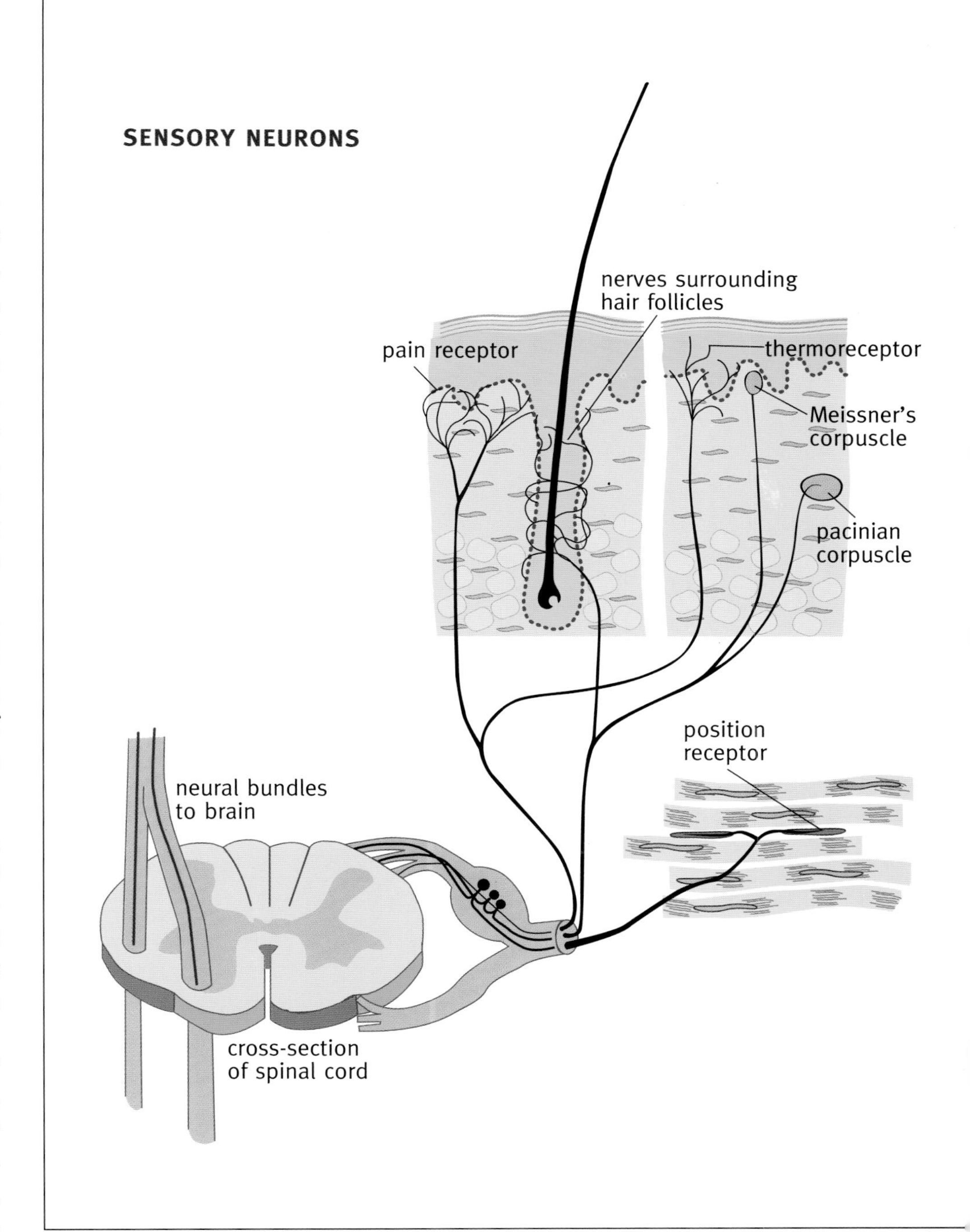

thetic. Most organs are connected to neurons from both divisions. The sympathetic and parasympathetic nerves attached to an organ send opposite signals. In the heart, for example, the sympathetic fibers stimulate, and the parasympathetic fibers inhibit. This provides a way to control heart rate. For example, if the heart is beating too slowly for the body's needs, impulses through sympathetic fibers increase the heart's rate. When the heart starts going too fast, parasympathetic fibers signal it to slow down.

SPECIAL SENSES

Certain neurons and support cells form complex organs that can sense features of the world around us. These are the special senses of smell, taste, hearing, and seeing.

Smell (Olfactory sense) Olfaction, or smelling, is the simplest of the special senses. It is made possible by neurons in the inner lining of the nasal cavity. There are different types of olfactory neurons—about fifty at the latest count—each of which responds to a specific smell.

The dendrites of these neurons are very sensitive to certain chemicals in the air. When such chemicals enter the nose, they penetrate a mucous layer covering the neurons and come in contact with dendrites. This activates an impulse that travels to the brain. For a chemical to have a smell, it must be carried in the air, and must also dissolve in the mucous membrane inside the nose. Only a small portion of all chemicals share these two properties.

How does the brain detect different smells? Since different types of olfactory neurons respond to different chemicals, only a fraction of all the neurons are activated by one smell. By sorting out the source of incoming signals, the brain can detect which chemical is present in the nose. Olfaction is extremely sensitive; some chemicals can be smelled when only one out of every million molecules in the air is that chemical.

Taste (Gustatory sense) The sensation of taste is sponsored by the 2,000 taste buds located mostly on the tongue, though some are also found in the throat. Each taste bud contains about twelve sensory neurons that respond to one of just four basic sensations: sweet, sour, salty, and bitter.

The sensation of taste is produced when specific molecules in the food we eat dissolve in the saliva on the tongue and then bind to the ends of neurons in the buds. A nerve impulse is activated and travels to the brain. As with incoming olfactory signals, the brain sorts out which type of neurons were stimulated, and we experience the matching taste sensation.

We can experience many more taste sensations than just the four basic types. Combinations of several tastes often give new flavors. In addition, taste is affected by smell. As food is taken into the mouth, odors drift up into the nasal cavity and

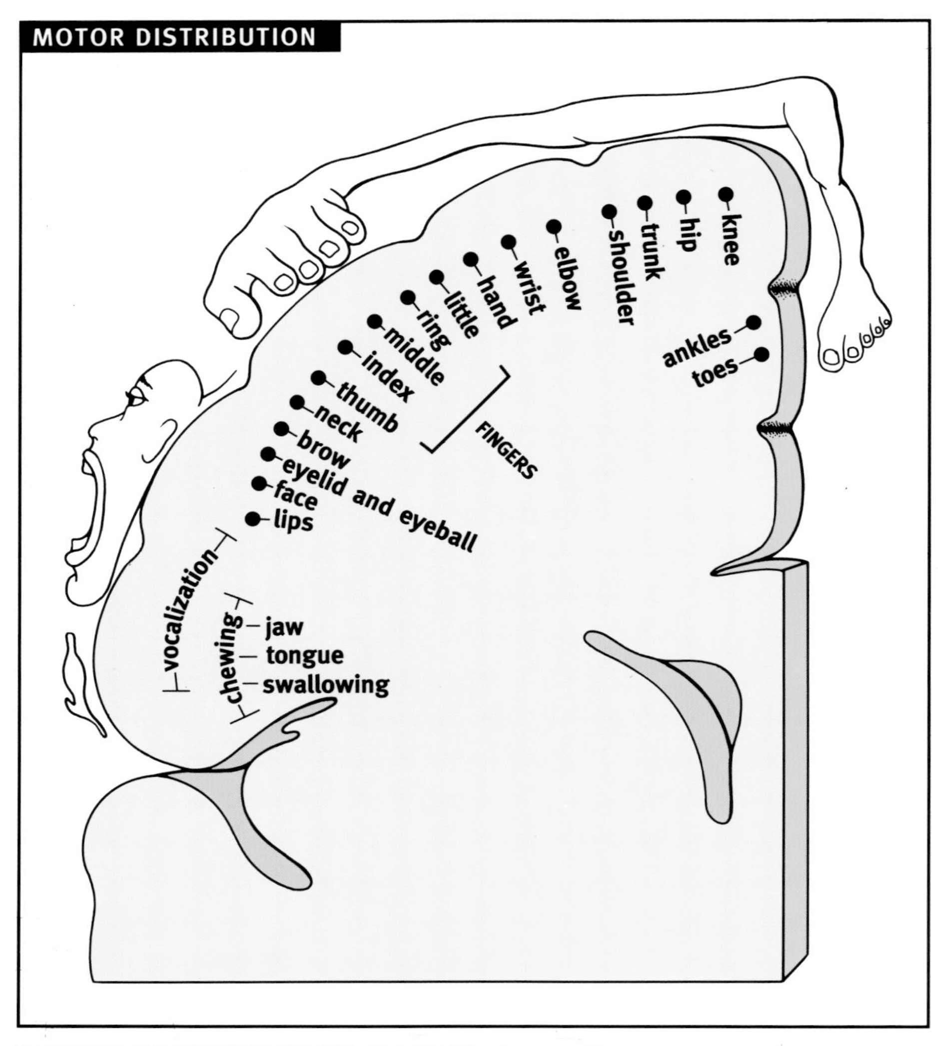

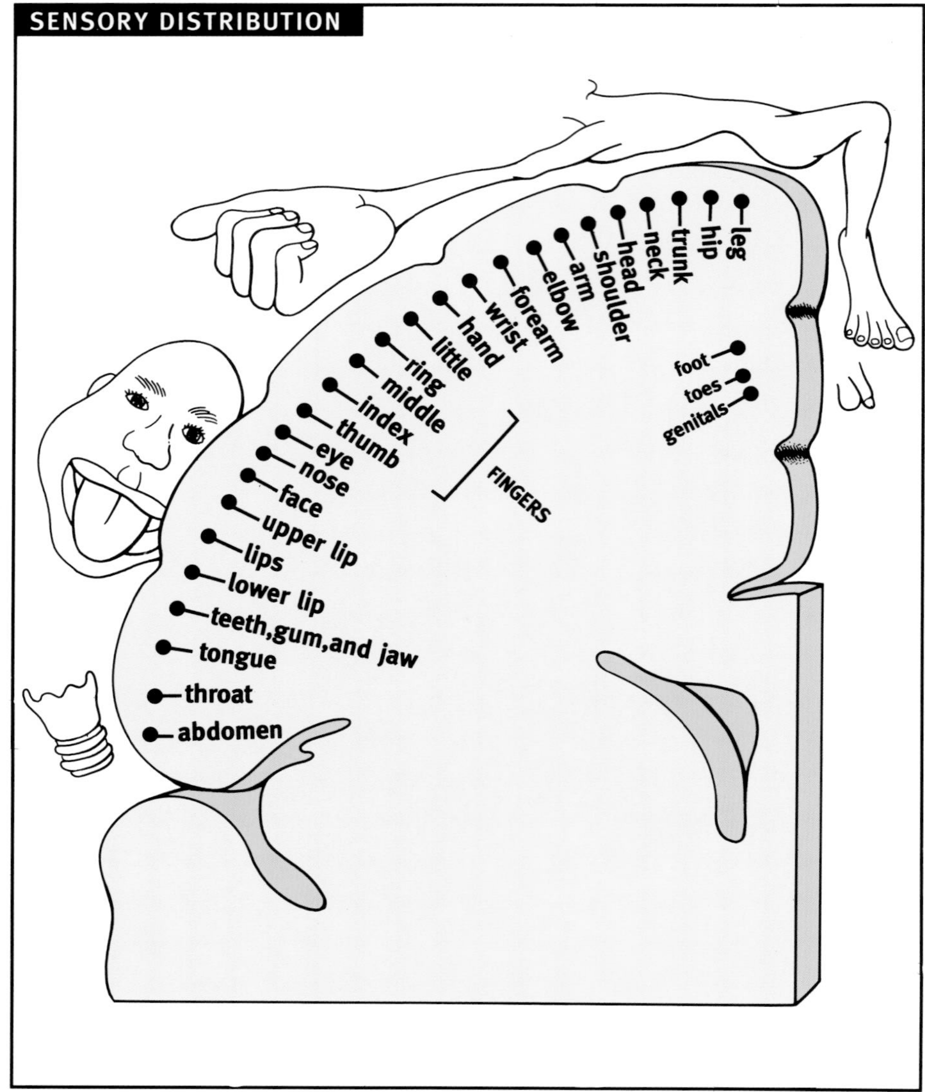

enhance the total sensation. You may have noticed that food doesn't have much flavor when you have a cold. The virus that causes a cold triggers two responses that interfere with the olfactory senses. First, mucous secretions inside the nasal sinuses increase and thicken. This helps trap and eliminate virus particles, but it also prevents efficient penetration of odoriferous substances. Second, cold viruses bring on inflammation and swelling of nasal membranes, which interferes with proper functioning of the delicate olfactory dendrites. In this way a cold eliminates our sense of smell, leaving only the four basic tastes working, and with these limited sensations, even if you feel like eating, food is not very exciting.

Hearing (Auditory sense) The ability to perceive sound waves is highly developed in humans. The outer ear, or **pinna**, is a funnel-shaped flap of skin and cartilage that directs sound waves into the **external canal**. This opening is about 1 inch (2.5cm) long, and is covered at the inner end by the **tympanic membrane**, or eardrum, a thin layer of tissue stretched tightly across the canal.

Attached to the inside of the eardrum are three bones, the **malleus, incus**, and **stapes**—also known as the hammer, anvil, and stirrup because of their shapes. These small bones form a bridge to the **cochlea**, a shell-shaped organ filled with a special kind of fluid called perilymph. The stapes fits against the cochlea at the **oval window**. Inside the cochlea is a row of sensory neurons with end hairs that sit against the **tectorial membrane**.

When sound waves enter the ear, they cause the eardrum to vibrate. This makes the ear bones rock back and forth, transferring the signal to the cochlea. As the stapes moves against the oval window, vibrations flow through the internal fluid. This makes the tectorial membrane move, pushing it against the sensitive hairs of the sensory neurons. That contact stimulates impulses in the neurons that are sent toward the brain.

THE AUTONOMIC SYSTEM

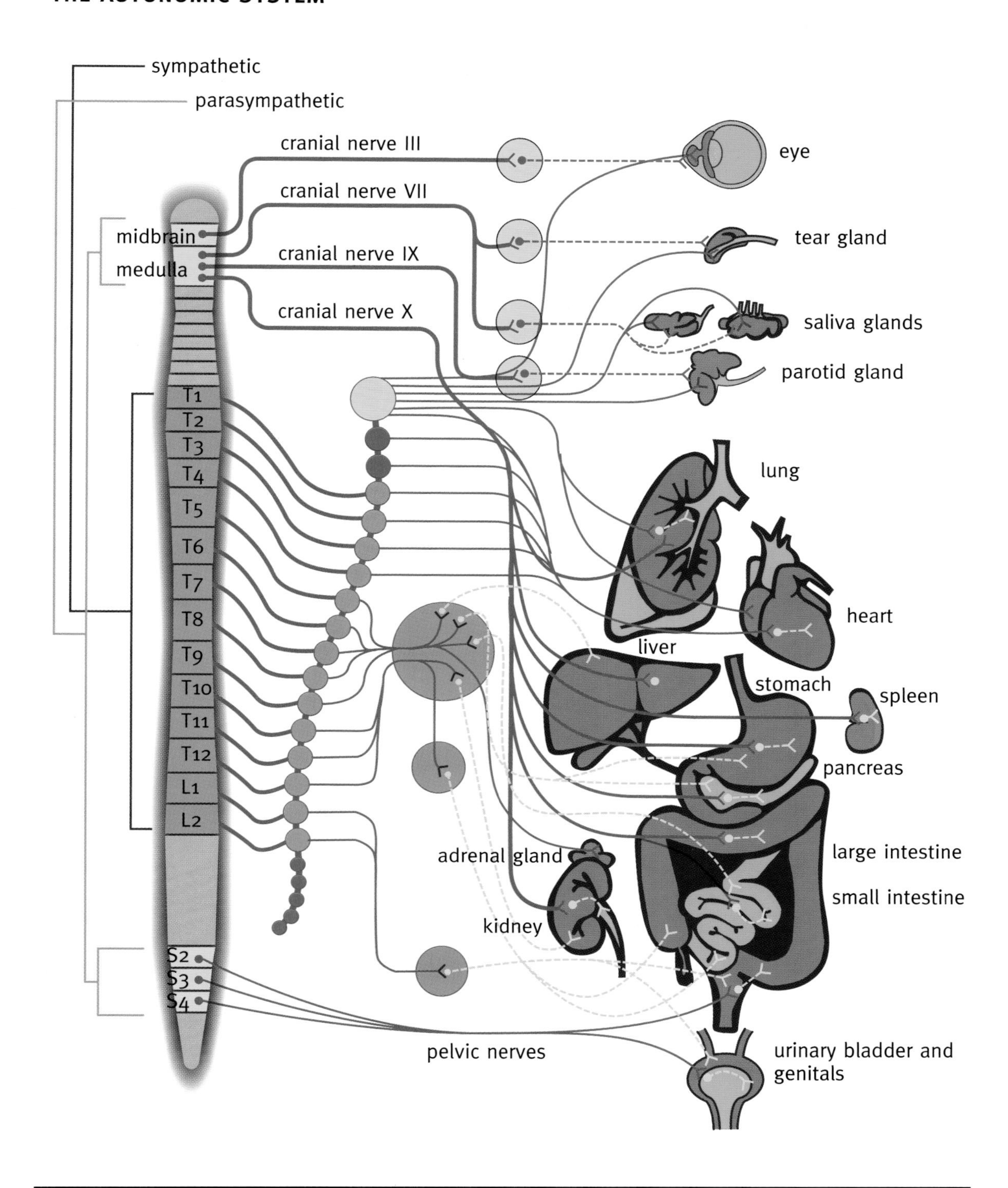

MIND-BODY CONNECTIONS

The autonomic nervous system functions independently of our conscious thoughts . . . or does it? For the most part, autonomic functions certainly carry on by themselves. But there is solid evidence that meditation—a relaxation technique that requires concentrating on soothing, pleasant thoughts—can affect some of these functions.

Deep meditation has been shown to lower oxygen consumption, decrease heart rate, and reduce blood pressure. Changes in brain wave patterns have also been measured, as well as reduction in the blood level of lactic acid, a somewhat harmful waste product.

Based on the principles of meditation, the science of biofeedback has emerged. This is a technique in which a patient monitors some feature of his or her own body, such as blood pressure, and then consciously tries to affect it. With practice, it is possible to learn to control these autonomic functions and thereby directly improve one's own health.

Biofeedback has been used to successfully treat a variety of conditions, including asthma, anxiety, pain, high blood pressure, headaches, and stomach disorders.

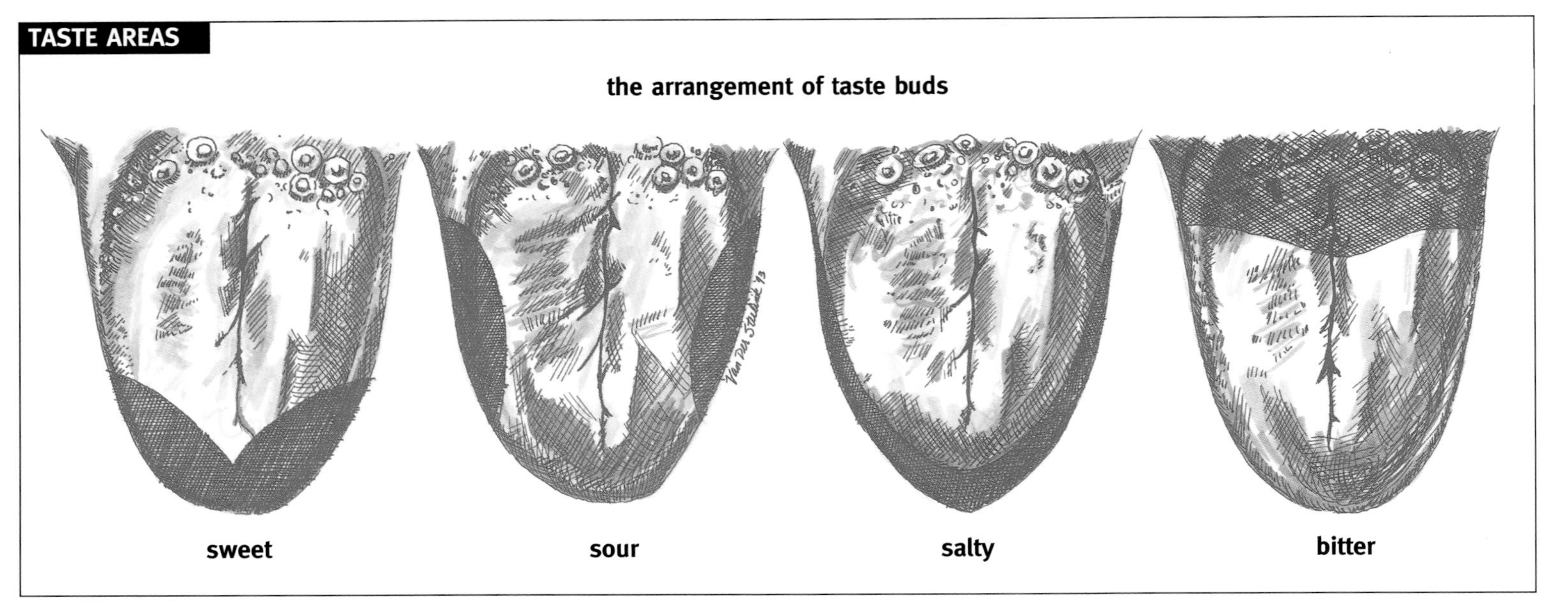

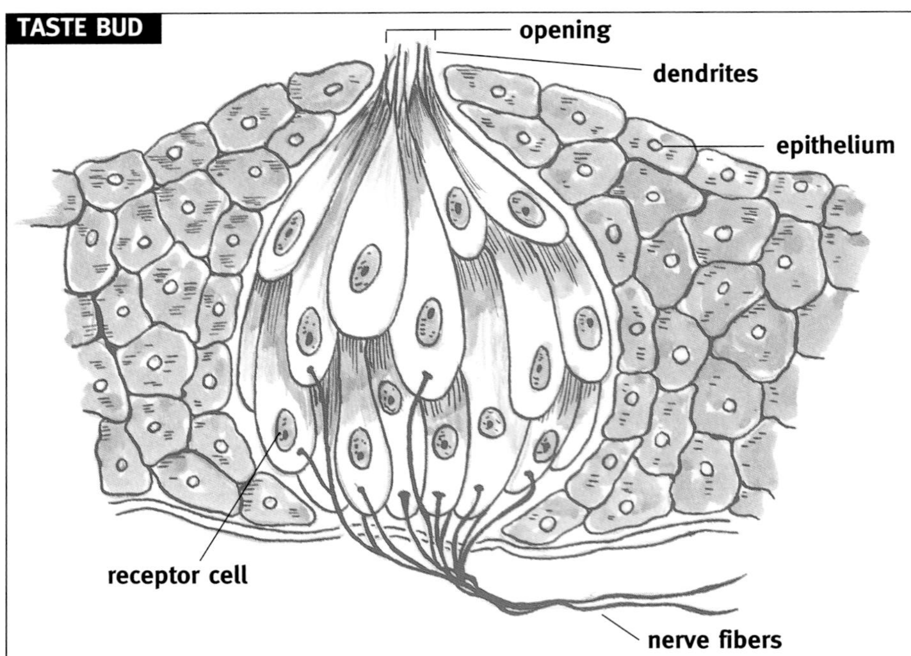

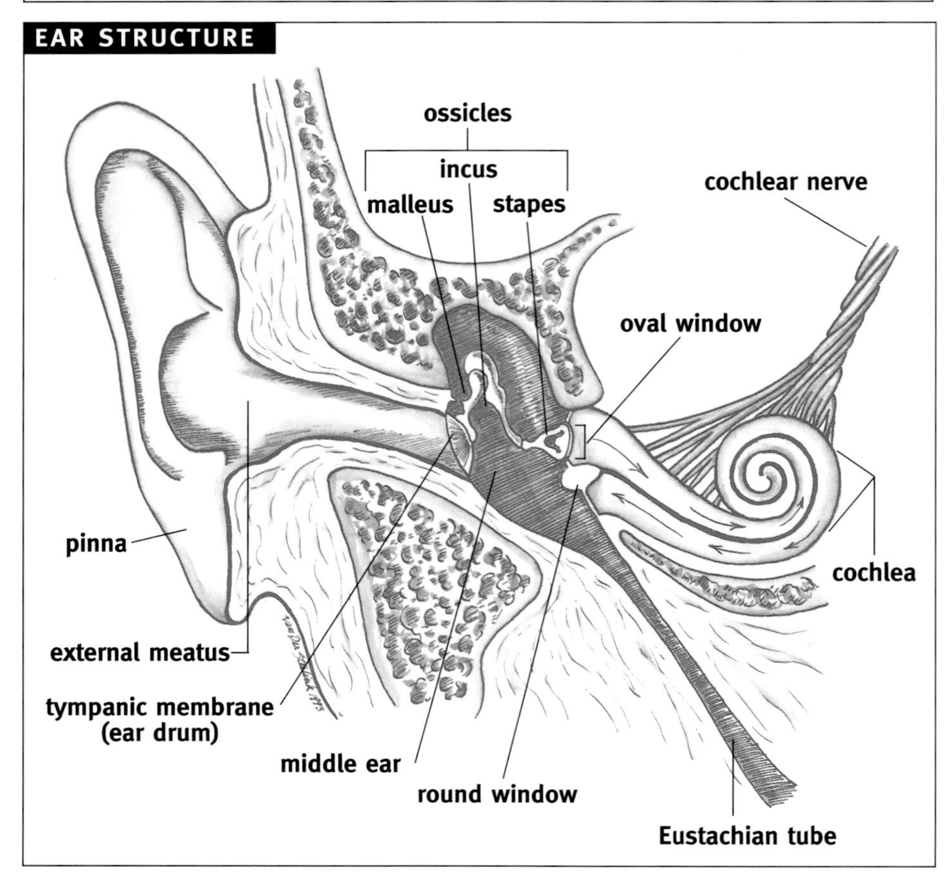

The auditory system is very complex both structurally and functionally. This is necessary to create the sensitivity of our hearing, the many different kinds of sounds we can detect.

There is another system of fluid-filled tubes in the inner ear in addition to the cochlea. These are the **semicircular canals**, similar in structure to the cochlea, but with a different function. Along with the cerebellum, these canals maintain our equilibrium—they help us keep our balance. This is why ear infections can cause dizziness; pressure in the inner ear interferes with the semicircular canals and throws off our balance.

Seeing (Visual sense) The most highly developed and amazing sense of all is vision. Our eyes permit us to perceive different colors of light, which is one kind of energy.

On the outside of the eyeball is the eyelid, a moving flap of skin that closes for protection during sleep or when there is dirt or dust in the air. The lids snap shut for a fraction of a second—a process called blinking—several times every minute. This spreads fluid from the **lacrimal glands**, or tear ducts, over the eye, keeping it moist. Secretions from the lacrimal glands, also known as tears, contain **lysozyme**, an enzyme that breaks open bacteria and kills them. Thus, blinking helps prevent infections in the eyes. Forming a clear protective covering over the inner eye is the **cornea**, behind which is the **iris**, a muscle layer that controls how much light is allowed to enter. Next is the **lens**, which focuses incoming light on the tissue layer at the back of the eyeball—the **retina**. Between the cornea and lens is the **anterior chamber**, and between lens and retina is the **posterior chamber**. Both of these compartments are filled with fluid. The retina feeds into the **optic nerve**, which connects with the visual center in the brain.

When light enters the eye, it is directed through the lens to the retina. Special sensory neurons in the retina known as **rod cells** and **cone cells** are activated when light hits them. Cones respond to various colors, while rods help us see when light is scarce.

The molecular basis of vision is now known. As an example, let's examine the rods. These cells make large amounts of a protein complex called rhodopsin. The protein part, opsin, is bound to a molecule called retinaldehyde. When light energy strikes this complex, the retinaldehyde changes shape, partially separating it from opsin. This separation triggers an impulse that is sent on to the brain through nerve fibers, where incoming signals are interpreted as the various colors we see.

HIGHER BRAIN FUNCTIONS

Perhaps the most fascinating aspect of human beings is our ability to reason. No other living creatures are able to use logic and make rational decisions at the level that humans can. This process involves such complex activities as learning and using memory and language, all of which probably take place in the brain. So far, very little is known about how the mind actually operates, and scientists are still working hard trying to figure it out.

One subject of study about which research may soon provide some answers is memory. The process of memory involves storing information. There are different ways this might be done—one guess is that every

AUDITORY NEURONS

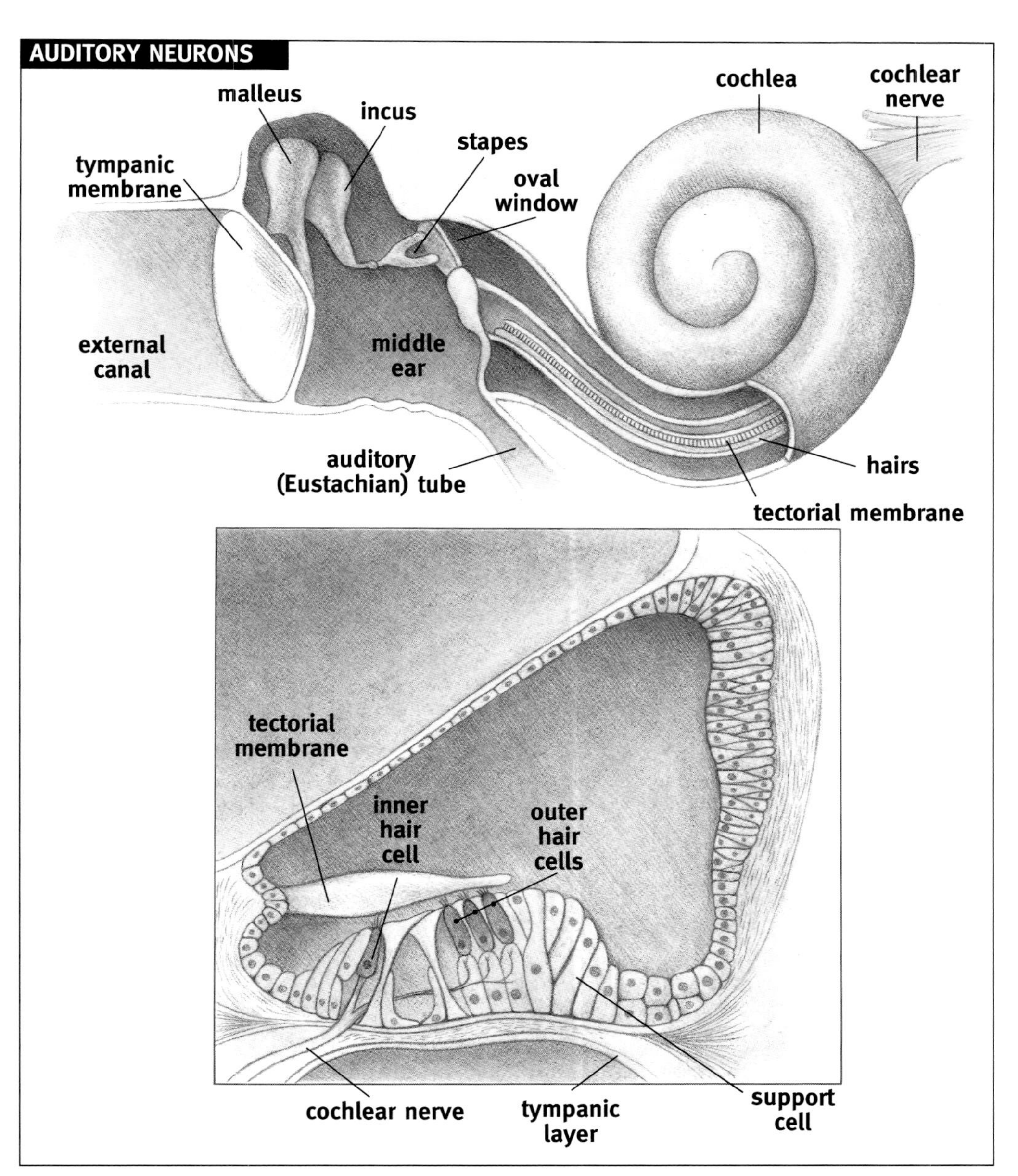

SEMICIRCULAR CANALS

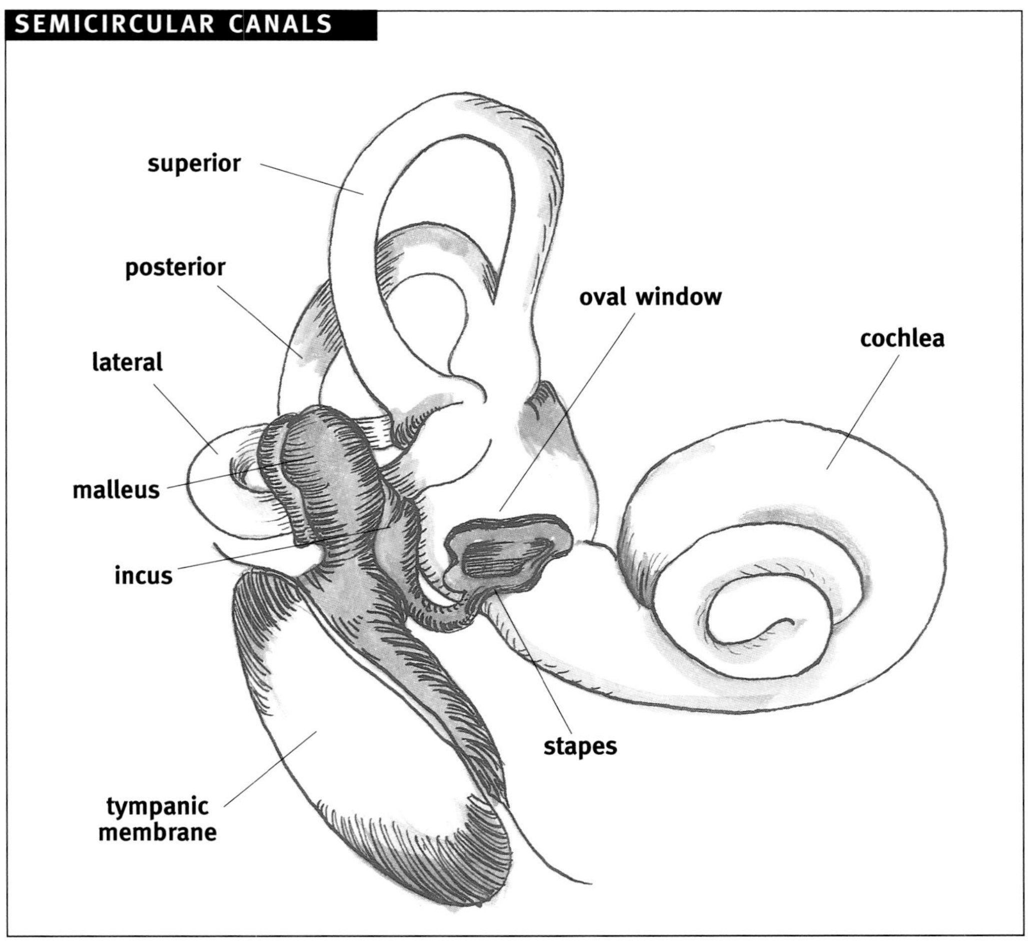

EYEGLASSES

normal eye
object
myopic eye
object
hyperopic eye
object

experience we have lays down specific patterns of molecules inside neurons in the brain. For this theory to be true, there would have to be specific "memory molecules" inside brain neurons, which could be set in a particular arrangement to store a memory.

If such memory molecules exist, they should be detectable, and experiments are being done to search for such arrangements. With further research, scientists expect to discover the principles by which our minds work.

RODS AND CONES

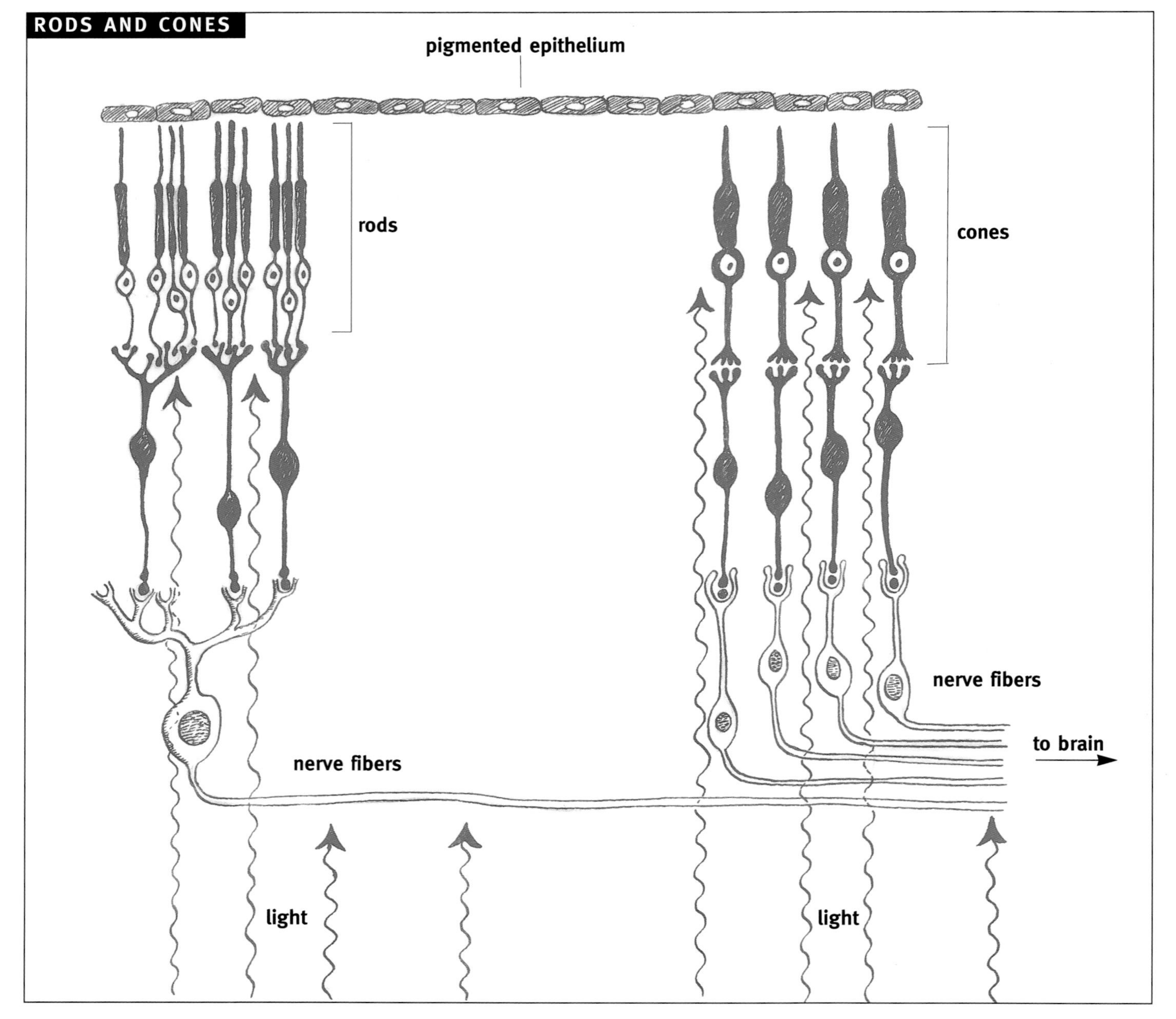

EYE STRUCTURE

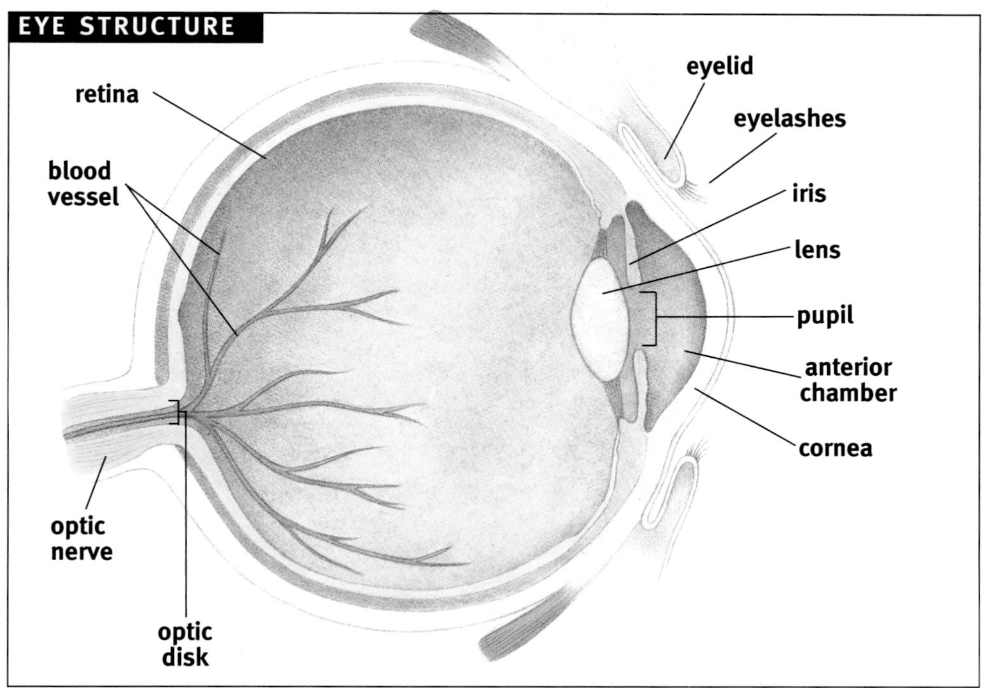

SMELL

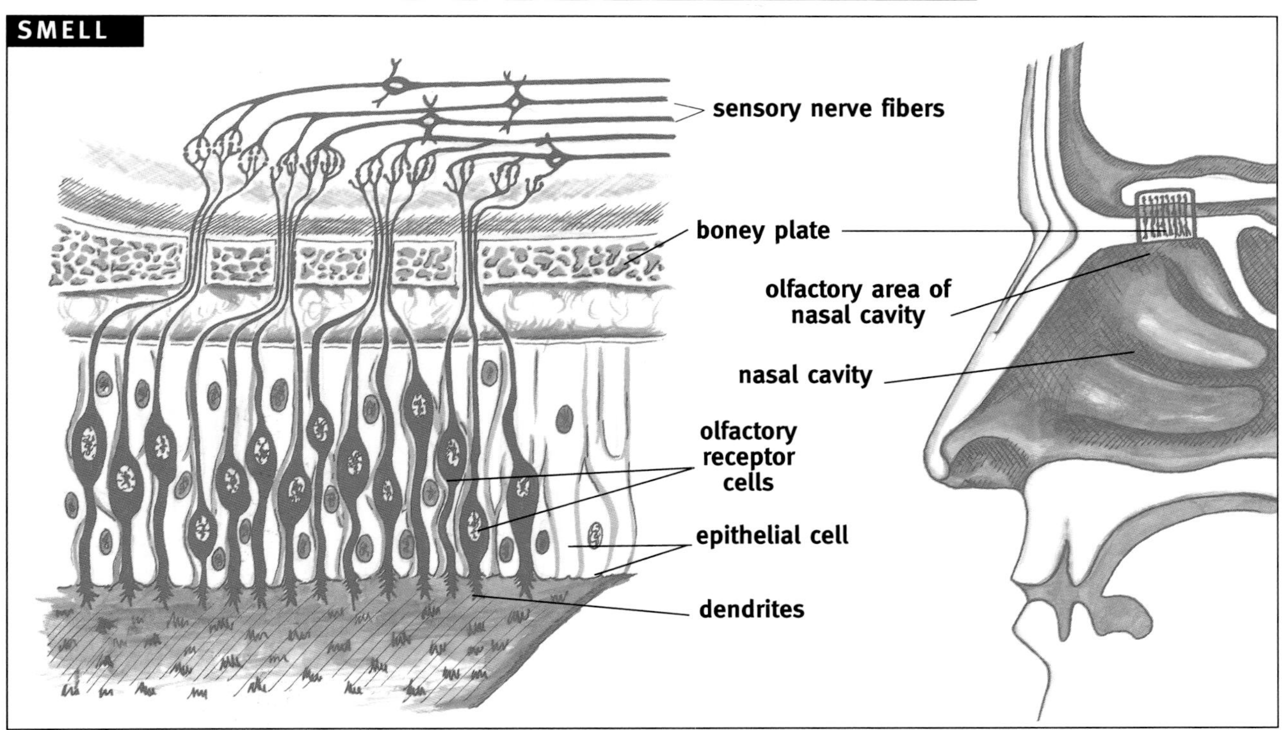

NEARSIGHTEDNESS AND FARSIGHTEDNESS

Normally the eyeball is fairly circular in shape, but some people's eyes may be more oblong. This causes objects to appear fuzzy or blurred, and makes it difficult to see fine details.

To focus, the lens of the eye bends, or refracts, incoming light so that it focuses exactly on the surface of the retina. If the eye is too long, however, the focused image occurs slightly in front of the retina, and a blurred picture hits the retina. This condition is known as myopia, or nearsightedness, since objects can be seen clearly if they are close up, but not far away. Eyeballs that have too short a distance between lens and retina cause hyperopia, or farsightedness. In this case, the focused image is projected behind the retina, again giving a blurred picture. Faraway objects can be seen clearly, but images close up are out of focus.

Both of these conditions can be corrected with eyeglasses, which simply place an extra lens in front of the eyes. A concave lens is used for myopia. This type of lens bends incoming light slightly outward, making it enter the eye at a wider angle. This lengthens the focal point, placing it exactly on the retina instead of in front of it. For hyperopia, a convex lens is used. The effect is to bend light rays inward before they contact the eye lens, shortening the focal point to fall on the retina.

Contact lenses work on the same principles as eyeglasses, except contacts are made of special plastic instead of glass. And while glasses fitted in frames sit in front of the eyes, contact lenses fit right against the eyes themselves.

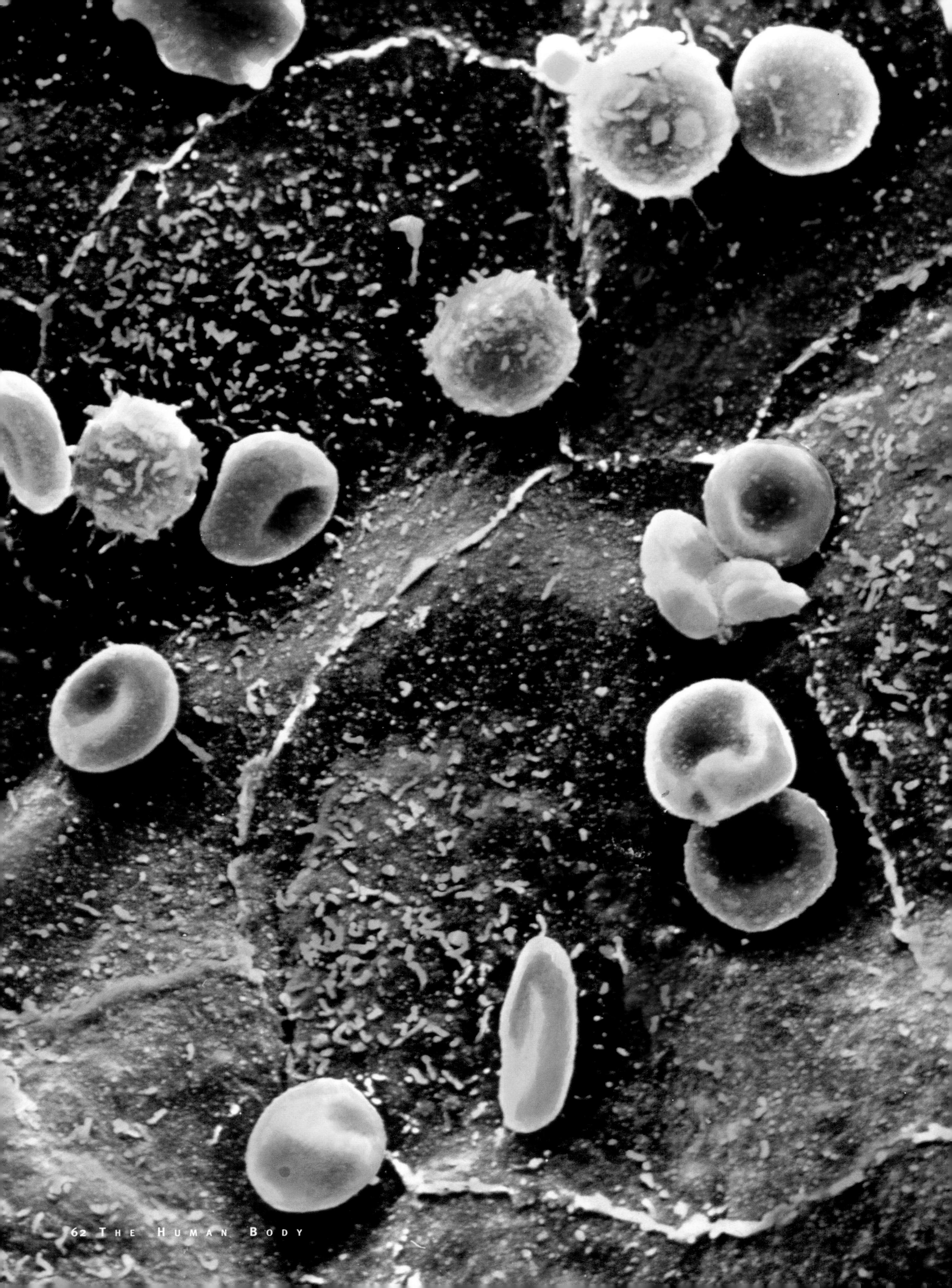

Chapter 6

THE CIRCULATORY SYSTEM

The specialization of human cells allows them to perform individual tasks that together benefit the whole body. But there is a trade-off; the more specialized a cell becomes, the less able it is to perform, on its own, the basic functions necessary to survive. Nerve cells in the brain, for example, do an amazing job of processing information and controlling body functions. But these neurons are also very fragile and delicate—so delicate that they are permanently damaged when oxygen is absent for more than a few minutes.

Since tissues and organs are groups of specialized cells that are not self-sufficient, a constant supply of oxygen, nutrients, and many other substances must be brought to them regularly in order for them to survive. This means a system is needed that can deliver vital substances to every single cell in the body.

The circulatory system, also called the cardiovascular system, is the body's transportation network. It is made up of the blood, blood vessels, lymphatic vessels, and the heart. Together these organs and tissues supply the rest of the body with the substances needed to maintain life.

BLOOD

Blood is a complex tissue made of different kinds of cells, free proteins, other chemicals and factors, and water. There are three types of cells in blood: **white blood cells, red blood cells**, and **platelets**. Together these cells account for 45 percent of the blood's total volume.

WHITE BLOOD CELLS Several kinds of cells found in the blood are colorless or "white" in appearance. All of these cells play a role in protecting the body from disease. Although these white cells are located in the blood, they function as part of the immune system, which we will examine in chapter 11.

RED BLOOD CELLS The most numerous cell type in the blood, and the one that trans-

ERYTHROCYTES

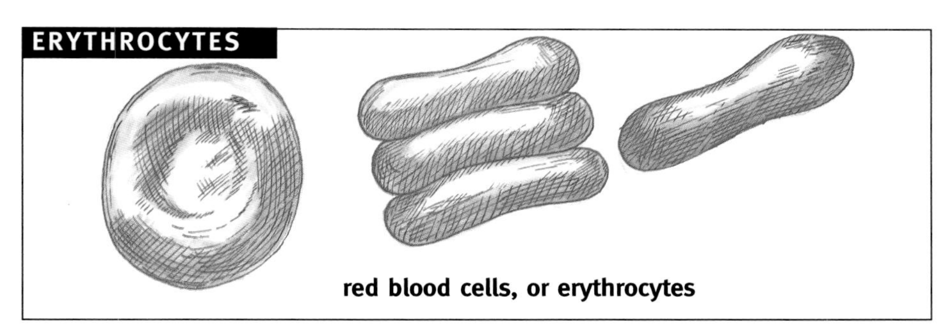

red blood cells, or erythrocytes

HEMOGLOBIN

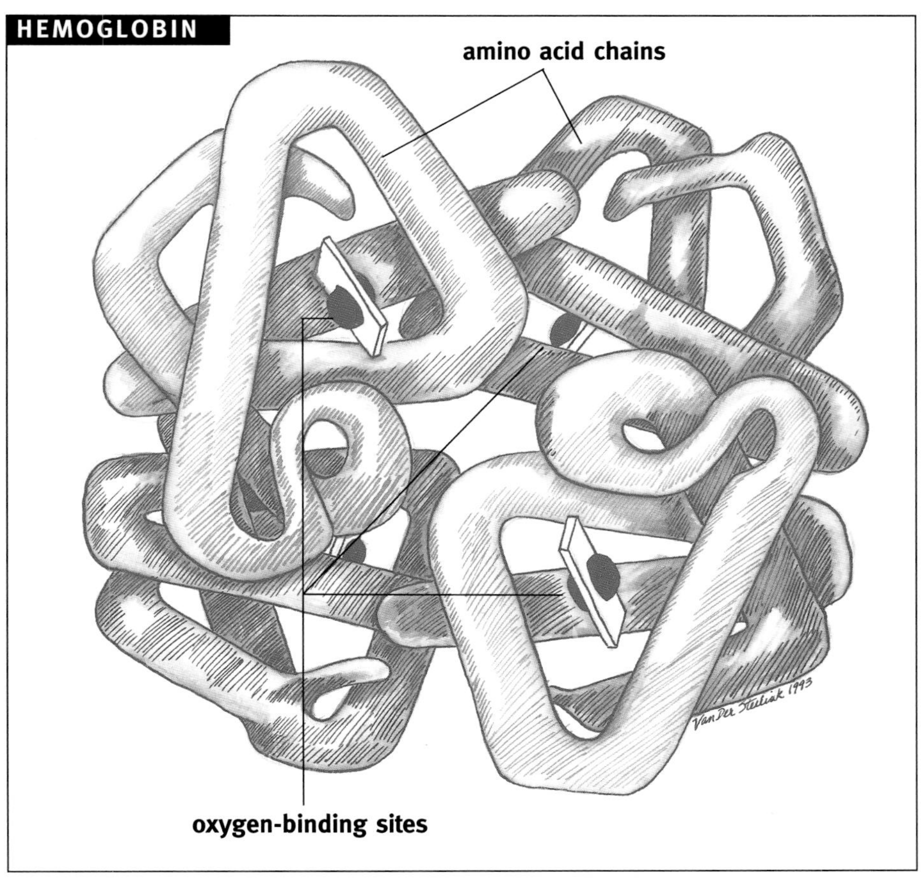

PAGE 62: Heart tissue Electron micrograph inside a chamber of the heart. Erythrocytes (red blood cells) are visible as smooth, almost donut-shaped discs, while leukocytes (white blood cells) appear as bumpy spheres. The membrane beneath these blood cells is composed of large, flat endothelial cells, their edges joined in prominent lines, forming a continuous sheet that covers the inner surface of the heart.

ports materials throughout the body, is the **erythrocyte**, or red blood cell. These have a flat, disclike shape—a feature that gives erythrocytes maximum surface area and allows them to exchange gases better. There are about 80 million erythrocytes in every cubic inch of blood. The typical life span of erythrocytes is about 120 days, which means they must be continually replaced. New erythrocytes form in the bone marrow by division of stem cells, whose only function is to divide and produce new cells. To keep up with the number of cells that wear out and die, the body must produce 2 million new erythrocytes every second.

Mature erythrocytes have a high content of **hemoglobin**, a protein specially designed to carry oxygen. In fact, each erythrocyte contains about 280 million hemoglobin molecules, accounting for a full one-third of the cell's weight. Since every molecule of hemoglobin carries four oxygen molecules, one erythrocyte can transport over a billion oxygen molecules through the blood. Hemoglobin contains iron atoms that actually attach to the oxygen molecules, and it is this iron that gives blood its reddish color.

Once new erythrocytes form and fill up with hemoglobin, the nucleus is no longer needed and is actually extruded or "spit out" of the cell. Within a few days after losing the nucleus, the cell also discards all of the ribosomes and endoplasmic reticulum. Thus, mature erythrocytes are best described as bags of hemoglobin circulating in the blood. After a few months of service, when erythrocytes get old and begin to break apart, they are taken out of the bloodstream through the spleen and the liver.

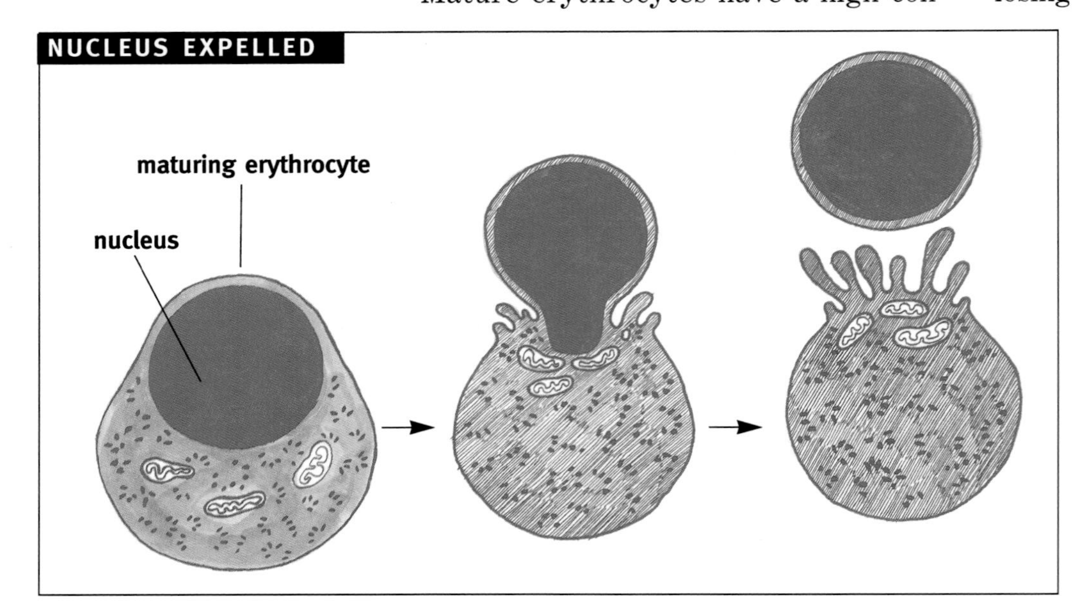

PLATELETS Platelets, also known as **thrombocytes**, are actually pieces of cells called **megakaryocytes** that break up when they mature. Under the microscope, platelets look like tiny dishes or plates, which is how they got their name.

BLOOD COLOR

The major pigment found in blood is hemoglobin. Blood generally appears red because iron atoms attached to the hemoglobin molecule reflect light in the red wavelengths. You may have noticed, however, that blood doesn't always appear to be red. If you look at the inside of your arm, in the crease opposite your elbow, you can see a few veins just under the skin. Blood in these veins doesn't look red—it has more of a bluish tone. What causes this difference in color?

Hemoglobin molecules actually change shape when they bind oxygen. This rearrangement plays a role in how well hemoglobin picks up oxygen in the lungs and releases it in the tissues. But it also gives the blood slightly different colors. When hemoglobin is fully loaded with oxygen,it gives off a bright red color, but when no oxygen is bound, it has a deep purple tone.

The vessels you can see in your arm and elsewhere are veins, which are usually positioned closer to the skin than arteries. Thus veins are more visible than arteries. The blood in these veins has very little oxygen attached to it, and thus displays a dark red or purple color. The pigments in the skin darken this color even further, giving veins a purple or blue appearance.

This explains the blue color of vessels just under the skin, but why is blood from a cut or scratch always red, even when it is flowing from a vein? The answer is that as soon as blood leaves the body, oxygen in the air—which is plentiful—instantly binds to hemoglobin and changes its color to bright red.

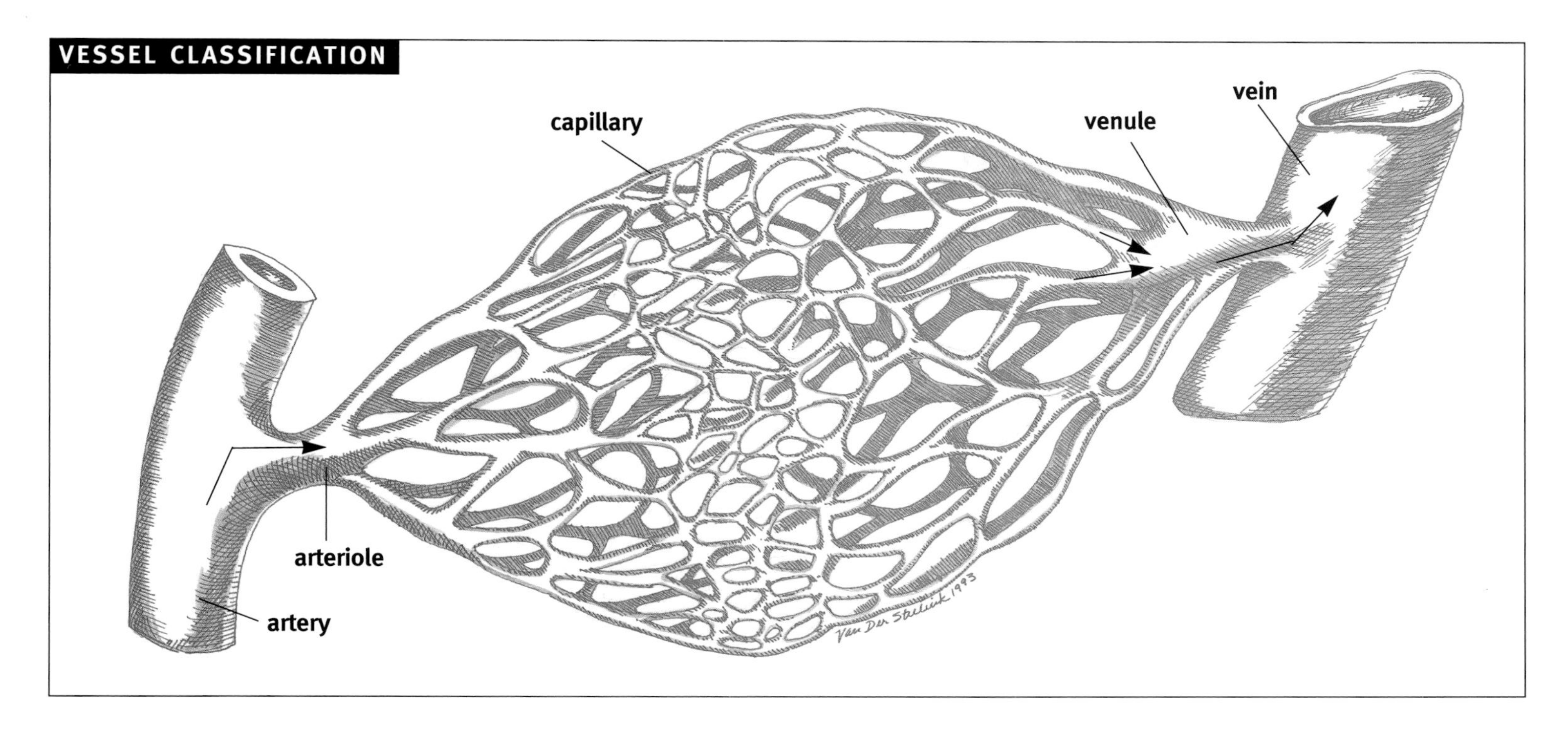

They circulate for only four days before being removed from the bloodstream. The role of platelets is to detect broken blood vessels and start the clotting process.

Plasma The 55 percent of blood that is not cells is called **plasma**. It is made up of about 90 percent water and 10 percent other compounds such as proteins, gases, food substances, and other chemicals.

There are several different blood proteins in plasma. One example is albumin, which helps regulate blood pressure by keeping water in the blood. Fibrinogen is another example; it is an essential factor in clotting, which stops blood flow after vessels are broken.

Food substances like nucleotides, amino acids, sugars, and fatty acids are carried in the plasma as it circulates throughout the body. There are also dissolved gases—such as oxygen and carbon dioxide—and many chemicals the body uses, such as sodium, potassium, calcium, magnesium, phosphate, and carbonate.

When a blood vessel is broken due to a cut or a bruise, it is critical to seal it off so that too much blood does not escape. The total amount of blood in the body, about 5 quarts (4.75L), is more than is needed for adequate circulation, so losing some blood from a wound is not necessarily dangerous. However, if too much blood is lost, the heart cannot pump correctly, blood flow stops, and cells and tissues begin to die. Thus it is very important that leaks in the system are stopped quickly.

The process of **coagulation**, or clotting, is the body's way of stopping blood flow from a damaged blood vessel. This process is triggered by circulating platelets, which stick to broken edges of blood vessels. When platelets detect broken blood vessels, they start a series of reactions that eventually cause fibrinogen molecules to hook together to form a net over the damaged area. This seals off the break and stops any more blood from passing out. The healing process eventually replaces the blood clot with new tissue.

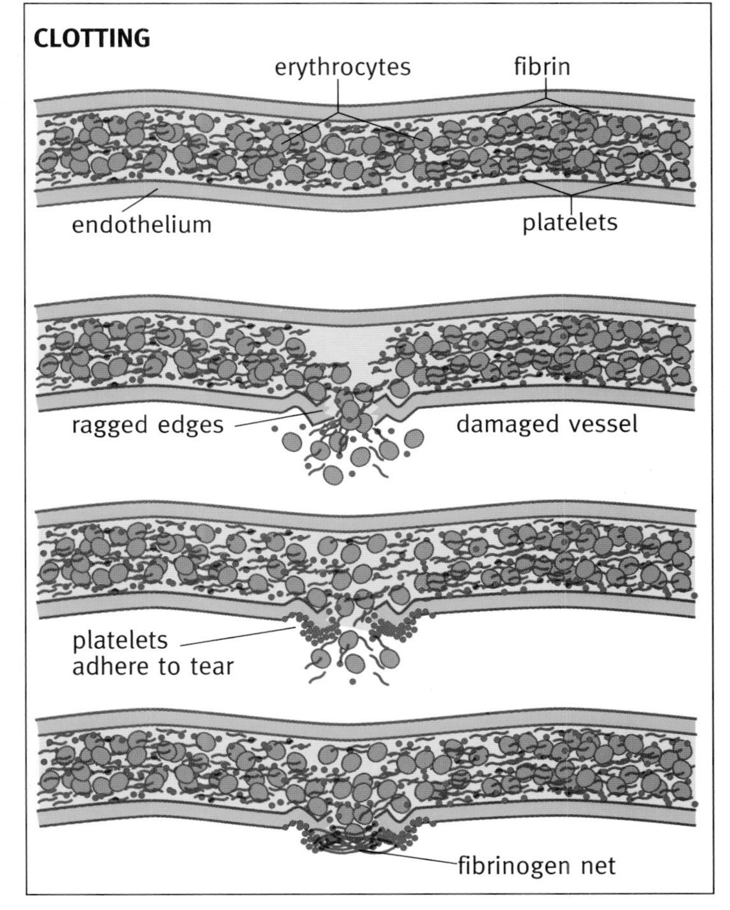

Blood Vessels Since every cell relies upon the bloodstream for oxygen and nutrients, the network of blood vessels passes through every organ and tissue. There are so many of these vessels in the body that if they were placed end to end they would be about 60,000 miles (96,000km) long.

Large blood vessels that carry blood away from the heart are called **arteries**. These are the strongest vessels, built to withstand the high pressure of blood being forced through them and out into the

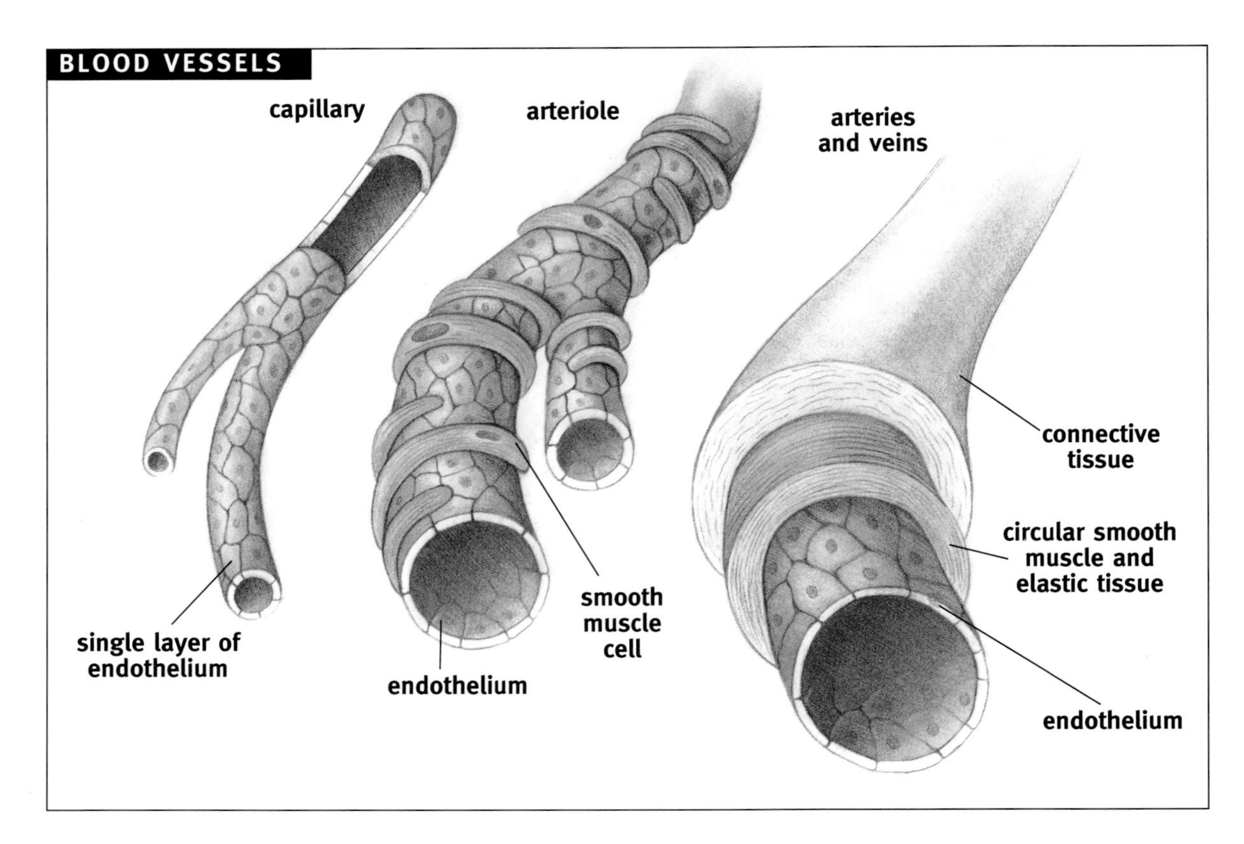

network of vessels. Arteries split up into **arterioles**, which branch into many **capillaries**. The capillaries join into **venules**, which join to form **veins** that carry blood back to the heart.

Blood vessels are hollow tubes with an inner lining of **endothelial** cells. These cells form a tight layer that keeps blood inside the tube. The smallest vessels, called capillaries, are very thin—so thin that erythrocytes must pass through in single file—and have only a single layer of endothelium, with no other covering. Larger vessels that carry more blood have additional layers of connective tissue for strength. Some vessels have smooth muscle wrapped around the outside, which helps regulate blood flow to different areas.

Lymphatic Vessels Within the tissues, cells are continually bathed in a substance known as **interstitial fluid**. This fluid mixture provides a junction between blood and cells. Gases and nutrients delivered by the blood pass through the capillary walls into the interstitial fluid and from there into individual cells.

The pressure of blood flowing through capillaries forces some water and other substances out into the interstitial fluid, causing a buildup. The excess interstitial fluid collects into lymphatic vessels, which are similar in structure to blood vessels. You may have noticed that sometimes when you scratch or scrape your skin a clear fluid comes out instead of blood, or along with blood. This fluid is called lymph.

The lymphatic vessels that begin in tissues join into larger and larger vessels and eventually feed into major veins to mix lymph with the blood. In this way interstitial fluid is circulated through the tissues, although more slowly than blood.

There are special structures in the lymphatic system called **lymph nodes**. These are where certain cells of the immune system called **lymphocytes** can be found. We will consider lymphocytes in detail in chapter 11.

THE HEART

At the center of the circulatory system is the heart. It is a muscular organ about the size of your fist, and has the job of pushing blood through the long network of blood vessels throughout the body. Every day the heart beats about 100,000 times, pumping the equivalent of 1,000 gallons (3,800L) of blood through the vascular network.

There are four separate chambers in the heart: the **right atrium, left atrium, right ventricle**, and **left ventricle**. Located at the entrance and exit of these chambers are **valves**, which force blood to flow in one direction only. The atrio-ventricular valves, for example, open when the atria contract to force blood into the ventricles, and then shut tightly so that blood cannot flow backward into the atria when the ventricles contract.

The heart walls are made of cardiac muscle, a type of muscle tissue that is very

ARTIFICIAL HEART

Compared to most other organs, the heart is quite simple in design and function. It is basically just a pump that moves the blood around. In 1982 an artificial heart, called the Jarvik 7 after its inventor, Dr. Robert Jarvik, was used for the first time to keep a patient alive. Dr. Barney Clark, the patient, had suffered heart failure and volunteered to undergo surgery to receive the new artificial heart.

The Jarvik 7 consists of two plastic chambers driven by compressed air that replace the two ventricles. The new heart is connected to the patient's atria, aorta, and pulmonary arteries. Two air hoses that make the new heart pump are connected to a compressor outside the patient's body.

Like most new medical techniques, there were problems with the first artificial heart experiments. Some patients suffered paralysis and some died from broken blood vessels in the brain, a condition known as a stroke. But the fact that life was extended for some heart patients, along with knowledge gained from such studies, was beneficial. Researchers are now working to improve the design of future artificial hearts to make them safer and more efficient.

strong and durable. The individual cells are similar in appearance to skeletal muscle, except that cardiac cells do not fuse to form giant fibers like skeletal muscle. Cardiac cells are joined by gap junctions, which spread electrical impulses from one cell to the next.

A key feature of cardiac cells is their ability to contract on their own, unlike skeletal muscle, which requires nerve impulses to contract. If each cell in the heart contracted at different times, however, no blood would be pumped through. Efficient pumping requires the coordinated contraction of the entire heart at once to squeeze blood along.

A group of cells called the **sino-atrial node**, located in the wall of the right atrium, serve as the heart's pacemaker by making sure all the cells contract together. Cells in the sino-atrial node depolarize about once every second, sending electrical impulses out to surrounding cardiac cells. The signal spreads first over both atria, causing these two chambers to contract simultaneously and push blood into the two ventricles.

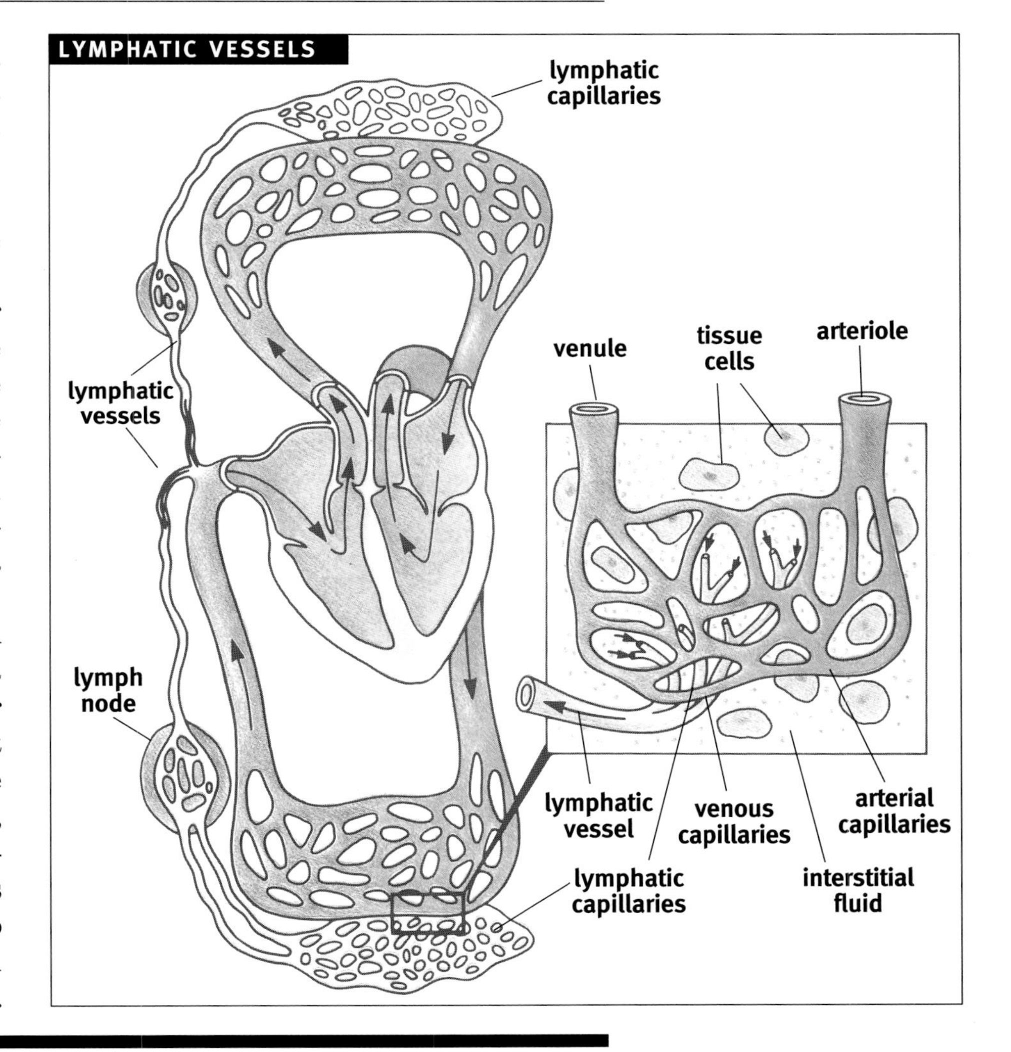

HEMOPHILIA

Some people have a disease called hemophilia, which is caused by defective blood clotting. There are thirteen separate factors in the clotting process, and if just one component is missing, a clot will not form. This is a very dangerous condition, since even a slight scratch will continue to bleed for a long time. Researchers have now identified the entire coagulation pathway. This means that the blood from patients with hemophilia can be analyzed and the defective clotting factor can be identified. Once it is known which factor is missing, that substance can be given to the patient to control bleeding.

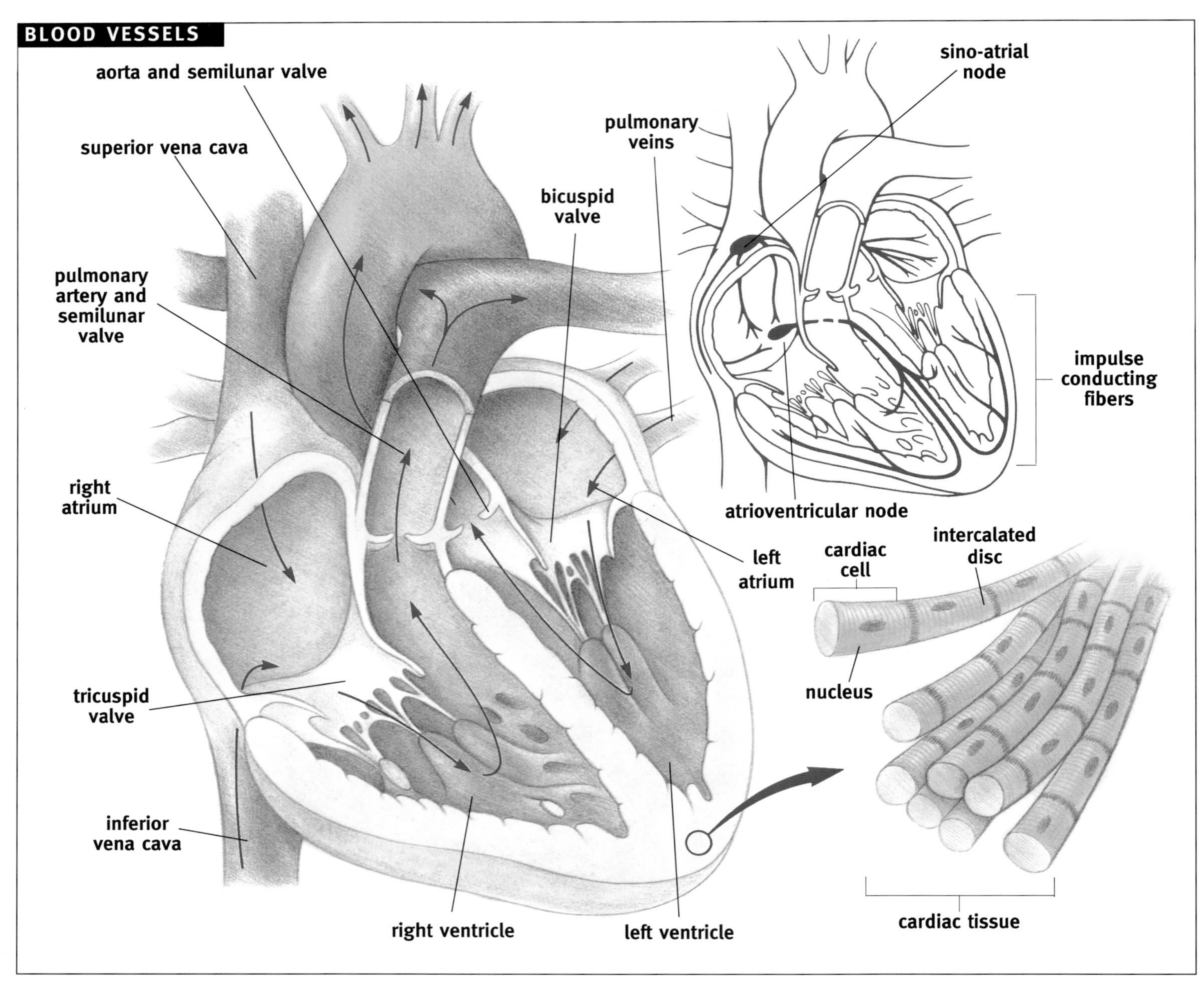

Impulses from the sino-atrial node reach the nearby **atrioventricular node**, which sends the signal through a network of fibers to all areas of the ventricles. The ventricles then contract, a fraction of a second after the atria, forcing blood out into the aorta and pulmonary arteries.

Since contractions of cardiac muscle are caused by electrical impulses, the activity of the heart can be detected and monitored. The resulting measurement is called an electrocardiogram, or ECG. The wave marked P on the ECG represents atrial contraction. The stronger ventricular contraction produces the QRS pattern. Repolarization of the ventricles is responsible for the T wave, but atrial repolarization is hidden under the QRS complex. By monitoring ECG patterns, doctors can learn how well a patient's heart is working and detect what is wrong with a heart that is not functioning properly.

Although the heart beats in a constant rhythm on its own, there are several extra controls over the timing of contractions. This is important because increased blood flow to certain tissues is sometimes needed. When you run, for example, your muscles need about fifteen times more oxygen than when you are resting. This means that blood must circulate faster to bring more oxygen to muscle tissues, and the only way to make blood flow faster is to speed up the heart.

Nerve fibers from the autonomic nervous system attach to the heart and influence its pace. When you run, the heart is stimulated by sympathetic nerve bundles to contract faster, pushing more blood through the system and delivering oxygen to the muscles.

Heart rate is also influenced by certain chemicals in the blood. The chemical **adrenaline**, which is produced by the adrenal glands, stimulates the heart to speed up. Adrenaline is released into the blood when you get excited or scared.

BLOOD FLOW

Let's now follow the cycle of blood flow through the body to get the overall picture of how the circulatory system works. Blood from the right atrium is pumped into the right ventricle, then into the **pulmonary artery**, which carries blood to the lungs. In the capillaries of the lungs, gases are exchanged: oxygen is picked up and carbon dioxide, a waste product, is given off. The freshly oxygenated blood returns to the heart through the pulmonary veins. These large veins feed into the left atrium, which empties into the left ventricle.

Contraction of the left ventricle forces blood into the **aorta**, the major artery to the rest of the body except the lungs. The aorta divides into many arteries that carry blood to the tissues. In the capillaries, oxygen is passed to interstitial fluid and then into the cells. Carbon dioxide given off by cells is taken up by blood in the capillaries and flows back toward the heart. All of the blood returning from the tissues collects into the **superior vena cava** and **inferior vena cava**, the two largest veins in the body. These veins feed blood into the right atrium, completing the cycle.

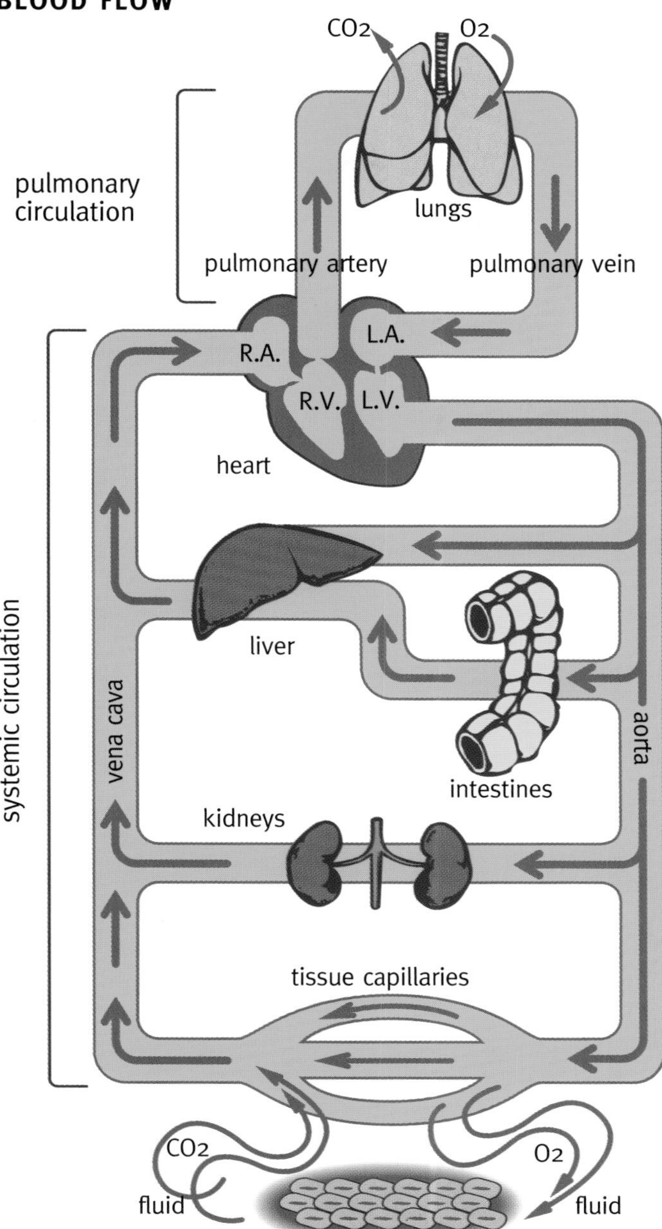

Along the way blood passes through all of the organs of the body, many of which contribute to its contents. As blood flows through the stomach, for example, nutrients from food are picked up and carried along to the tissues. When blood passes through the spleen, old cells are taken out of circulation. The liver removes toxins and adds proteins to the blood, the kidneys adjust the water content and remove waste products, and marrow in the bones adds new erythrocytes. Thus the circulatory system is like a crowded highway network, carrying many different materials to various locations in the body.

ATHEROSCLEROSIS

Cardiovascular disease is the leading health problem in most of the world's deveoped nations, killing millions of people each year. Most cases of heart disease can be attributed to atherosclerosis, or "hardening of the arteries."

Atherosclerosis begins with the development of plaques, or thickenings, on the inner wall of blood vessels. These initial plaques act as anchors for further deposition of fatty materials and calcium deposits, until the inner arterial walls become lined with hardened substances. The most dangerous aspect of this process is the closing off, or occlusion, of the arterial channel, severely restricting blood flow to the heart. When this occurs in the coronary arteries that feed heart muscle, the heart itself becomes oxygen-starved and fails, resulting in a heart attack.

The exact cause of atherosclerosis is not known, but several important factors have been identified. High-cholesterol and high-fat diets, high blood pressure, cigarette smoking, and elevated blood sugar levels all add significantly to the risk of developing atherosclerosis. Stressful and competitive life-styles have also been linked to this disease. A low-fat diet and regular exercise may help to prevent it.

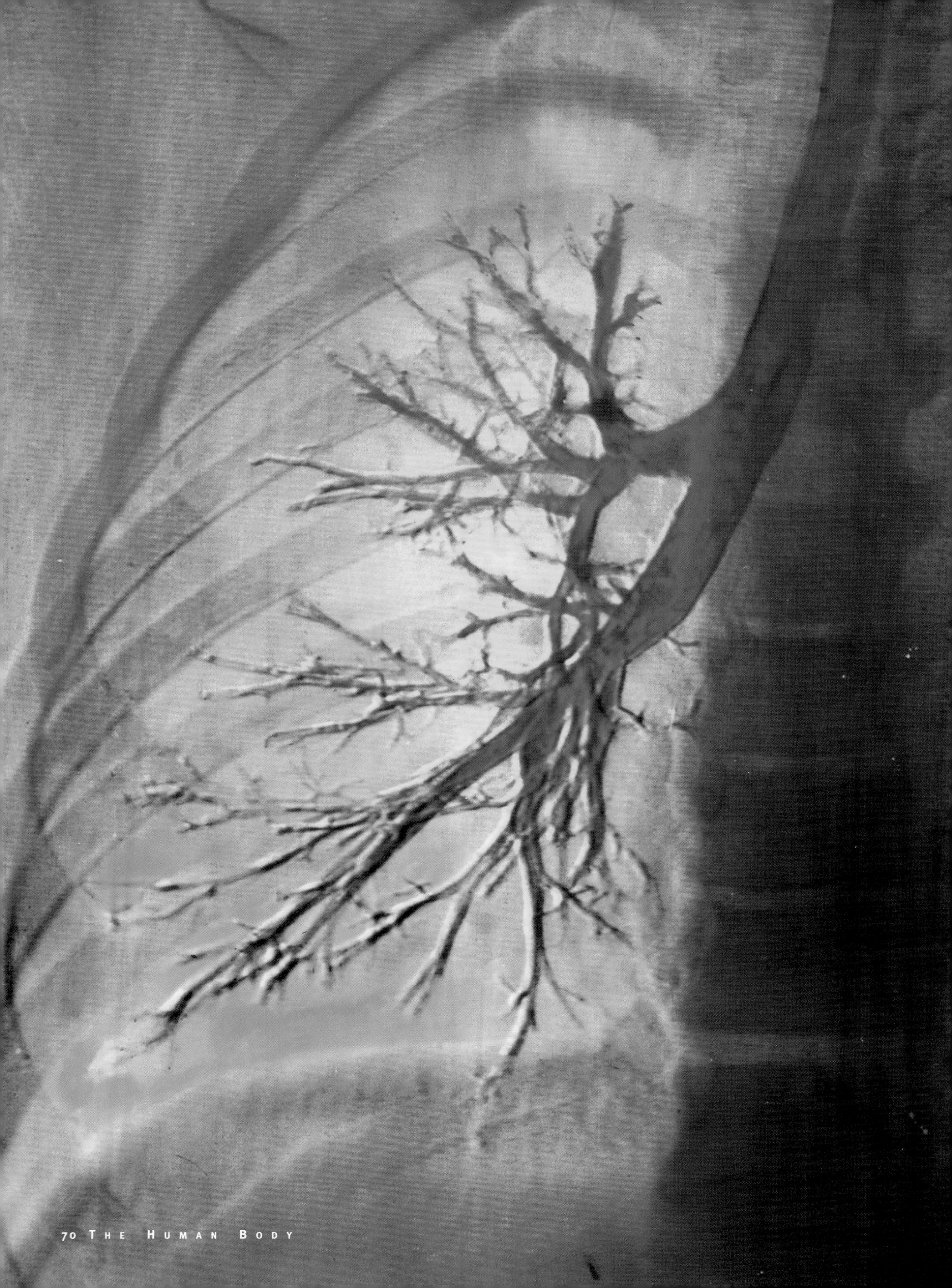

Chapter 7

THE RESPIRATORY SYSTEM

The function of the respiratory system is to take in oxygen from the atmosphere and deliver it to the bloodstream. The air around us is rich in oxygen; it makes up 21 percent of the atmosphere. But most body cells are sealed off from the air around us and thus cannot take up gases freely. They rely on the circulatory system to deliver oxygen to them, and the bloodstream relies on the process of respiration for a constant input of oxygen.

We all know how important the respiratory system is, and that if breathing stops for more than just a few minutes, cells start to die and tissues can be permanently damaged. Most people also know that oxygen is the gaseous chemical we need to survive. But why is oxygen such a key molecule? What makes it so important that two whole systems are involved in bringing it to every cell?

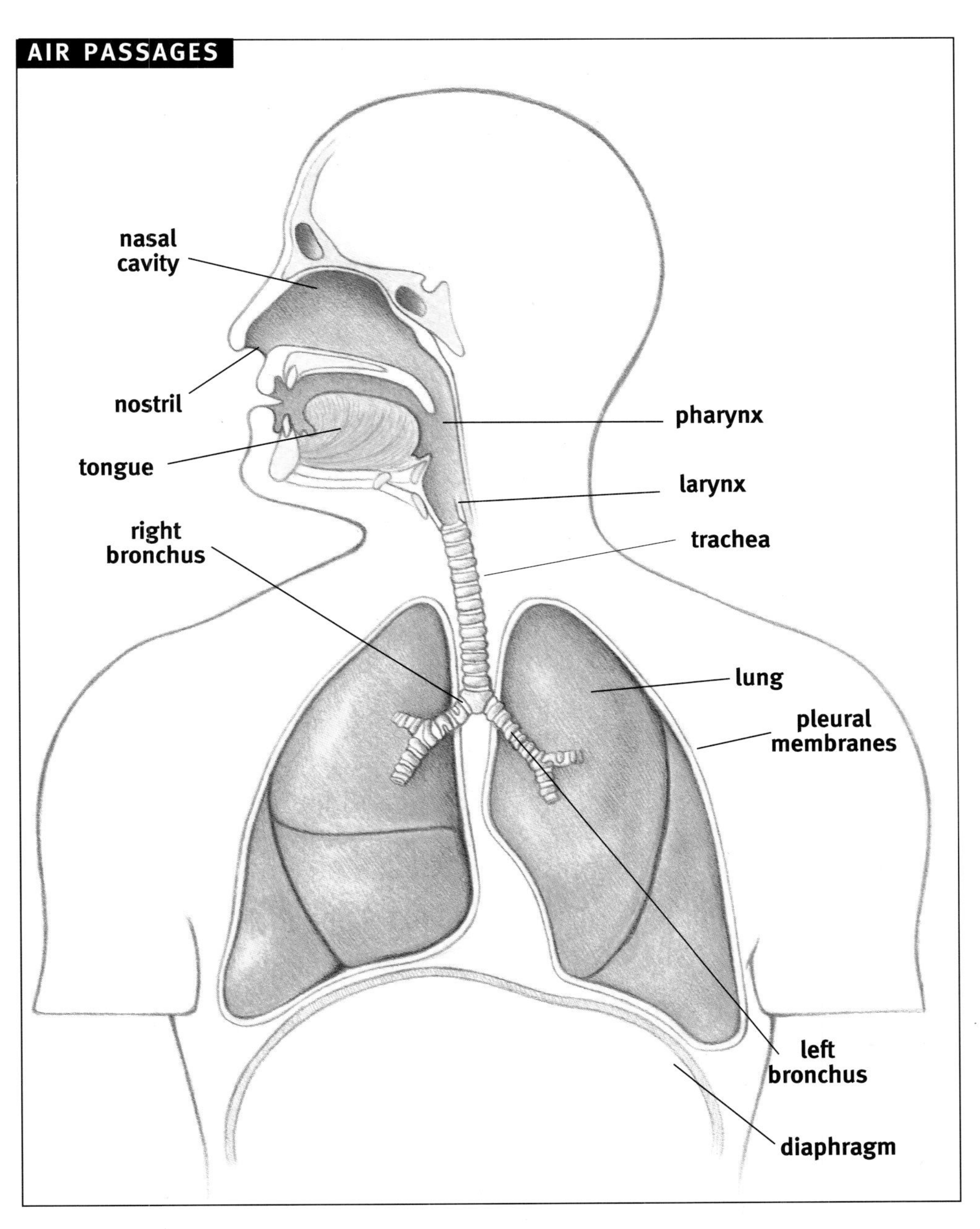

THE ROLE OF OXYGEN

Oxygen plays a vital part in the cellular process that produces energy. Every cell in the body requires energy to do its job—muscle cells for contraction, neurons for sending impulses, bone cells for laying down new matrix. Cells get this energy from food, which is broken down to produce an energy-rich molecule called **adenosine triphosphate (ATP)**.

The major reaction that produces ATP is written as follows:

$$C_6H_{12}O_6 \text{ (GLUCOSE)} + 6\,O_2 \rightarrow 6\,CO_2 + 6\,H_2O \text{ (36 ATPs)}$$

In this equation, C stands for a carbon atom, H for hydrogen, and O for oxygen. The symbols show that glucose is combined with six oxygen molecules to produce thirty-six molecules of ATP. The six oxygen molecules in this reaction must

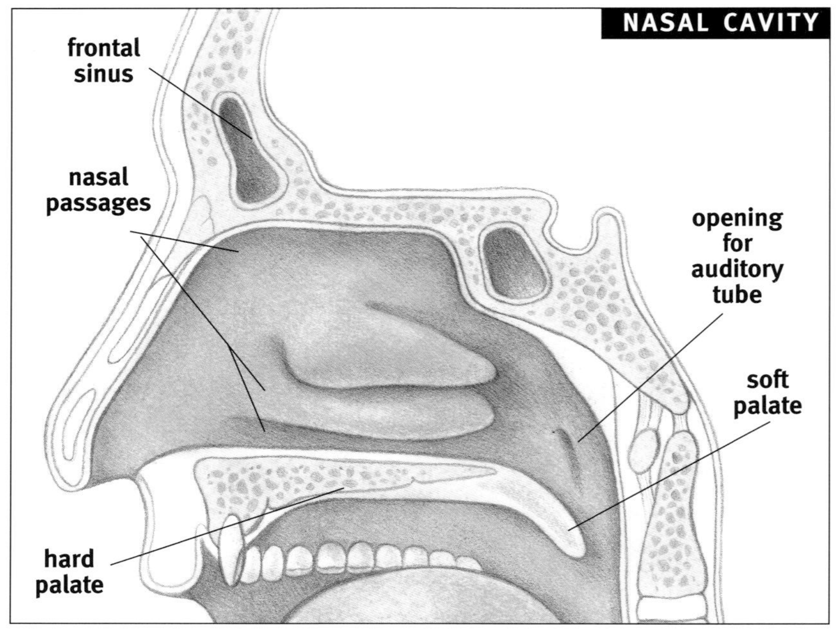

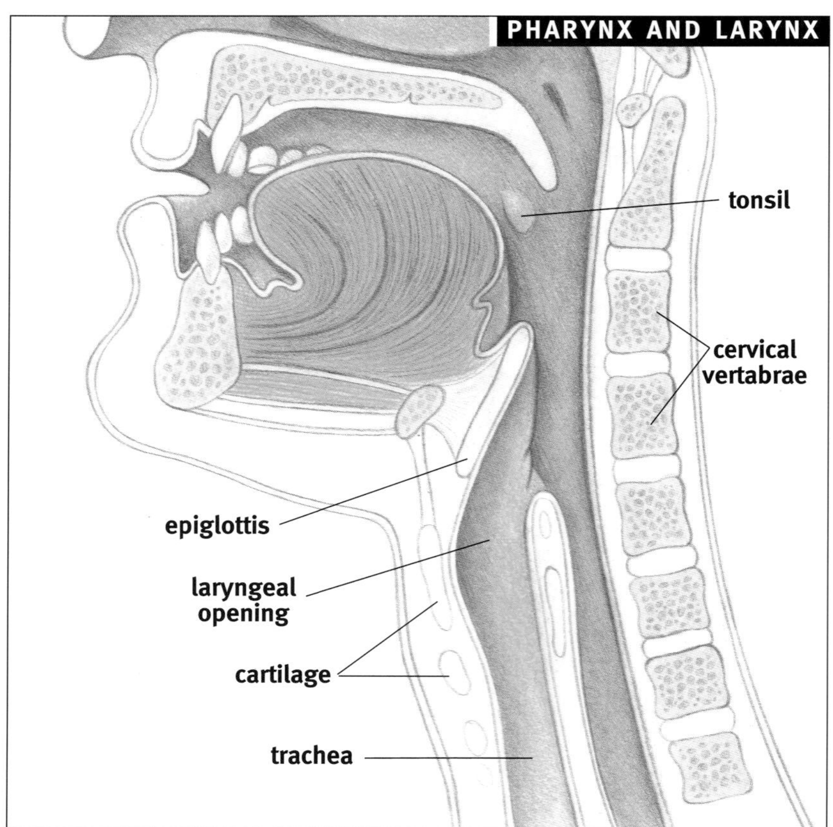

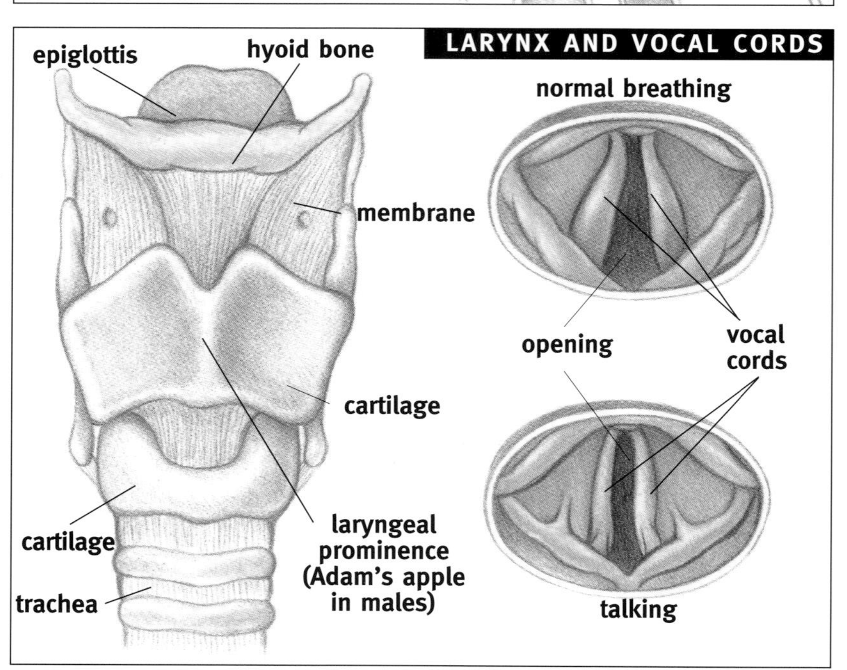

be delivered by respiration (through inhalation). Six molecules each of carbon dioxide and water are given off as by-products (through exhalation).

Glucose is a sugar found in most types of food, and many of the chemicals in things we eat can be converted into this simple sugar. In the above reaction, glucose is broken apart, releasing energy that is stored in ATP molecules. During this process, hydrogen molecules are attached to oxygen to form water. If oxygen is not available to accept the hydrogen molecules, the whole system quickly backs up and stops working, halting the production of ATP.

Fragile cells such as neurons rely totally on constant ATP production to survive, and if their energy system is blocked they die quickly. This is why a continuous supply of oxygen is so vital to the body.

The two other products of this reaction, carbon dioxide and water, must be eliminated. As we will see, the respiratory system is responsible for removing these two waste products from the blood as well as bringing in oxygen.

Let's now consider the physical organs of the respiratory system: the air passages, lungs, and diaphragm. We will then examine how these structures work together to carry out oxygenation of the blood and the elimination of carbon dioxide and excess water from the body.

AIR PASSAGES

Air comes into the body through a series of channels known as air passages. In normal relaxed breathing, air is brought into the nostrils—the openings into the nose—and through the **nasal passage**. The inner lining of this channel contains cells that produce **mucus**, a thick, sticky fluid that covers the surface of the passageway. This moist layer traps dust, microorganisms and other particles that are floating in the air. The inside of the nose is also protected with nasal hairs that extend

RESPIRATORY REFLEXES

The regular pattern of breathing is sometimes interrupted by respiratory reflexes that occur in response to various conditions.

Coughing—This reflex is triggered by sensory neurons in the throat and bronchial tubes when dust particles, bits of food, or mucus buildup irritate the sensitive cells that line the air channels. To produce a cough, the epiglottis closes tightly over the trachea, the diaphragm contracts to build up air pressure in the lungs, and then the epiglottis opens quickly. A stream of air shoots through the air passages, clearing material out.

The coughing reflex is partially under voluntary control, allowing you to cough on your own in addition to the automatic coughing that occurs without your attention.

Sneezing—A more forceful and totally involuntary reflex is the sneeze. It occurs in much the same way as a cough, except for a deep breath before the sneeze and a rapid diaphragm contraction that blasts a large volume of air up through the mouth and nose.

It is thought that irritation of sensory neurons in the nasal passage stimulates sneezing. Irritating substances such as pollen, pepper, dust, and other particles are detected by these neurons, which then direct a sneeze to clear the foreign material out of the system.

Hiccups—Perhaps the most annoying reflex of all is hiccups. This is caused by spasms in the diaphragm and epiglottis, throwing the smooth breathing pattern out of rhythm. They are involuntary and can last from a few seconds to several hours in severe cases.

The best guess is that hiccups are caused by irritation of sensory neurons in the digestive tract. You may have noticed that hiccups often follow eating too rapidly—this can evidently disturb the stomach and intestines, producing mixed signals in the neural network that temporarily confuse the respiratory center.

Favorite remedies for hiccups include holding your breath, getting someone to scare you, breathing into a paper bag, or drinking a glass of water while bent over at the waist. The effectiveness of such treatments is not documented, but whatever benefit they do provide may be through a common mechanism. All these activities would interrupt breathing, and possibly reset the disturbed respiratory control center.

PAGE 70: The lung X-ray image of the right lung. The arteries that carry blood from the heart and branch out to all areas of the lung are clearly visible. In the lung tissue, blood picks up oxygen and then carries this vital substance to all areas of the body.

into the passageway and block larger materials from getting deep into the body.

Behind the nose is the **nasal cavity**, a convoluted pocket that is also lined with mucous membranes. Air is filtered and cleaned in this compartment, and also warmed and moistened. The nasal cavity has many twists and turns that expose incoming air to a total surface area that is quite large. Contact with these surfaces transfers heat and water to the air before it goes on. The nasal cavity also contains the olfactory neurons that let us smell.

Next, air passes through the **pharynx**—a tube that runs down through the neck. This channel also connects to the back of the throat so that air can be taken in through the mouth. Both air and food pass through this single tube. The walls of the pharynx are made of skeletal muscles that contract to push food through.

The bottom of the pharynx divides into two separate tubes, the **trachea** and the **esophagus**. The esophagus is the tube through which food passes to enter the stomach; the trachea is the passageway for air going to the lungs. Between these two channels and the trachea is the **epiglottis**, a flap of tissue that acts as a gate. When you swallow food, the epiglottis covers the trachea, opening the esophagus. When you take a breath, the epiglottis swings the other way to allow air to pass through the trachea while blocking off the esophagus.

Just past the epiglottis, at the top of the trachea, is an organ called the **larynx**, or voice box. The front of this structure makes a bump in the throat called the Adam's apple that you can feel move when you swallow. The larynx contains the **vocal cords**—two flaps of tissue stretched across the air passage that constrict and vibrate to produce speech.

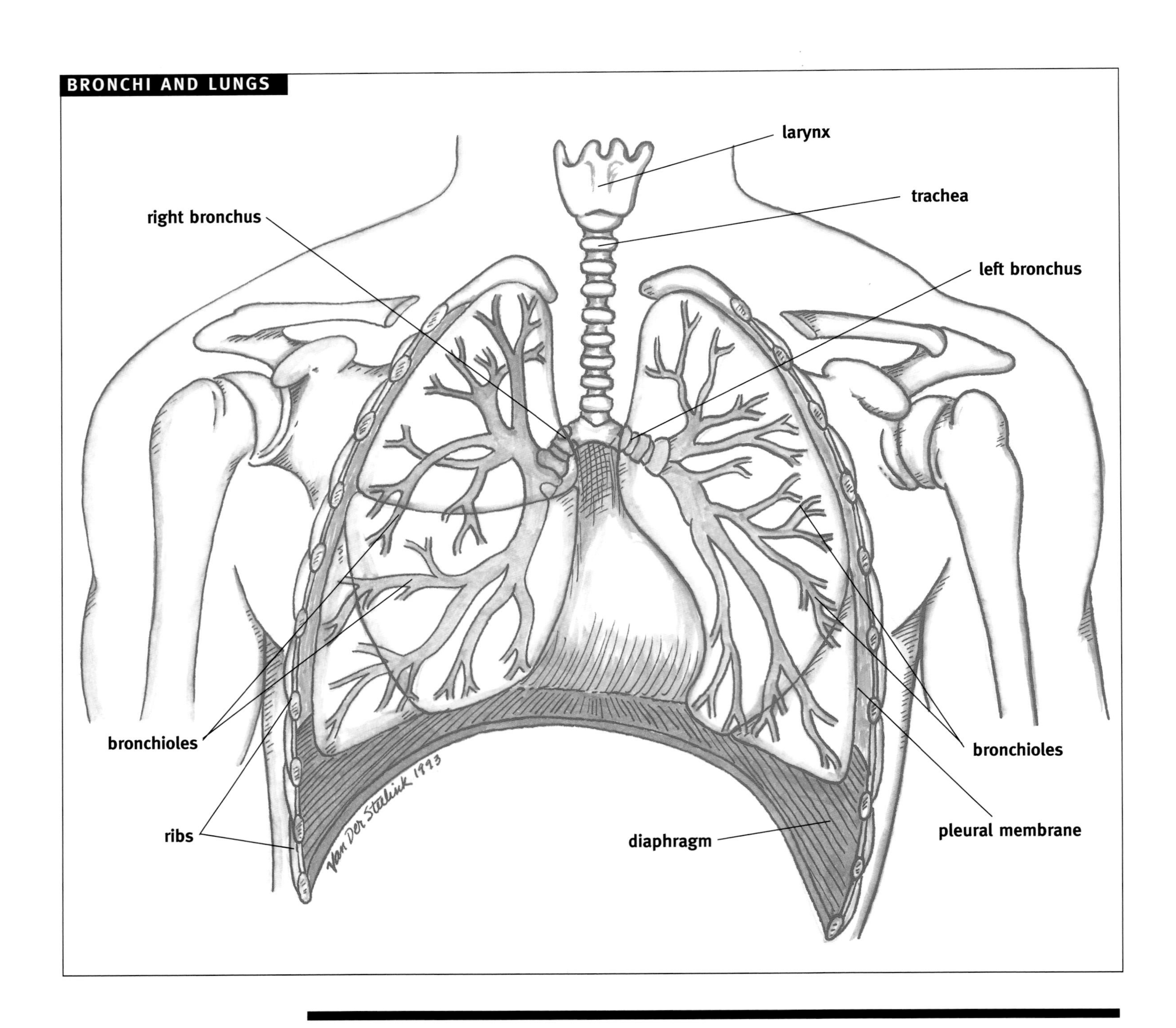

SMOKING

Scientific research has confirmed the link between cigarette smoke and several diseases, including emphysema and lung cancer. With all of the safeguards built into the respiratory system to keep foreign particles out, it doesn't make much sense to suck thick smoke down into the lungs, where it can damage the sensitive alveoli. Yet many people ignore the danger and subject themselves to potentially fatal diseases by continuing to smoke.

Cigarette smoke contains carbon monoxide, a gas that binds permanently to hemoglobin and prevents it from carrying oxygen. In addition, the tiny particles in smoke penetrate into the alveolar pockets and irritate the sensitive lung tissues. It is thought that constant irritation by these particles leads to changes in the DNA of alveolar cells, resulting in cancerous growths.

Smoking is difficult to stop because some of the chemicals in cigarettes are addictive—they cause the brain to crave more of the same chemical. Cigarette smoke also stimulates certain chemicals in the body that produce a feeling of calm and well-being. But the effect is temporary and artificial, and carries with it the highest risk—losing your life.

THE LUNGS

The bottom of the trachea splits into the right and left **bronchi**. These tubes enter the lungs, the major organs of the respiratory system. Inside the lungs the bronchi divide into several smaller **bronchioles**, which connect to many narrow passages called **terminal bronchioles**—very small tubes deep in the lung tissue.

The lungs sit inside the chest, or **thoracic cavity**, and are wrapped in an airtight sac called the **pleura**. The pleural sac is actually double layered with fluid in between. When you breathe and the lungs expand, the fluid between the two pleural membranes allows them to slide over each other smoothly. This allows the outer lung surfaces to move with minimal friction as you breathe.

ALVEOLI

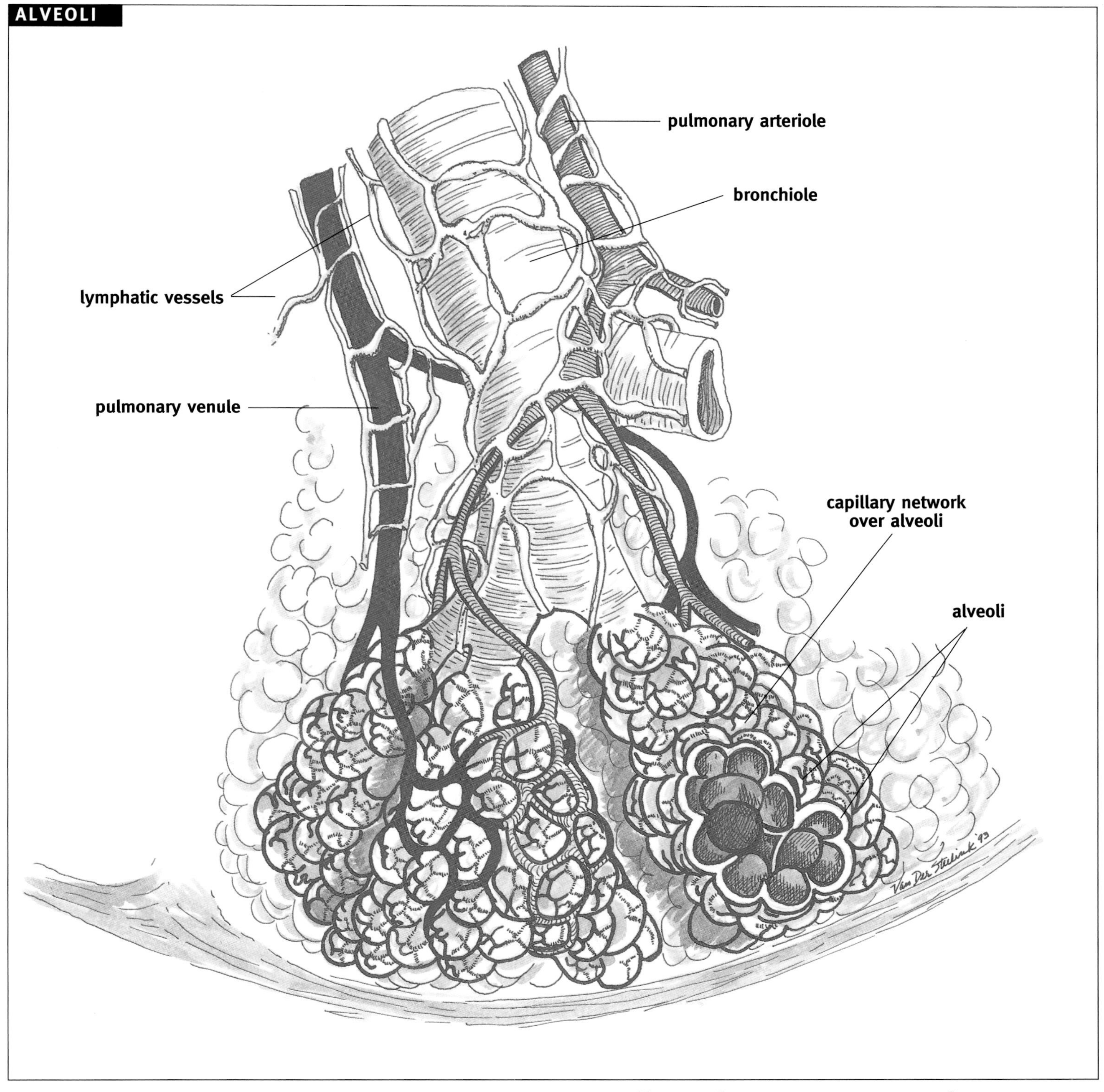

At the end of the smallest bronchioles are tiny air sacs called **alveoli**. The lungs contain approximately 300 million alveoli, providing a total surface area of about 750 square feet (675 sq m) for gaseous exchange. The inside of each alveolus is open to an air passage and the outside is in contact with blood vessels.

A rich supply of lymphatic vessels is also found in the lungs. Bringing outside air deep into the lungs presents a special challenge for the body's defense mechanisms. Although many harmful microbes are filtered out of incoming air in the nose and nasal cavity, some bacteria and viruses make it through to the lungs. To combat these disease-causing agents, lung tissue contains many white blood cells and numerous lymphatic vessels to carry away invading microbes.

Alveoli are thin sacs made of epithelial cells. The inside of each sac is lined with a special fluid called surfactant, which helps gases dissolve and pass through the alveoli. With blood capillaries lying against the alveoli, oxygen and carbon dioxide can pass easily between the air and the blood.

THE DIAPHRAGM

The last component of the respiratory system is a large muscle stretched across the bottom of the abdominal cavity, known as the **diaphragm**. In its resting position, the diaphragm forms a curved platform under the lungs. When it contracts, this muscle flattens out, pulling down on the thoracic cavity, which encloses the lungs.

Other muscles, the **intercostals**, which lie between neighboring ribs, also play a small role in breathing. When you take a deep breath, these muscles expand the rib cage, pulling more air into the lungs. During normal relaxed breathing, though, the diaphragm is the only muscle involved.

RESPIRATION

With an understanding of the anatomy of the respiratory system, we are now ready to consider how this system delivers oxygen to the blood and removes carbon dioxide from the blood.

Before you take a breath, the air pressure inside your lungs is the same as the

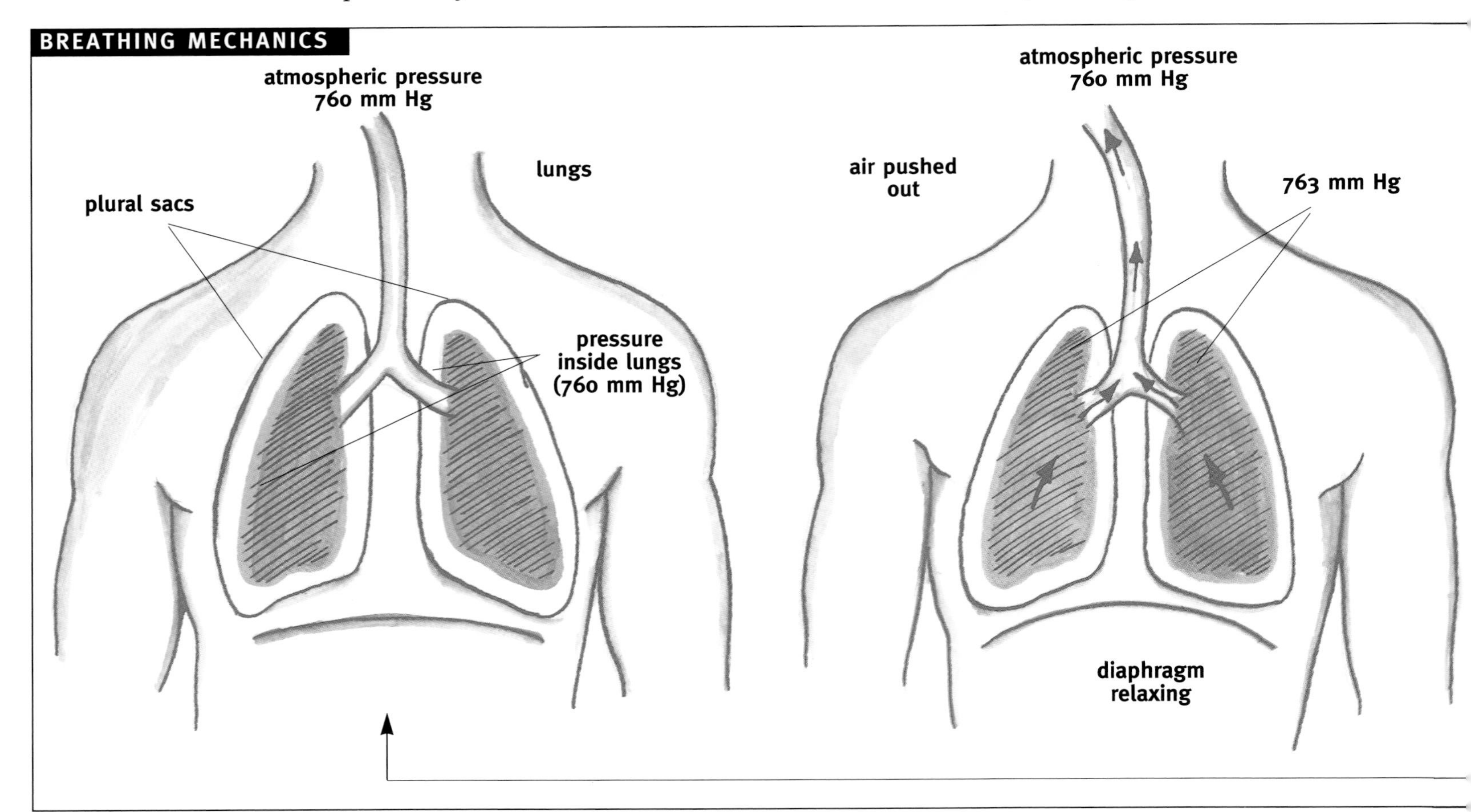

pressure of the atmosphere outside your body. Since there is not a difference in pressure between these two locations, there is no movement of air.

The process of inspiration, or "breathing in," begins when the diaphragm contracts, pulling downward and expanding the size of the thoracic cavity. This creates a partial vacuum, reducing pressure inside the chest, which causes the lungs to expand. The lower pressure inside the lungs makes air from the outside rush in until the air pressure inside the lungs equals that outside the lungs, the atmospheric pressure.

When you exhale, or "breathe out," the diaphragm relaxes, moving upward to its original position. This action reduces the total size of the thoracic cavity and causes pressure to build inside the lungs. The result is a flow of air out of the lungs through the nasal passages and into the air.

Gaseous Exchange Inspiration and expiration circulate air in and out of the lungs efficiently. This constant turnover of air provides a way for the lungs to get oxygen into the blood and carbon dioxide out of it.

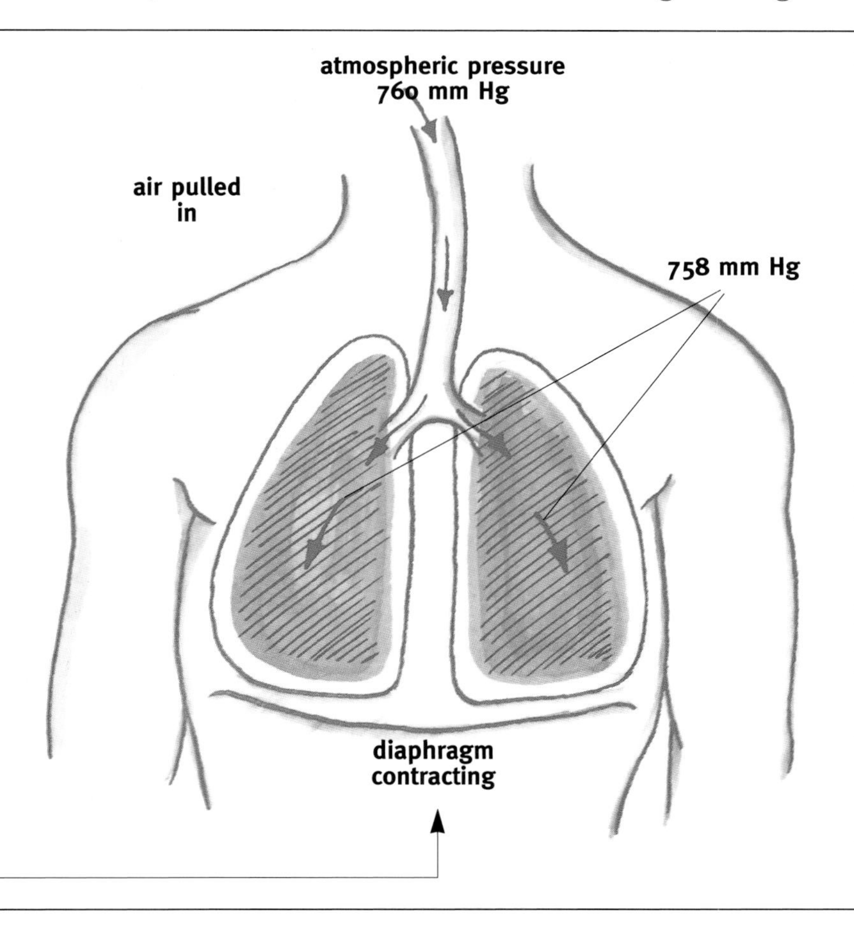

To understand gaseous exchange, we can think of the pressure produced by individual gases in the air. Oxygen is responsible for part of the pressure of air, and that partial pressure depends on how much oxygen is present. In air outside the lungs, oxygen has a partial pressure of 160 millimeters of mercury, which means it can force the liquid element mercury to rise 160 millimeters in a thin tube. This measurement is written like this: ppO_2 = 160. Carbon dioxide has a very low partial pressure in outside air ($ppCO_2$ = 0.3) because it is very rare in the atmosphere.

The difference in pressure of these gases between the alveoli and the blood is what moves them back and forth between the lungs and the bloodstream. Gases always move from an area of higher pressure to an area of lower pressure. Blood entering the lungs has a lower ppO_2 than alveolar air, so oxygen moves into the blood. The $ppCO_2$ is higher in blood entering the lungs than in the alveoli, so carbon dioxide moves out of the bloodstream and into the lungs.

When blood from the lungs reaches the individual cells, the situation is reversed. Now the ppO_2 is highest in the blood, so oxygen moves into the tissues. The built-up carbon dioxide in cells moves out of the tissues and into the blood, to be returned to the lungs and expelled.

Almost all of the oxygen held in the blood is carried by hemoglobin inside erythrocytes, with a small percent dissolved in the liquid portion of blood. Some carbon dioxide attaches to

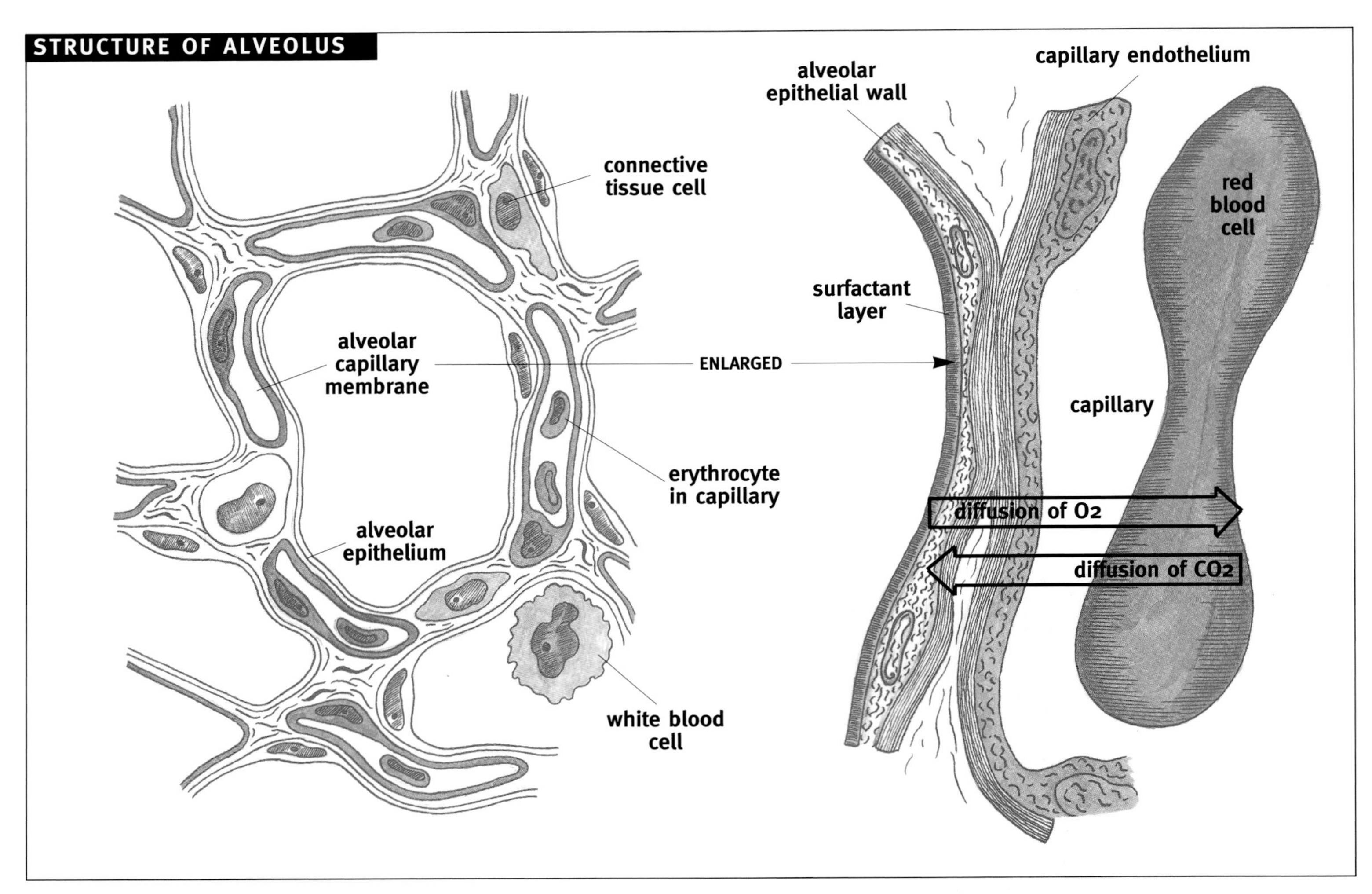

hemoglobin for transport to the lungs, but most of it combines with water to form carbonic acid, and some dissolves in the blood fluids.

An important feature of hemoglobin is that it binds oxygen and carbon dioxide weakly. If oxygen bound strongly to this protein, it would not be released to the tissues, and carbon dioxide would not pass out through the lungs. There are other gases that do combine with hemoglobin more tightly. Carbon monoxide—a chemical found in the exhaust of gasoline engines—is a gas that binds irreversibly to hemoglobin: once it binds, it does not release. This makes carbon monoxide a deadly poison, because it binds at the same place on hemoglobin as oxygen. This prevents hemoglobin from carrying oxygen to the tissues, and cells begin to die rapidly.

Control of Respiration A group of neurons in the midbrain known as the respiratory center controls breathing. Nerves from this center are connected to the diaphragm and direct it to contract in a constant rhythmic pattern. This occurs involuntarily, so that you do not have to think about it every time you breathe.

The respiratory center also has connections to the cerebral cortex, which means we have partial voluntary control over breathing. By thinking about it, you can override the normal pattern of breathing and slow, deepen, quicken, or even stop breathing. This is useful when you need to control respiration—when holding your breath underwater, for example.

Voluntary control over breathing is not total, however. If you try to hold your breath too long, carbon dioxide builds up in the blood and signals the respiratory center to take over. In extreme cases, prolonged breath holding signals the brain to shut off consciousness, causing you to faint. This releases the respiratory center from voluntary control and breathing resumes.

EMPHYSEMA

A common and dangerous lung ailment is emphysema. This disorder is characterized by destruction of the alveoli. As alveolar tissue is destroyed and replaced with thick, inflexible scar tissue, gaseous exchange is diminished and normal breathing becomes difficult. In advanced stages of this disease, the lungs expand, giving the patient a "barrel-chested" appearance, and decreased oxygen delivery begins to damage many vital organs.

The usual cause of emphysema is long-term irritation of the sensitive alveolar membranes. Cigarette smoke, air pollution, and constant exposure to airborne chemicals, dust, or smoke are blamed for many cases of this disease. The lung damage associated with emphysema can often be halted and reversed if the irritant is identified and exposure is eliminated. Tragically, many cases of emphysema go undiagnosed, or informed victims choose not to eliminate the source of the problem until the disease advances to an irreversible stage.

RESPIRATORY CENTER

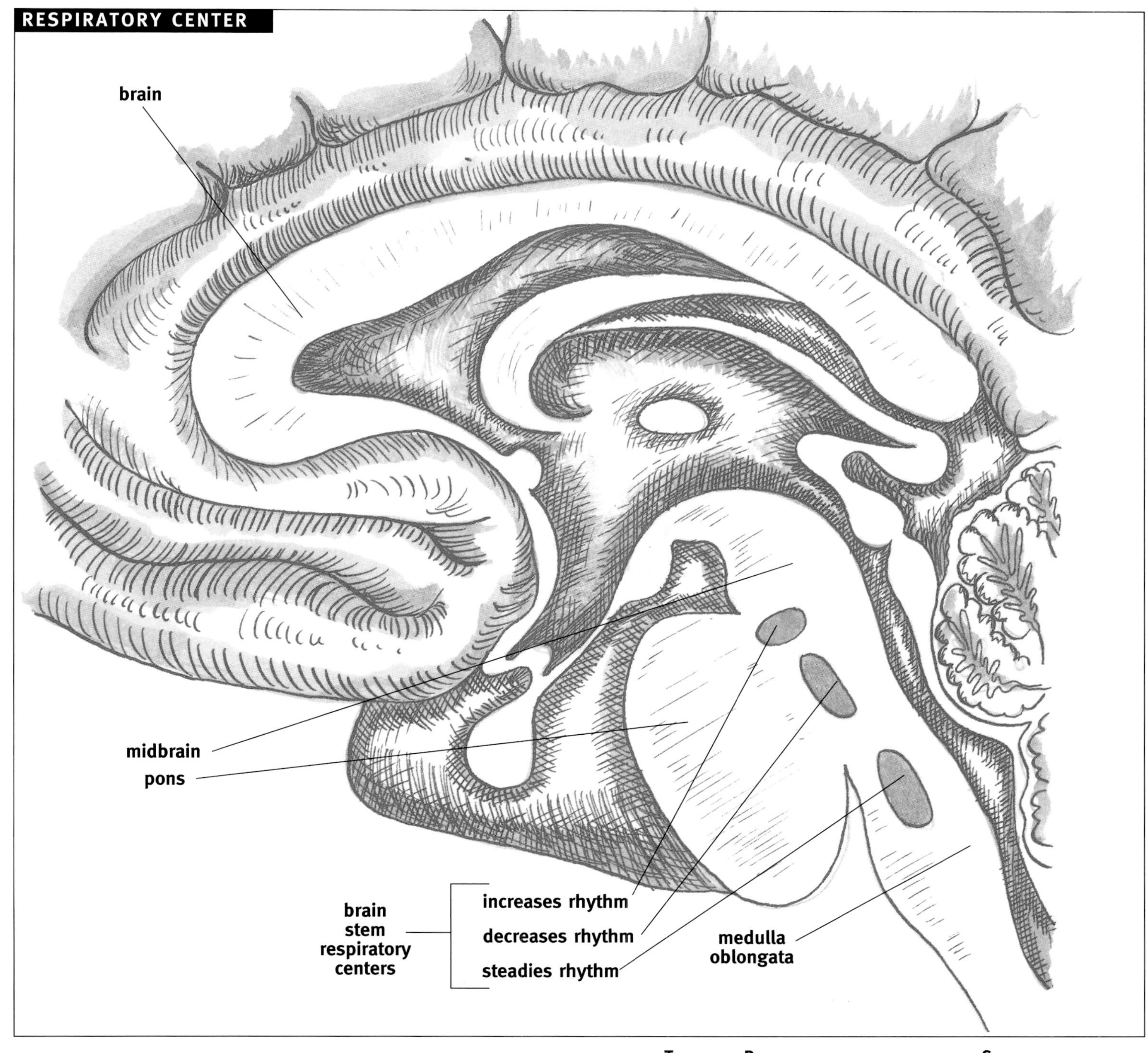

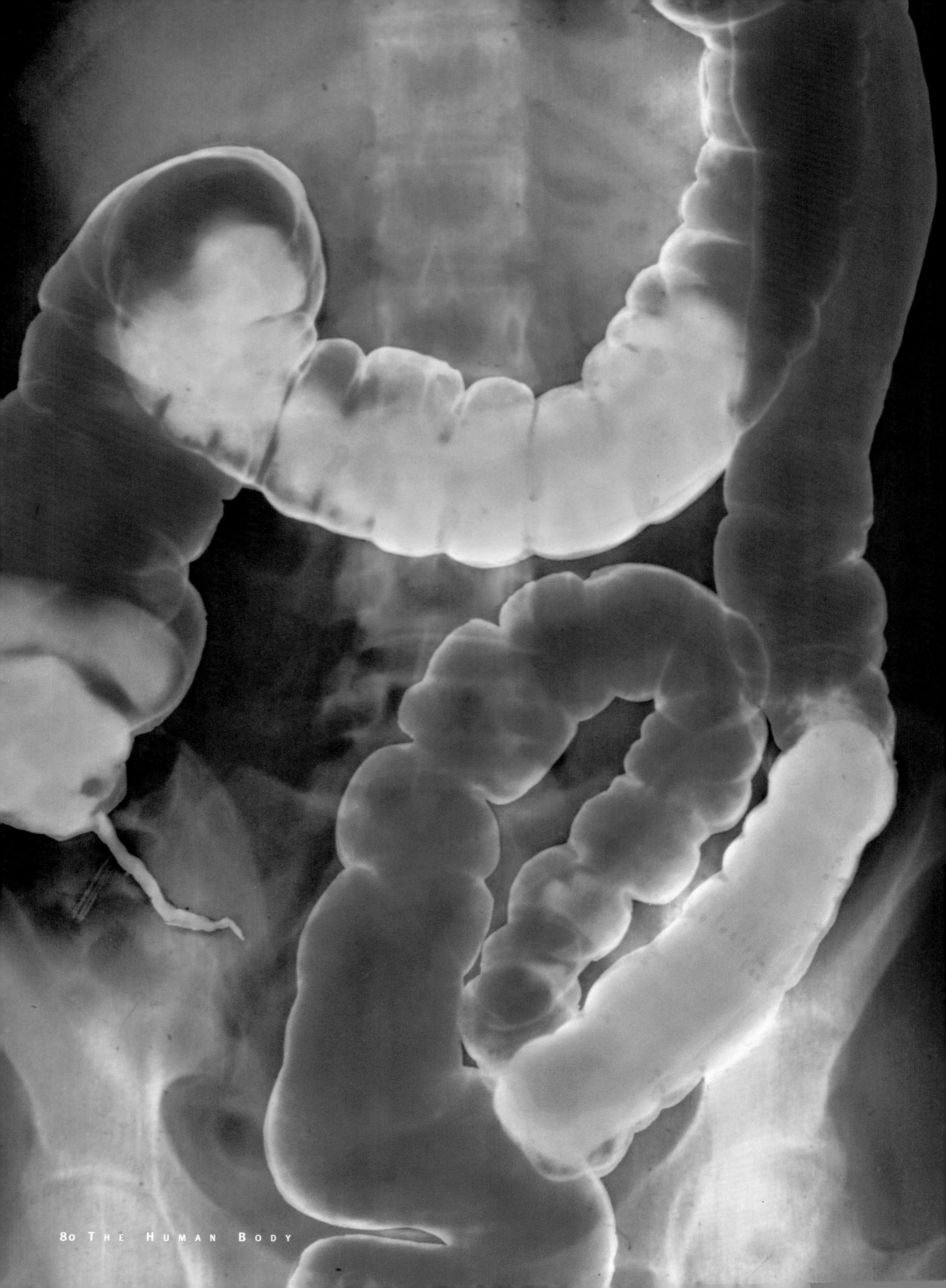

Chapter 8

THE DIGESTIVE SYSTEM

There are three reasons why we eat: (1) food provides energy-rich materials the body needs for fuel to enable it to perform work; (2) food contains the basic molecules the body uses to build new cells and tissues; (3) eating food is a lot of fun. Here we will consider just the first two uses of food—as an energy source and as a source of building materials for repair and growth.

The digestive system is a network of organs that brings food into the body, breaks it down, and sends the products into the blood for transport to the tissues and cells. The food we eat contains the same kinds of molecules our cells are made of: nucleic acids, proteins, carbohydrates, and fats. In the digestive process, these large molecules are broken down to their subunits as follows:

nucleic acids → nucleotides
proteins → amino acids
carbohydrates → sugars
fats → fatty acids and glycerol

These small building blocks are then absorbed into the blood and transported to the tissues for assembly into new macromolecules. The new macromolecules are incorporated into the tissues as the body grows, repairs damaged areas, and replaces worn-out cells.

A portion of these small molecules, usually part of the sugars and fatty acids that are absorbed, are put through the energy-producing cycle to make ATP, a form of stored chemical energy. Under extreme conditions, when sugars and fats are unavailable, amino acids can also be shut-

DIGESTIVE TRACT

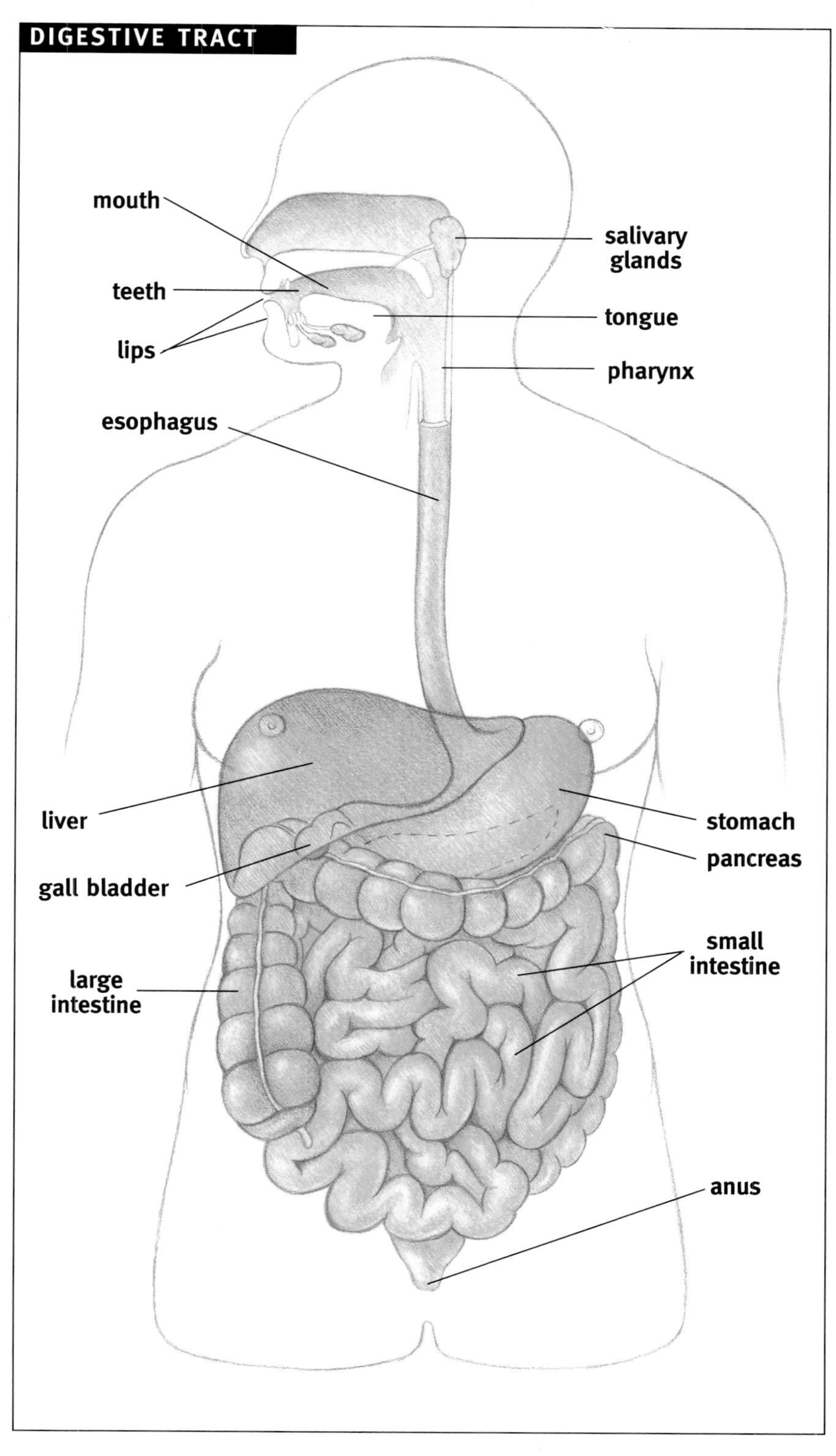

PAGE 80: The large intestine X-ray image of the large intestine. This final section of the digestive tract removes excess water and electrolytes from food we eat, and discards waste products from the body. The wormlike structure attached to the large intestine (middle, left) is the appendix.

VITAMINS		
VITAMIN	FUNCTION	SOURCES
A	—promotes growth and regulation of bone cells —activates synthesis of rhodopsin, the vision protein —maintains keratinocytes for healthy skin	—dark green, dark yellow, and orange fruits and vegetables
B_1 (thiamine)	—aids energy-producing enzymes —activates synthesis of acetylcholine, a neurotransmitter	—whole-grain cereals, pasta, bread; peas and lima beans; oysters
B_2 (riboflavin)	—aids carbohydrate and protein digestion —maintains erythrocytes	—dark green vegetables; eggs; whole-grain breads, pasta, cereals; dried legumes; mushrooms
B_6 (pyridoxine)	—helps fat digestion —promotes production of antibodies to fight infection	—whole-grain cereals and breads; spinach, green beans, potatoes; bananas; fish; poultry
B_{12} (cyanocobalamin)	—aids in erythrocyte production —activates synthesis of amino acids —helps produce energy	—animal products such as meat, milk, cheese; fish; oysters
C (ascorbic acid)	—forms collagen fiber in connective tissue —promotes wound healing —combines with poisons and inactivates them	—citrus fruits; tomatoes; strawberries; potatoes; dark green vegetables
D	—regulates calcium and phosphate, mineral components of bone	—eggs; milk; salmon; tuna
E (tocopherols)	—helps protect liver from toxic compounds —promotes wound healing —activates synthesis of nucleic acids —forms cell membrane	—vegetable oils; whole-grain cereals and breads; dried beans; leafy green vegetbles
K	—promotes synthesis of clotting factors	—spinach; cauliflower; cabbage; liver; also synthesized by intestinal bacteria
BIOTIN	—aids in synthesis of fatty acids and nucleotides	—yeast; liver; egg yolk; synthesized by intestinal bacteria
FOLIC ACID	—activates synthesis of nucleic acids —forms red and white blood cells	—green leafy vegetables; liver; synthesized by intestinal bacteria
NIACIN	—promotes digestion of fats —aids in energy production	—meats; liver; fish; peas; beans; nuts; whole-grain products
PANTOTHENIC ACID	—converts amino acids and fatty acids into glucose for ATP production	—cereal; green vegetables; yeast; kidney, liver; produced by intestinal bacteria

tled into the energy cycle and used for fuel to produce ATP.

In addition to these four basic types of molecules, food also provides our bodies with vitamins and minerals. These are elements and small chemicals the body cannot make on its own. Cells can actually manufacture nucleotides and some amino acids if needed, though it is easier to get them from food. But the only source of vitamins and minerals is the food we eat.

Most vitamins and minerals act as cofactors in the body. A cofactor is something that helps another molecule do its job. Iron, for example, acts as a cofactor in the hemoglobin molecule by attaching to oxygen and carrying it through the bloodstream. On pages 82 and 85 are lists of the vitamins and minerals the body requires.

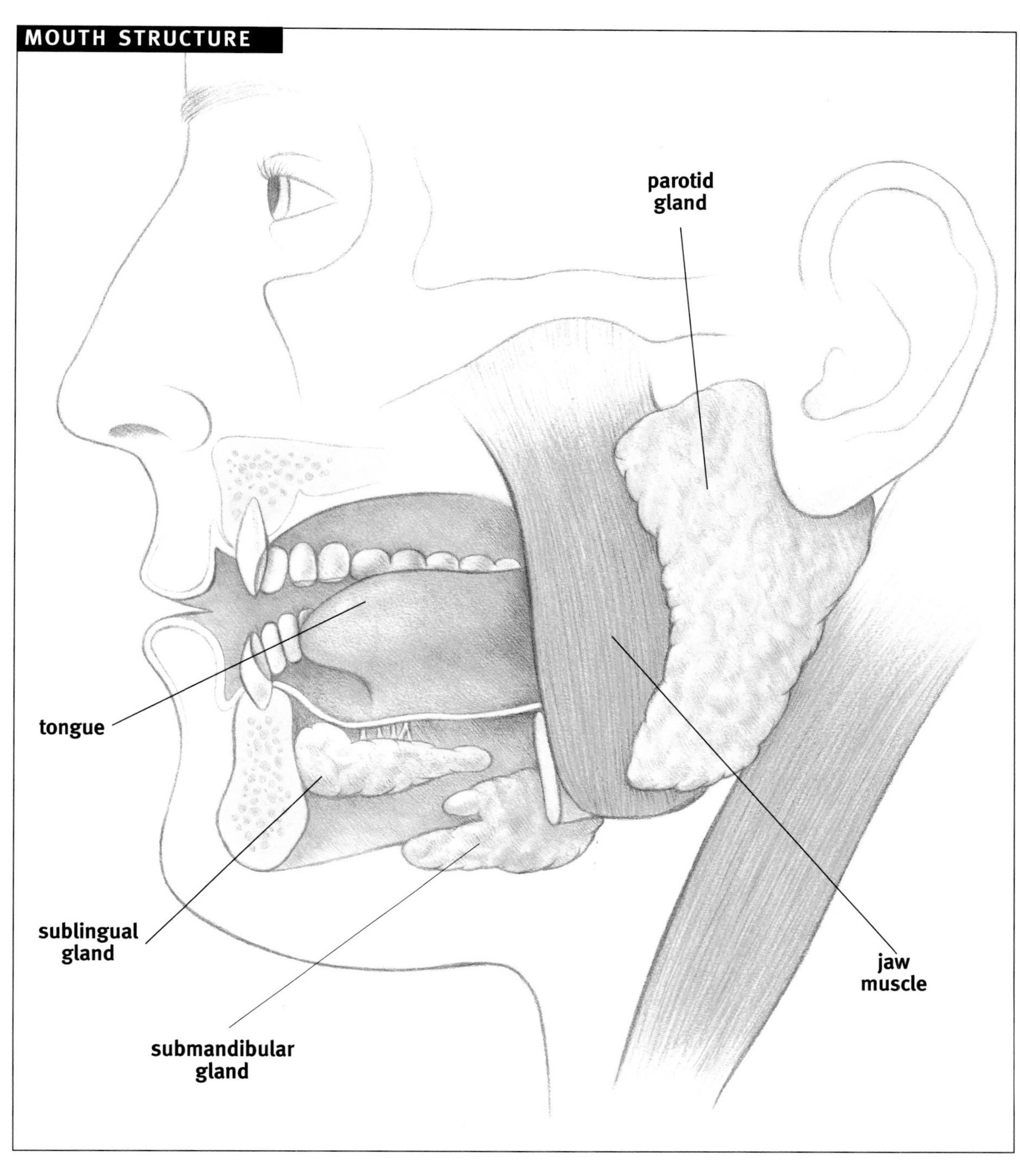

THE DIGESTIVE TRACT

Let's now examine each of the organs of the digestive tract in turn, and find out what happens to the food we eat.

MOUTH The first steps of food processing are carried out by the mouth. Here the materials we eat are physically broken up by the process of chewing. Strong jaw muscles help us to grind food between the teeth, shredding and tearing it into small pieces. The tongue—a strong and agile muscle—aids in this process by guiding food between the teeth. The cheeks and lips also help by keeping food in place as it is chewed.

In addition to mechanically breaking down food, the mouth also begins the process of chemical digestion. The **salivary glands**, located in tissues around the mouth, secrete a fluid called **saliva** into the mouth. This fluid contains digestive enzymes that break up chemical bonds in the food molecules. One of these enzymes, amylase, breaks up a type of carbohydrate called starch, which is made of long chains of sugar molecules hooked together.

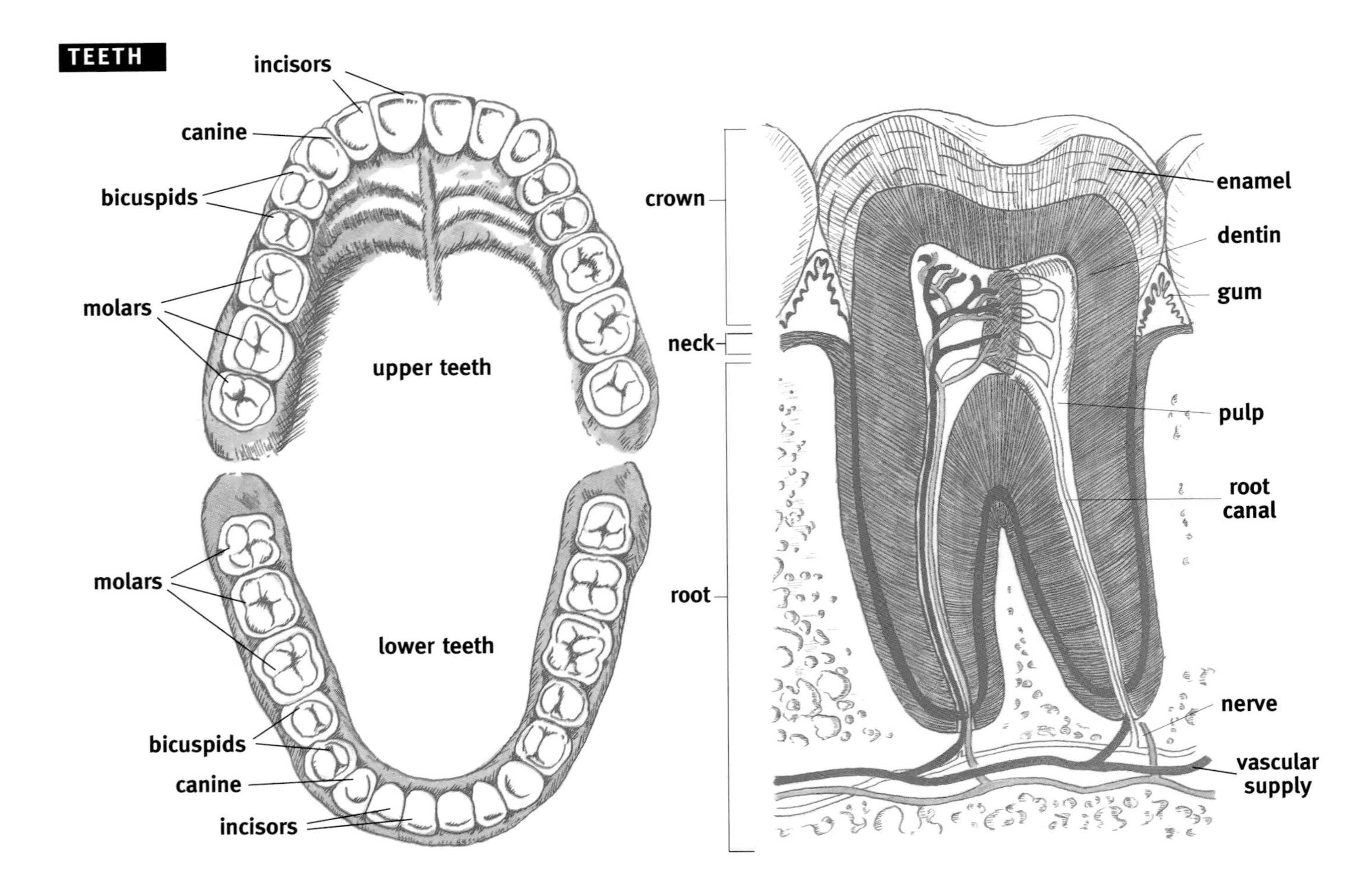

Amylase breaks the long chains into smaller branches, and these branches are further digested once they reach the intestines.

In addition to digestive enzymes, saliva contains antimicrobial enzymes. An example is lysozyme, an enzyme that breaks up bacteria and kills them. Many harmful microbes enter the mouth when we eat and breathe, but lysozyme and other protective enzymes usually kill them before they can cause infections.

Esophagus Once food is chewed into small bits it is moved to the back of the throat and into the esophagus, the passage that connects the mouth to the stomach. Skeletal muscles in the wall of the esophagus squeeze food down through this channel and into the stomach. No significant digestion takes place in the esophagus.

Stomach The bottom of the esophagus enlarges into the stomach, a muscular chamber where food is broken down further. The walls of this chamber contain layers of smooth muscle. The inner lining of the stomach is composed of special epithelial cells that are resistant to the harsh chemicals present. The interior of the stomach contains many deep folds that increase surface area and also help mix food when stomach muscles contract.

When food enters the stomach, a mixture of gastric juices is released to actively break food down into smaller pieces. These juices contain hydrochloric acid, a strong chemical that helps break up food molecules. Another important enzyme in the stomach is pepsin, which breaks proteins down into short chains of amino acids.

As food is digested in the stomach, rippling contractions pass through the stomach walls, mixing the food with the gastric juices. This mixing action helps digestive enzymes reach all of the food bits and break them down.

Small Intestine Next, the partially digested food is passed into the small intestine, where the final steps of digestion take place. This chamber is about 1 inch (2.5cm) wide and 20 feet (6m) long. The inner wall of the small intestine is lined with fingerlike projections called **villi**, which increase the surface area for absorption of nutrients. Between these villi are **intestinal glands**, which secrete fluids that protect the inner lining from harsh digestive juices.

The innermost lining of the small intestine is made of epithelial cells that pro-

MINERALS		
MINERAL	FUNCTION	SOURCES
CALCIUM	—necessary for formation of bones and teeth —promotes proper functioning of nerves and muscles —aids in chromosome separation during cell division —helps carbohydrate metabolism	—low-fat dairy products; green, leafy vegetables; sardines, canned salmon
CHLORINE	—promotes water balance —forms hydrochloric acid in stomach	—table salt; salty foods
CHROMIUM	—helps in production of insulin	—whole grains; animal products
COBALT	—activates vitamin B_{12}	—cabbage, spinach, lettuce, watercress; liver
COPPER	—necessary for synthesis of hemoglobin —activates synthesis of melanin	—nuts; cocoa powder; raisins; dried beans
FLUORINE	—hardens teeth and prevents cavities	—fish; animal products; tea
IODINE	—forms part of thyroid hormone	—seafood; table salt
IRON	—forms part of hemoglobin —necessary for ATP formation	—whole grains; eggs; meat; dried beans
MAGNESIUM	—forms part of many enzymes —helps form bone tissue —aids proper functioning of nerves and muscles	—whole grains; nuts; meat; fish
MANGANESE	—activates many enzymes —promotes synthesis of hemoglobin	—liver; meats
PHOSPHORUS	—aids in formation of bones and teeth —forms part of nucleic acids —promotes proper functioning of nerves and muscles	—dairy products; meat; fish; poultry; nuts
SELENIUM	—prevents chromosome breakage; antioxidant	—seafood; egg yolks; milk; mushrooms; garlic
SODIUM	—promotes water balance —allows conduction of nerve impulses	—table salt; salty foods
SULFUR	—forms part of vitamins and amino acids	—beef; liver; lamb; poultry; eggs; cheese; beans
ZINC	—regulates carbon dioxide —forms part of hormones —aids taste sensations —helps in formation of reproductive cells	—meats; most other foods

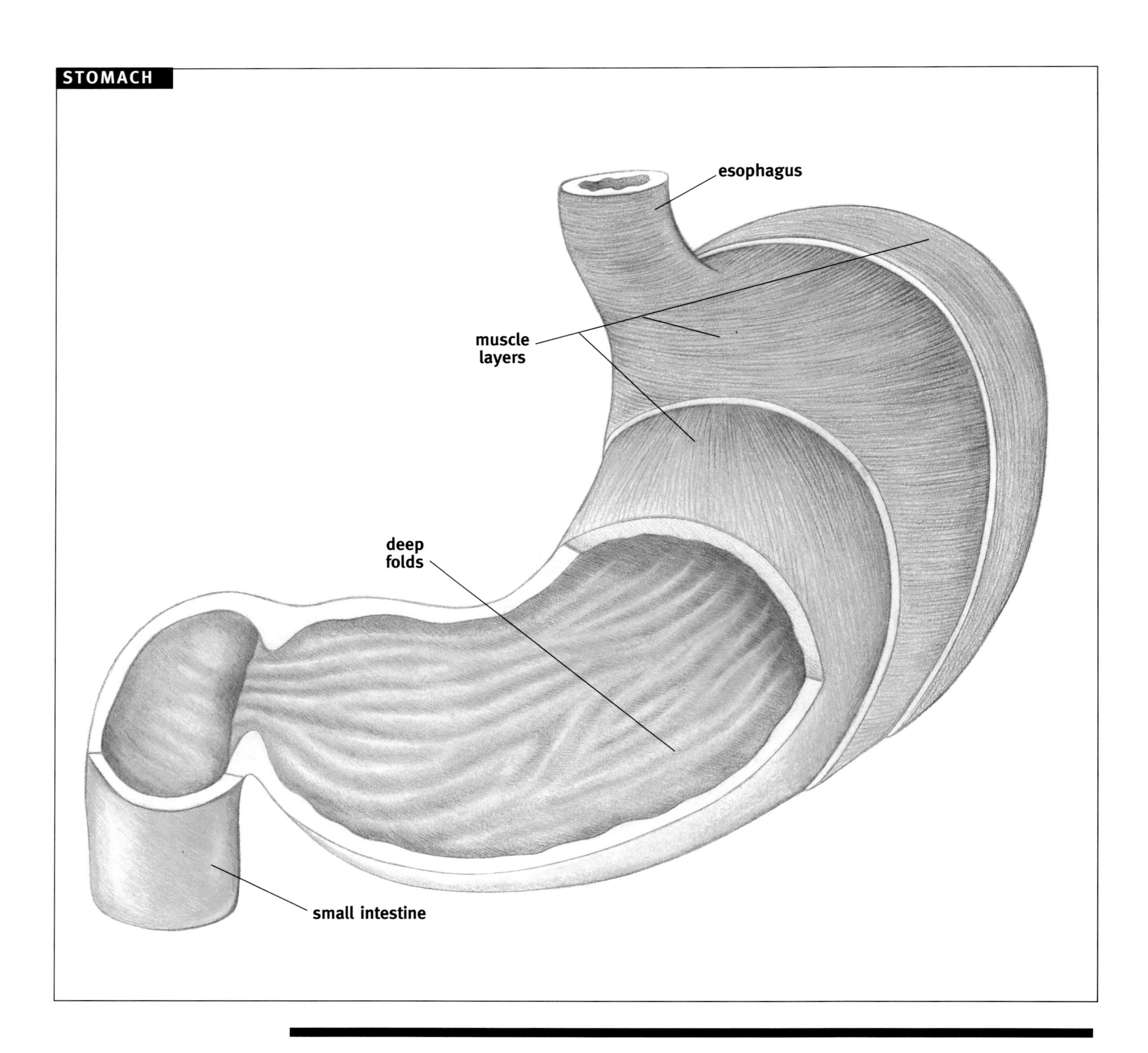

LACTOSE INTOLERANCE

Some people have a condition known as lactose intolerance, which means if they drink milk or eat products made from milk—such as cheese—they experience stomach cramps, abdominal pain, and diarrhea. In severe cases, dehydration can result, producing a serious health problem.

The cause of this condition is a lack of the enzyme lactase, which breaks down the milk sugar lactose. Cells in the lining of the small intestine usually produce this protein and secrete it into the digestive juices along with other enzymes. If this enzyme is not present when milk products are ingested, lactose cannot be absorbed. This interferes with other materials being absorbed, and also causes a reaction by the tissues of the small intestine.

The occurrence of lactose intolerance varies widely between races. About 7 percent of Caucasians have this condition, while the rate for blacks is about 70 percent. Almost no Asians can tolerate milk—the incidence of lactose intolerance in Asiatics is about 95 percent.

duce digestive enzymes. There are also layers of smooth muscle surrounding this tubular chamber, which slowly contract and mix juices and food for maximum digestion.

In addition to its own digestive factors, the small intestine receives digestive fluids from two abdominal organs, the pancreas and the liver.

Pancreas The pancreas is positioned near the top of the small intestine and is connected to it by the **pancreatic duct**. Cells within the pancreas synthesize the following enzymes:

Enzyme	Function
Pancreatic amylase	breaks carbohydrate chains into sugars
Trypsin Chymotrypsin Carboxypeptidase	cleave proteins into short chains of amino acids
Pancreatic lipase	digests fats
Ribonuclease	breaks RNA into ribonucleotides
Deoxyribonuclease	breaks DNA into deoxyribonucleotides

VILLI

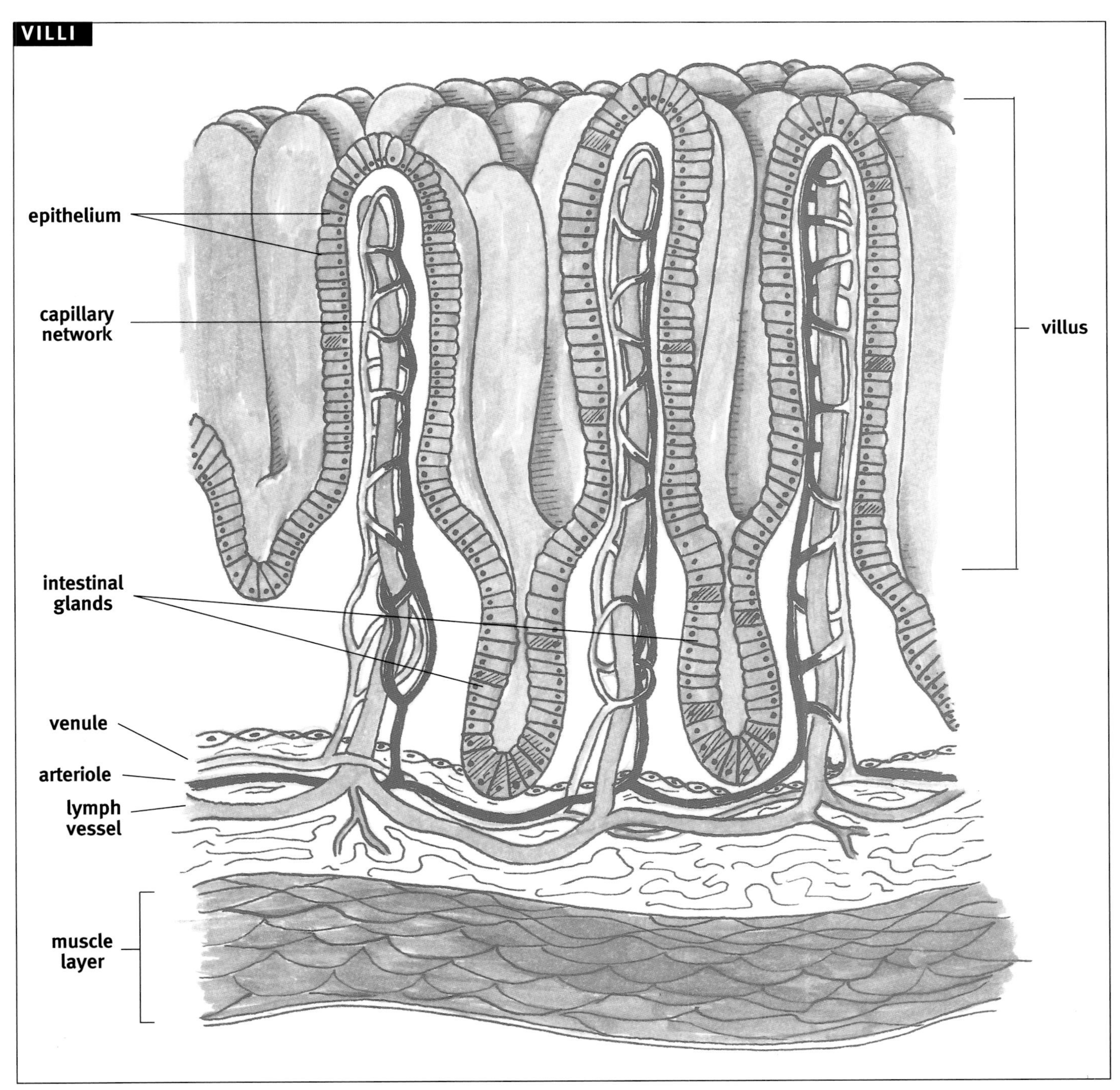

LIVER AND PANCREAS

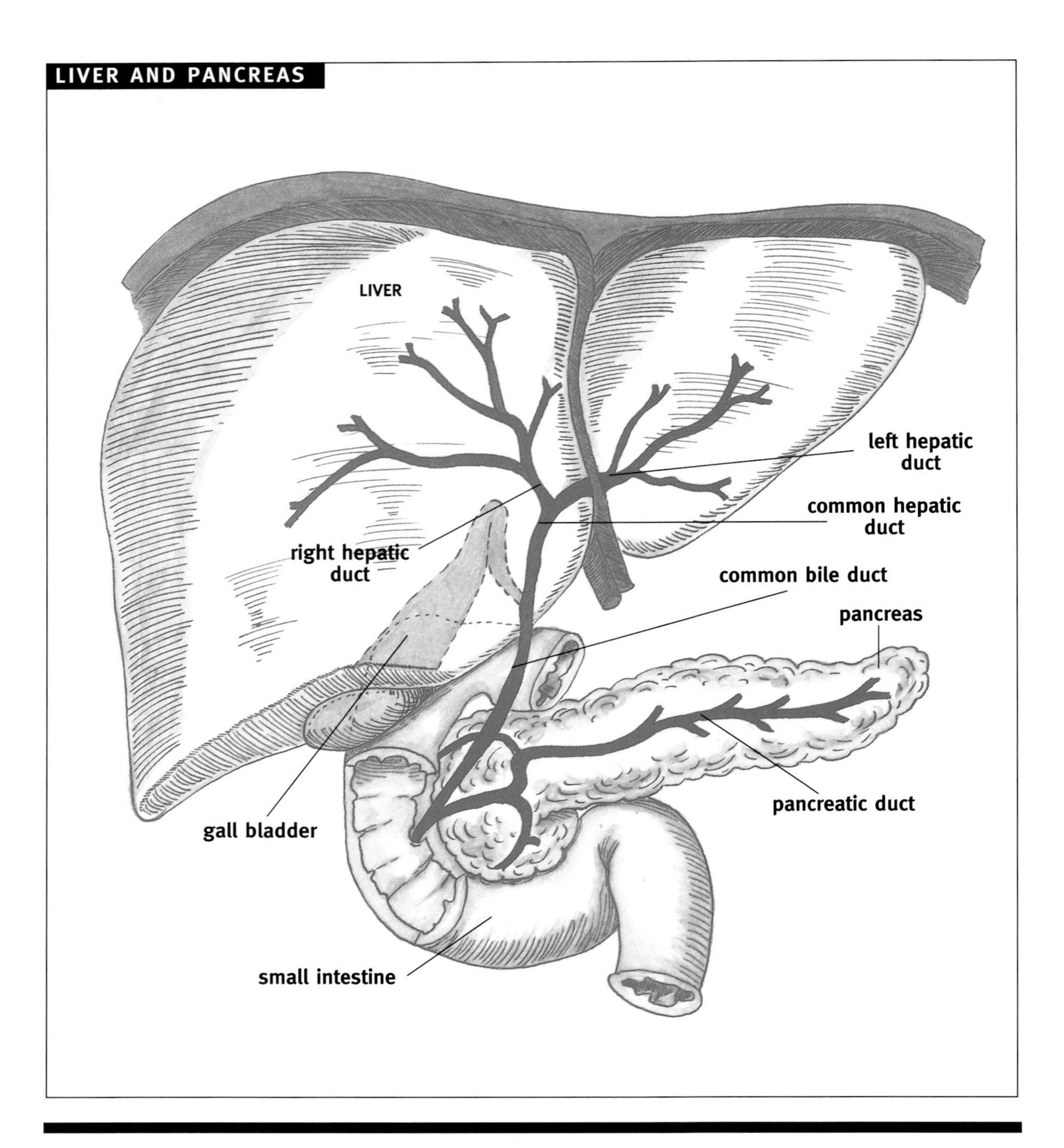

OBESITY

Obesity is a condition in which body weight is 15 percent or more above the ideal weight of an individual according to height. In affluent nations, this is a common problem—in the United States, for example, about one-fifth of the population is between 10 and 20 percent overweight. Even moderate obesity can have a pronounced negative effect on a person's health. Disorders such as diabetes, cardiovascular disease, arthritis, high blood pressure, varicose veins, and pulmonary disease are all aggravated by being overweight.

Whenever the calorie intake is greater than the energy expended, a person will gain weight. The human body is designed to store excess food energy in the form of lipids in adipose cells, and will always do so if possible. Thus, obesity in many cases is the consequence of overeating, lack of exercise, or both.

Restricting calorie intake, following a healthy diet plan, and exercising regularly is very effective in reversing obesity. Health experts warn, however, that a diet must always provide sufficient protein during a weight-loss program. Starving the body of vital materials leads to loss of muscle, bone, and other vital tissues, and can cause serious harm. Studies show that gradual, carefully paced weight reduction is safer and longer lasting than quick-loss "crash diets," which are often followed by rapid regaining of lost pounds.

In some people, adipose tissue continues to proliferate as their body develops, leading to a condition called hyper-plastic obesity—a severe form of obesity that displays a strong genetic component. Those afflicted with this ailment usually gain weight rapidly in childhood and adolescence, and become grossly obese as adults, carrying 100 pounds (45 kg) or more of extra weight. Dieting and exercise are usually not effective in such cases, but the condition can be treated with drugs that alter metabolism, or by surgery to remove sections of adipose tissue.

All of these enzymes are found in a fluid called pancreatic juice, which is secreted into the small intestine.

Liver This organ produces a greenish fluid called bile, which contains salts, cholesterol, and phospholipids. Bile is secreted into the small intestine, where it emulsifies fats—breaks them into tiny droplets—so they can be absorbed. Excess bile produced by the liver is stored in the **gall bladder** until needed.

Once food is completely broken down, it is ready to be absorbed into the intestinal villi. About 90 percent of absorption takes place in the small intestine, with the rest occurring in the stomach and large intestine. Fatty acids and most sugars enter the villi by simple diffusion, which means they move through on their own. Some sugars, as well as all of the amino acids, must be actively transported through the intestinal wall. This involves a special energy-requiring system that pulls these molecules through. Vitamins and minerals pass through the epithelial layer and into the villi by diffusion and do not require energy for absorption. Water, along with the fluids from digestive juices, is also absorbed by simple diffusion.

Inside the villi there are blood and lymph capillaries. Most nutrients move into the bloodstream directly, but some types of fat molecules enter the lymphatic system first and eventually enter the bloodstream when lymph is returned to the blood.

Capillaries that carry blood out of the intestinal villi connect to the **portal vein**, which carries everything taken in through the small intestine—nutrients, toxins, minerals, and water—directly to the liver. Inside the liver, all of the recently absorbed materials, including toxins that penetrate the intestine along with food molecules, are removed from the blood. The liver cells then trap and inactivate poisonous materials, and send the purified nutrients back into the bloodstream. Thus the liver filters all materials absorbed by the small intestine before they continue on to the rest of the body. The liver also stores some of the nutrients it takes in, and distributes them later, when food is not available.

Large Intestine Connected to the small intestine is the final section of the digestive system, the large intestine, a tubular structure that is 2½ inches (3cm) wide and 5 feet (1.5m) long. Some absorption of remaining nutrients takes place here, along with water and some chemicals. All of the unabsorbed material, the feces, is pushed through the large intestine and out of the body. In this manner, all of the solid waste products are expelled from the body. There are also fluid wastes that must be eliminated, and this is the subject of the next chapter.

ABSORPTION

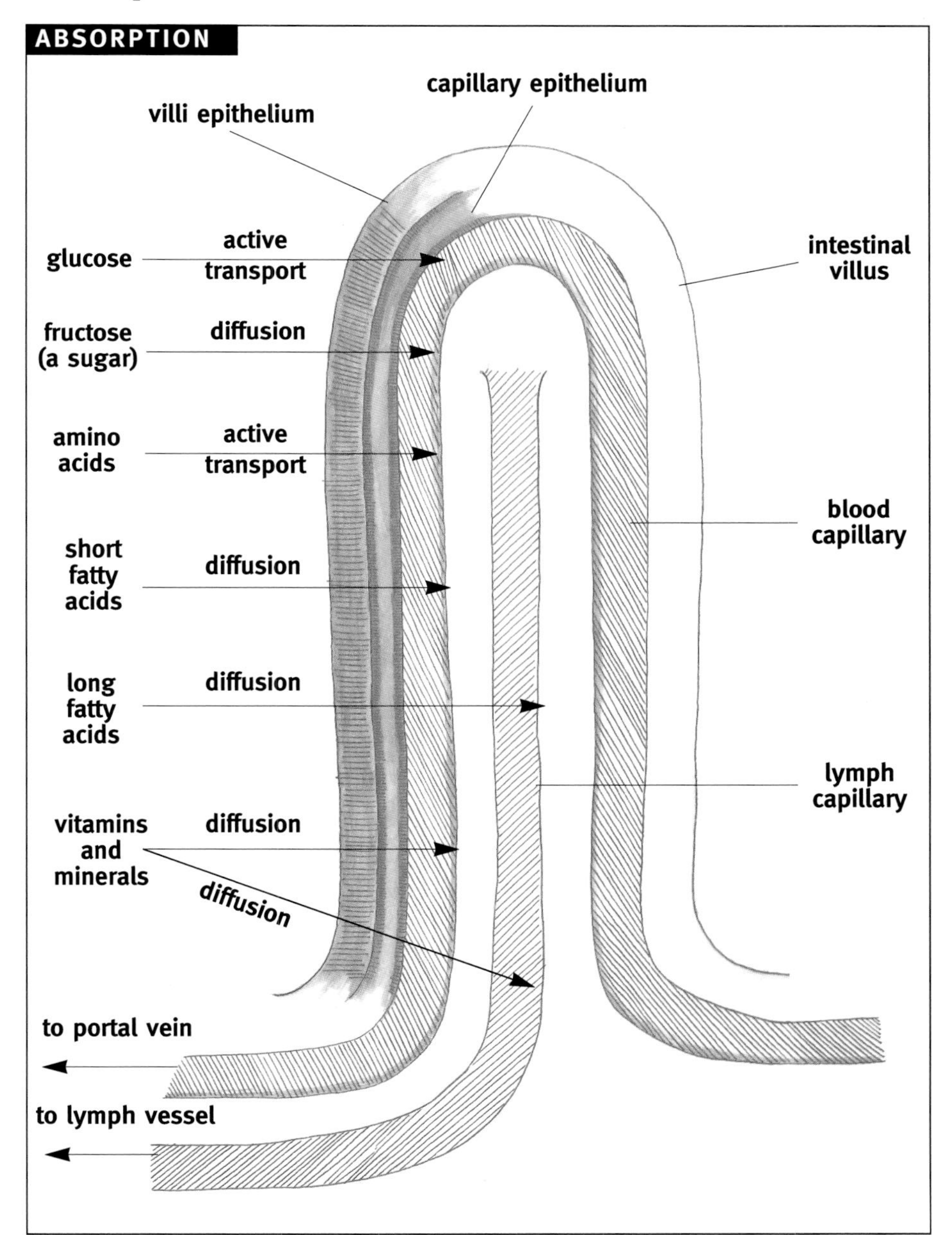

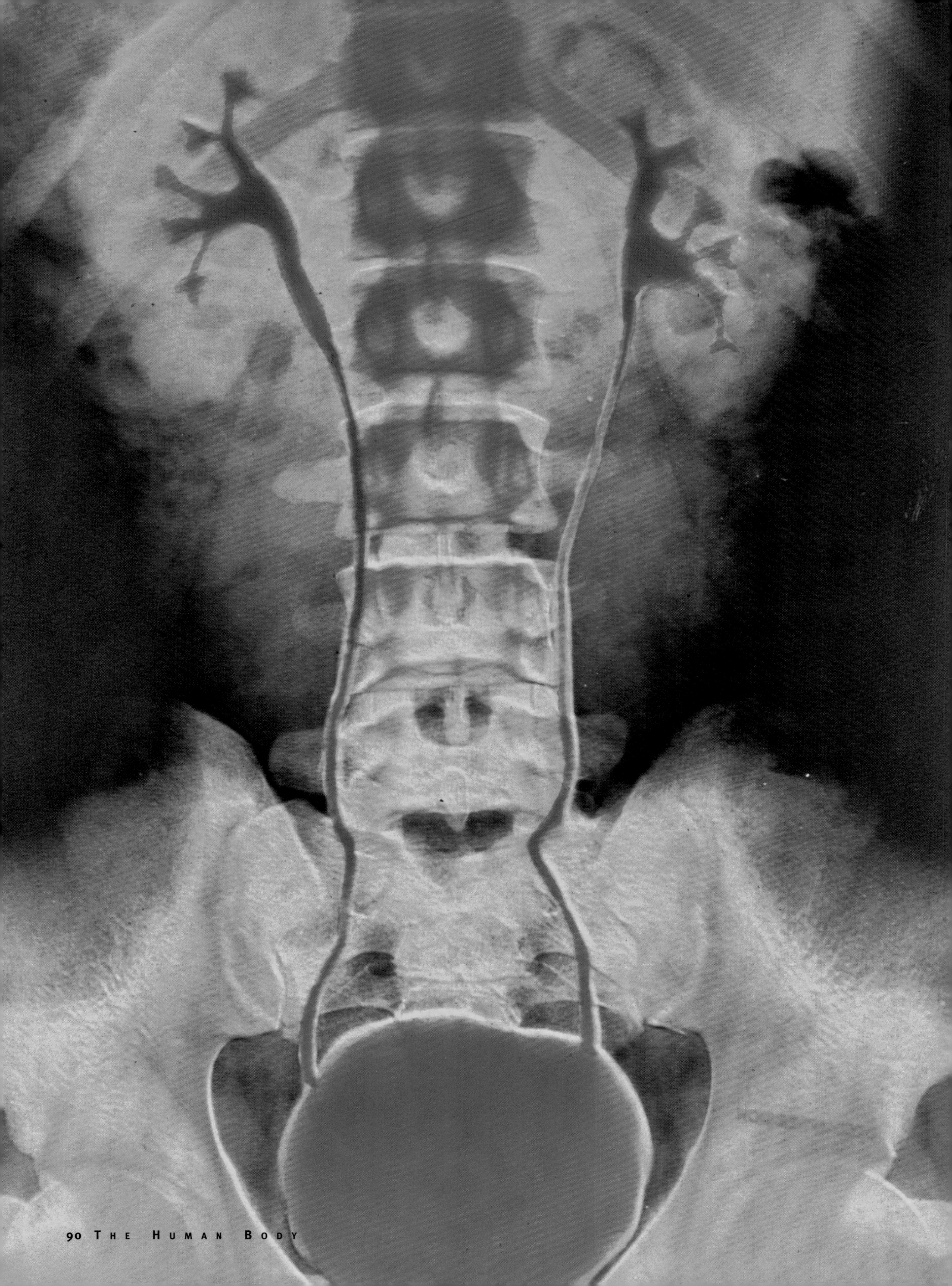

Chapter 9

The Urinary System

The food molecules that are delivered to the bloodstream by the digestive system circulate throughout the body to reach individual cells. Every cell depends on these substances for fuel and for raw materials used in growth and repair. As the cellular enzymes break apart molecular bonds in these food molecules to produce energy and build new macromolecules, chemical waste products are generated that must be eliminated from the body.

We have already examined how one of the main by-products of energy production—carbon dioxide—is transported to the lungs and exhaled. We also learned that the sweat glands get rid of some waste materials by secreting them onto the outer surface of the skin, and that solid wastes are discarded from the digestive tract. But many other waste compounds that are not handled by the lungs, skin, and digestive system build up in the interstitial spaces and eventually pass into the blood. It takes another group of organs—known as the urinary system—to filter the bulk of waste products from the blood and pass them out of the body.

ANATOMY OF THE URINARY SYSTEM

The key organs of the urinary system are the two **kidneys**. They are flattened, disclike structures (kidney beans are very similar in shape to these organs) about the size of your hand. They are positioned in the lower abdomen, just below the back part of the bottom rib.

Connected to the kidneys are two tubes known as the **ureters**. The ureters feed into the **urinary bladder**, which is a storage area for **urine**, the fluid mixture that contains waste products. Once urine builds up in the bladder, muscular valves called **sphincters** open up, and waste fluids are eliminated from the body through the **urethra**.

URINARY SYSTEM

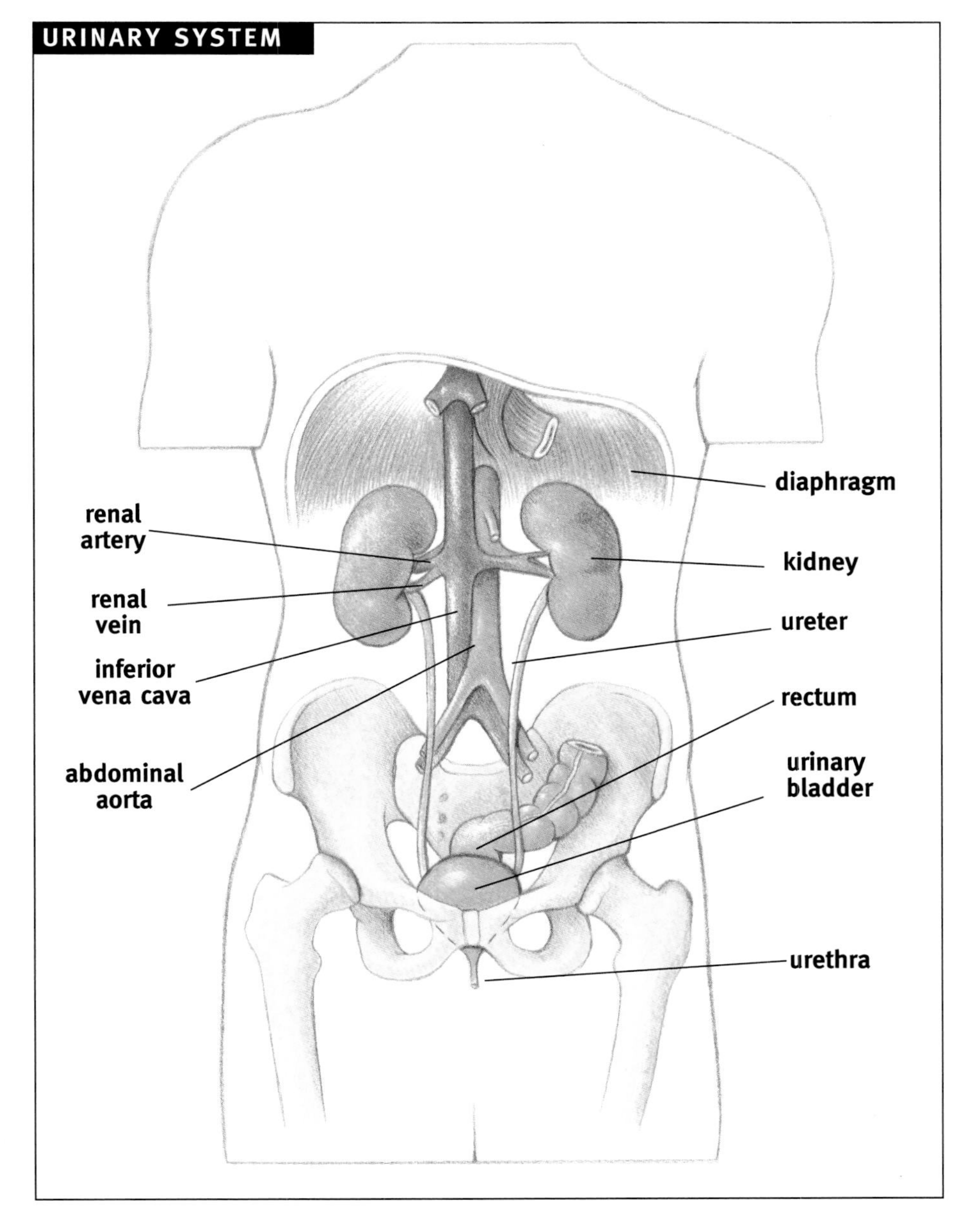

PAGE 90: The urinary system X-ray image of the kidneys (green), ureters, and bladder (red). The two kidneys, where blood is filtered, are the triangular-shaped organs on either spine. Waste products and excess fluid expelled by the kidneys form urine, which collects in the renal pelvis, the branching structures visible against the kidneys. Urine then moves down through the ureters, and is stored in the bladder until eliminated.

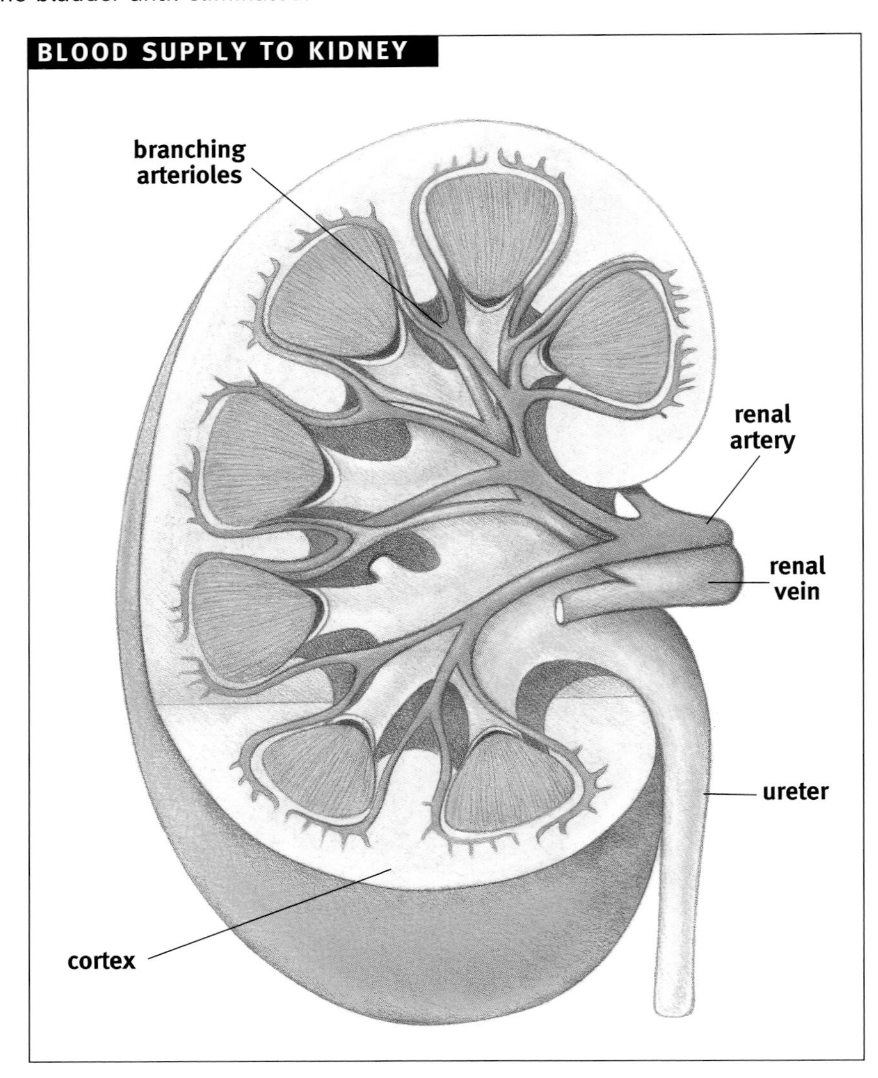

KIDNEY FUNCTION

The two kidneys have a very rich blood supply. The **renal arteries**, which branch off from the aorta, receive about one-fourth of the total blood flow pumped out of the heart. This results in a volume of 1⅛ quarts (1.2L) of blood passing through the kidneys every minute. At this rate, all of the blood in the body is filtered through the kidneys about sixty times every day.

As blood enters the renal artery, it is carried toward the **cortex**, or outer layer of the kidney, through a series of branching arterioles. In the cortex are found the functional units of the kidneys, the **nephrons**.

All of the filtration of the blood takes place in individual nephrons. Each kidney contains about 1 million of these units. The **incoming arteriole** branches into a group of looped vessels to form a structure known as the **glomerulus**. Surrounding this group of vessels is the **glomerular capsule**—a cup-shaped structure made of two membranes with a space between the inner and outer layers. Attached to the back of the capsule is a winding section of tubing known as the **proximal convo-**

SALT TABLETS

You have probably heard that it is very important to replace fluids when you engage in activities that cause you to perspire a lot, such as heavy exercise, a long hike in the mountains, or working outside on a hot day. This is important because the fluid volume of the blood must be maintained in order for the heart to pump efficiently.

Just drinking lots of water to replace lost fluids, however, isn't enough. When you sweat, it is not just water that is lost. The salty mixture ex–creted through the skin contains other substances as well, including sodium.

Sodium is one of the most important ions in the body, and its level is carefully regulated by the urinary system. When you drink water, it enters the blood through the intestines and travels to the kidney nephrons, where it passes into the tubules. But water alone, without the addition of some form of sodium, is not efficiently reabsorbed. This is because water follows sodium across the tubular membranes, and since there is very little sodium to reabsorb, almost all of the water continues through the tubules and out of the body.

Drinking more and more water just dilutes the sodium concentration further, so that less and less water can be reabsorbed. Since sodium plays a role in the proper functioning of several cell types, including neural and cardiac cells, reduction of sodium can develop into a dangerous situation.

Thus, it is important to replace not just water when you perspire heavily, but key ions as well. One way is to take salt tablets, which are made of sodium chloride. In earlier days, these tablets were a standard part of Boy Scout hiking gear. More recently, commercial drinks such as Gatorade have been developed to replenish the key substances lost from the body through heavy exercise. Getting some sodium back into the system lets water be reabsorbed in the kidneys, maintaining adequate blood volume and proper functioning of the heart and other tissues as well.

luted tubule. This tube connects to the **loop of the nephron**—a narrower U-shaped tube. The loop feeds into the **distal convoluted tubule**—another piece of twisting tubular material—which empties into a **collecting duct**.

Let's now follow what happens to the blood as it passes through the nephron. The filtration process begins when blood enters the glomerulus. The blood vessels in this structure have unusually large pores, or holes, which make it much easier for fluids from the blood to leak out. In fact, it is about 250 times easier for water to pass out of the glomerulus than out of regular blood vessels.

The pores are not so large that red and white blood cells or blood proteins can leak out. These particles remain inside the vessels and pass into the **outgoing arteriole**. When disease or accident damages the kidney, cells and proteins sometimes do pass through the glomerulus and mix with the urine. The presence of these large particles in the urine is a sign that the kidneys are not working properly. This is why doctors collect urine samples from patients and analyze them: the contents of urine sometimes indicate a health problem.

The pressure of blood entering the glomerulus is higher than pressure in the surrounding capsule. This difference in pressure forces water out of the bloodstream and into the capsular space. As water flows out of the vessels, many small, dissolved particles go with it. This includes food molecules such as glucose and amino acids, charged particles like sodium and chloride, and waste materials such as urea—a by-product of amino acid breakdown.

Once water and dissolved substances collect in the glomerular capsule, the fluid mixture is channeled into the proximal tubule, the first section of a long network of tubes in the nephron. The outgoing arteriole,

NEPHRON

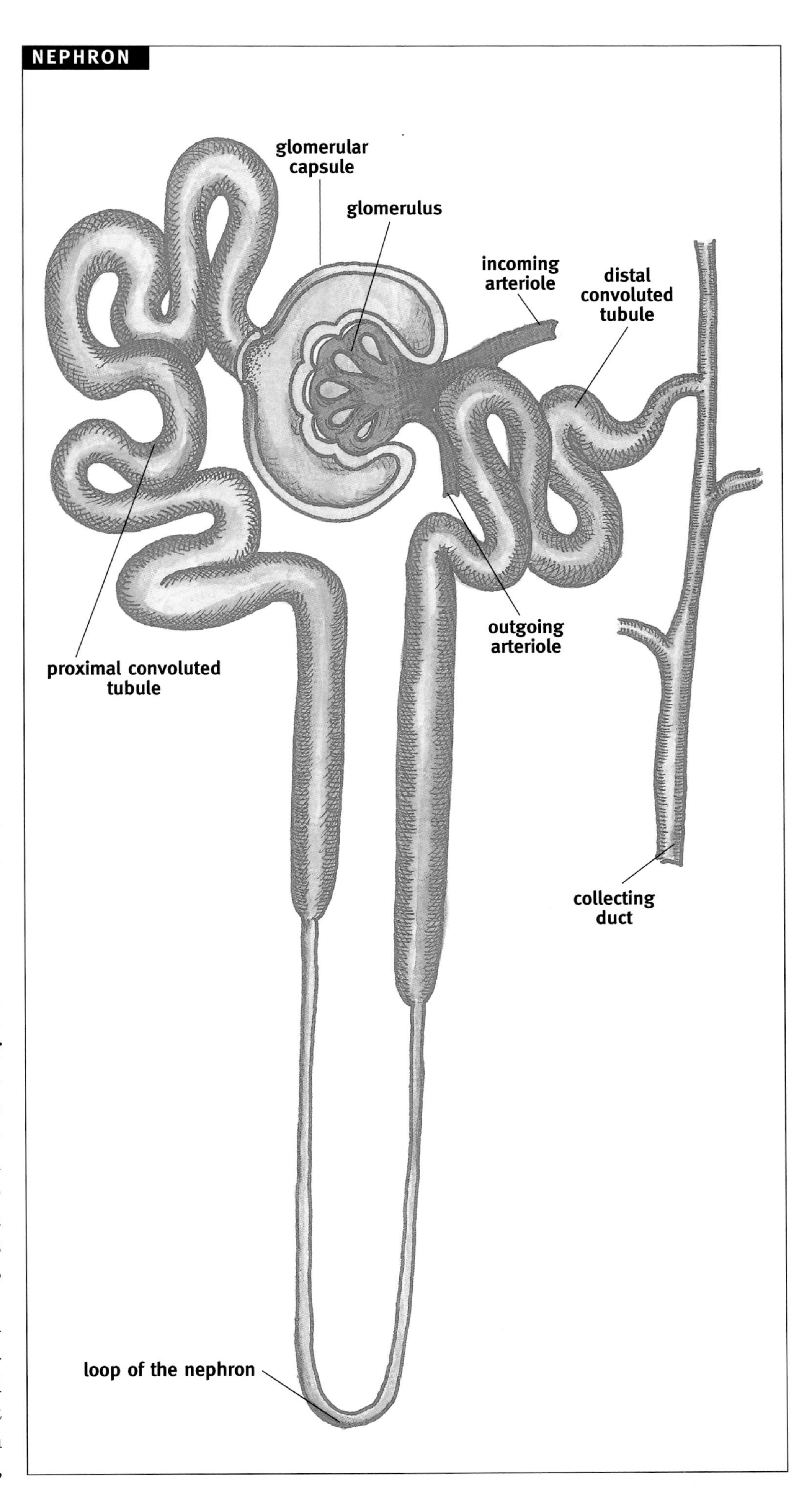

which carries blood out of the glomerulus, winds closely around the tubular network. As the fluid mixture flows through the tubules, certain materials are selectively reabsorbed back into the nearby blood vessels. The overall design of the nephron, then, is to allow water and all dissolved compounds to leak out of the blood into the capsule, and then selectively take back those items useful to the body as fluids pass through the tubules.

Nearly 200 quarts (190L) of fluid flow into the glomeruli and enter the tubules during a twenty-four-hour period. Yet only about 1 to 2 quarts (0.9–1.9L) of urine are expelled from the body each day. This means that almost all of the fluid—99 percent of it—is reabsorbed into the blood.

Reabsorption begins in the proximal tubule. The tubules are not leaky like vessels of the glomerulus—rather, the cells lining the inside of tubules selectively take up specific elements. In particular, these cells actively transport the charged particle sodium out of the fluid mixture. Sodium, which carries a positive charge, then passes into nearby segments of the outgoing arteriole.

Chloride ions, which carry a negative charge, are attracted to sodium ions and thus follow sodium out of the tubules and into the blood. In addition, water molecules, which associate with sodium and chloride, follow and reenter the bloodstream. In this way, about 65 percent of the water and ions that leave the blood in the glomerulus return to the blood from the proximal tubules.

Glucose and amino acids are also taken out of the tubules and returned to the blood—both by an active transport mechanism. Normally, all of the glucose and

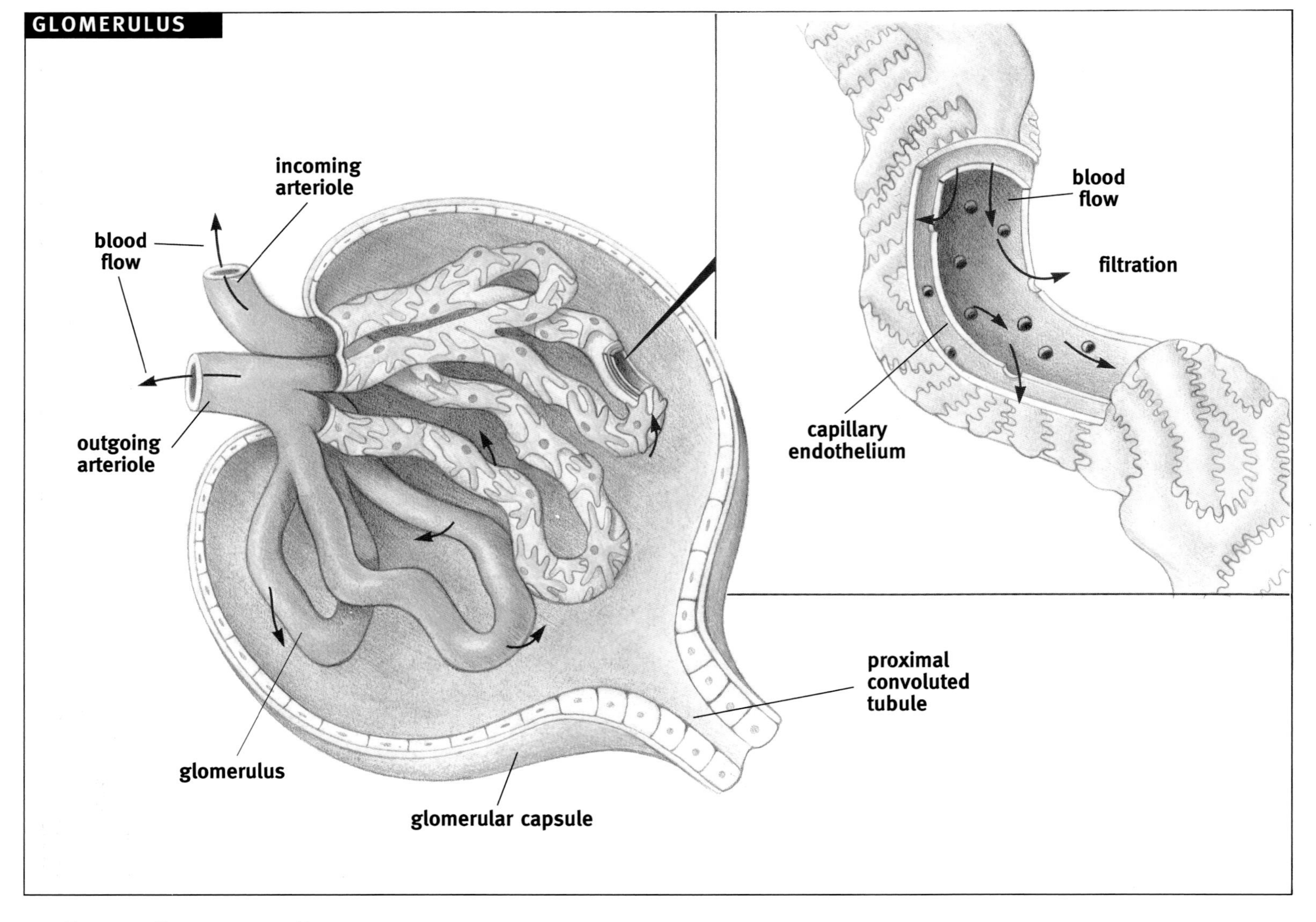

KIDNEY STONES

A large volume of fluid and dissolved material passes through the kidneys each day, usually without incident. Occasionally, however, minerals such as calcium form crystals in the renal pelvis. Calcium oxalate is the most common type of crystal, but calcium phosphate and uric acid can also solidify. Over time, such crystals can build in size to form a kidney stone, known as a renal calculus. Stones can cause extreme pain, and can even damage the sensitive renal tissues.

The body has a mechanism to combat the formation of renal calculi. A protein known as glycoprotein crystal-growth inhibitor (GCI) is present in urine, and interferes with the formation of calcium oxalate crystals. However, some people have a deficiency of this protein; such people have an increased incidence of kidney stones.

Most kidney stones eventually pass through the ureter and are eliminated, causing great pain and varying degrees of damage. Stones too large to pass were removed by surgery in the past, but a newer technique called lithotrypsy is now used instead. In this procedure, sound waves are directed into the kidney, breaking up the stones into smaller fragments, which can then move through the urinary tract and out of the body.

amino acids filtered through the glomerulus are returned to the bloodstream. Other compounds, such as urea, are not actively retrieved, though some portion diffuses back into the blood. In this way, the nephron selects which materials are returned to the blood and which are directed through the tubules to the collecting ducts.

The process of reabsorption continues in the loop of the nephron, so that 80 percent of the water, sodium, and chloride have been returned to the blood before the distal tubule is reached.

The distal tubules and the collecting ducts control reabsorption of the last 20 percent of the fluid mixture passing through the nephron. In particular, the amount of water that goes back into the blood is tightly regulated. When the volume of water in the bloodstream gets low, a special part of the brain called the **pituitary gland** releases a chemical known as **antidiuretic hormone,** or ADH. This hormone enters the bloodstream and travels to the cells lining the inner wall of the distal tubules and collecting ducts.

ADH causes the outer membranes of these cells to let water flow in more easily. This results in more water being reabsorbed and entering the blood, raising the water content of the bloodstream. If you drink a lot of liquids in a short time, the water content of the blood increases. This shuts down secretion of ADH into the bloodstream, so the distal tubules and ducts allow almost no water in, and fluids pass on through the collecting ducts. The result is an increased amount of urine, while the water in the blood remains at the proper level.

The kidneys also play a role in controlling blood pressure. The pressure of the blood is directly affected by the amount of sodium ions present, because where sodium goes, water follows. If sodium levels of the blood get low, blood pressure is also reduced. Extreme reduction can be dangerous because if blood pressure gets too low, the heart cannot pump effectively.

Specialized cells around the glomerulus sense this drop in pressure and respond by secreting an enzyme called renin into the blood. Renin converts a blood protein called angiotensinogen into angiotensin I. As angiotensin I passes through capillaries in the lungs, it is converted into angiotensin II. This blood protein then travels through the blood to the adrenal gland, where it signals cells to secrete another chemical, aldosterone. This hormone travels in the blood to the kidney, where it stimulates cells in the distal tubules and collecting ducts to increase reabsorption of sodium, which brings more water through the tubules and into the blood. The end result is a rise in blood pressure back to normal levels.

This renin-angiotensin pathway is complex and involves several different body systems, but it is typical of the kinds of

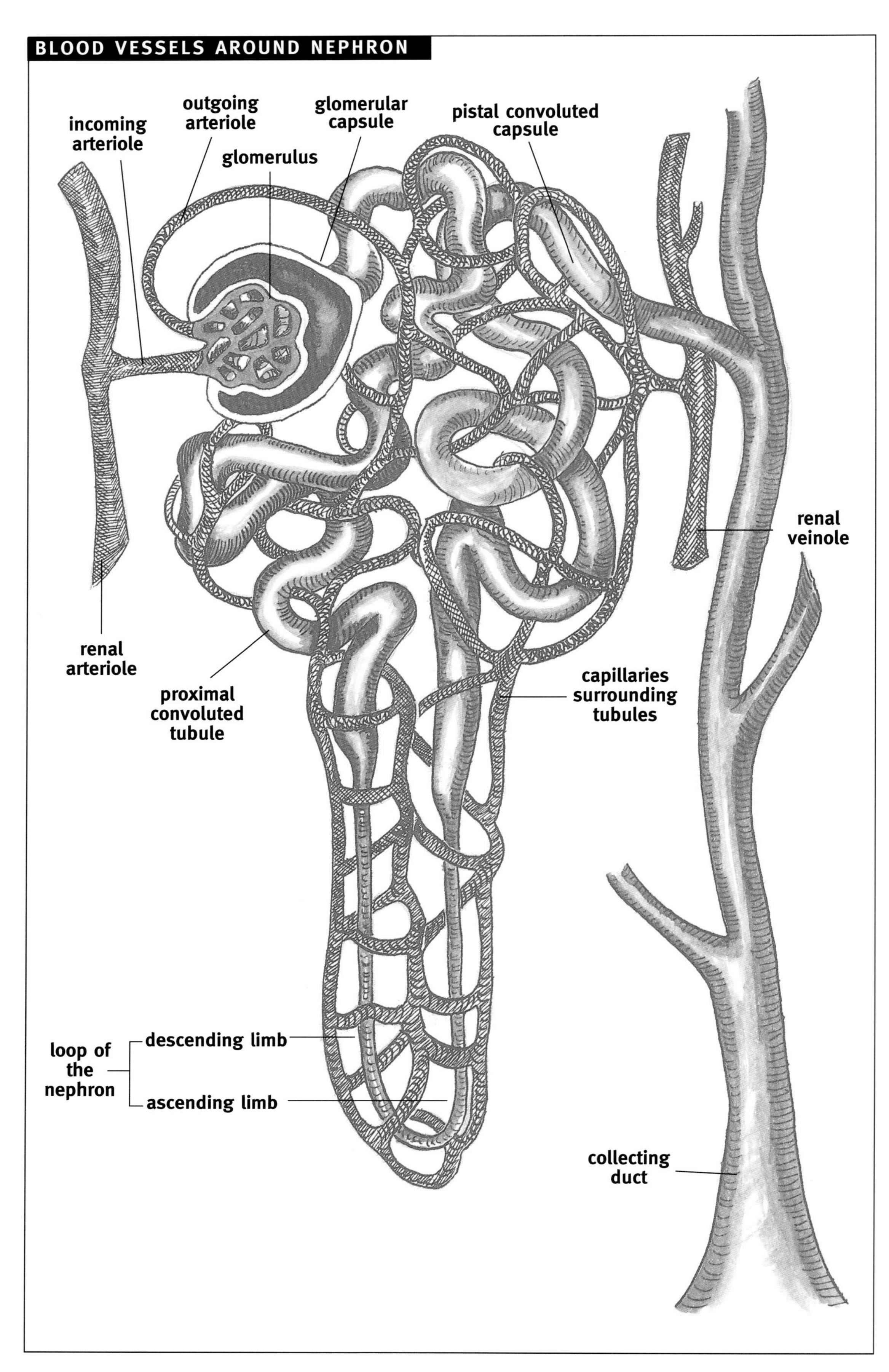

control cycles at work in the body. Most of the body's activities are carefully regulated to maintain a stable environment for tissues and organs to function in.

ELIMINATION OF URINE

Once the fluid mixture in the tubules passes through the collecting ducts, it is classified as urine. This fluid gets its name from one of the major chemicals in it—**urea**, a product of the breakdown of amino acids. The collecting ducts join into larger and larger tubes in the central area of the kidney called the **medulla**, and finally connect to the **renal pelvis**. From there, urine enters the ureters and travels down into the urinary bladder.

The urinary bladder is simply a hollow sphere made of muscle and connective tissue that holds urine until it is expelled. Strong muscular valves known as the **internal and external sphincters**, which are under voluntary control, open and allow urine to pass through the urethra and out of the body.

Proper functioning of the urinary system is vital to health. If the blood is not constantly filtered by the kidneys, waste materials—some of which are toxic—build up rapidly and begin to poison the body's cells.

Although most people have two kidneys, just one is enough to adequately filter the blood and maintain proper blood pressure. A few people are born with just one kidney, some people lose one of their kidneys from accident or disease, and some people give a kidney for transplant purposes. This usually does not interfere with leading a normal life.

Loss of both kidneys is a life-threatening condition. It is possible to filter the blood artificially by a process known as hemodialysis. A patient's circulatory system is connected to a machine that passes the blood through a series of membranes,

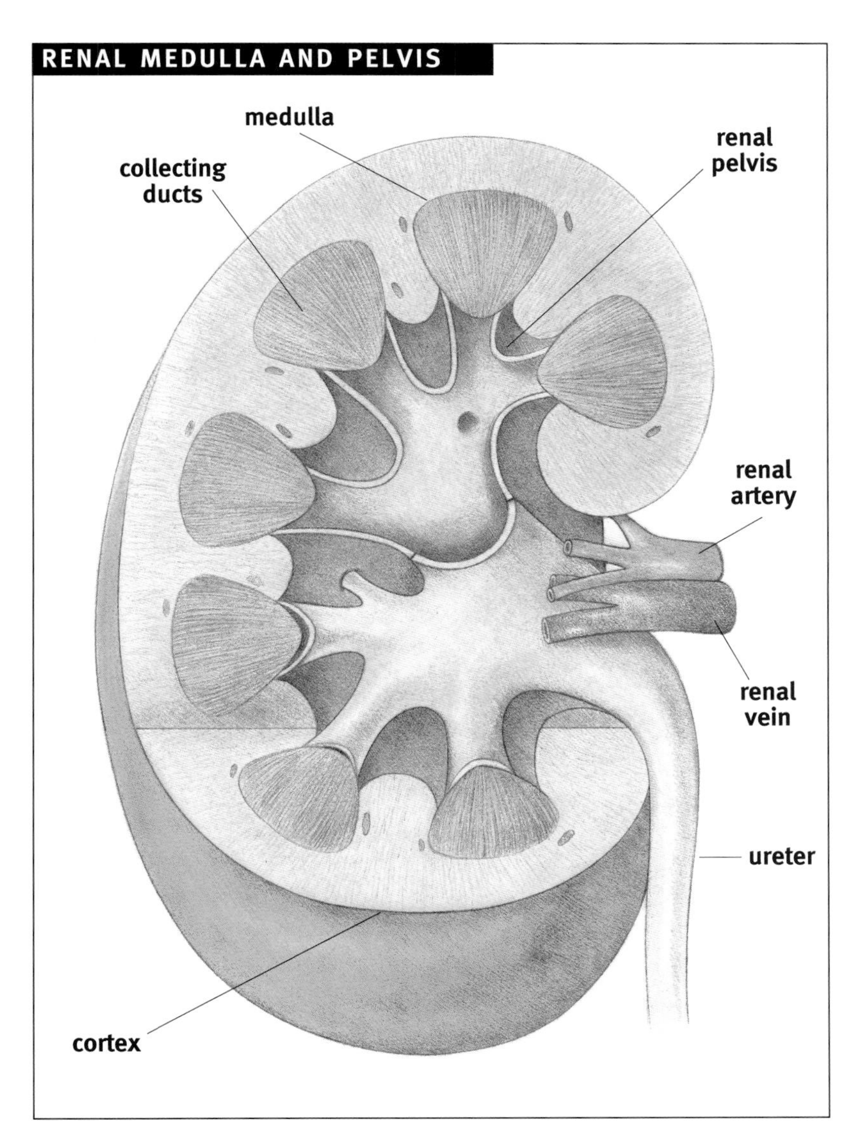

allowing waste products to move out of the blood and into a fluid mixture that bathes the membranes. The procedure is slow and must be repeated frequently, but patients without functional kidneys cannot survive without it. Scientists are currently working on better artificial kidney machines.

Another alternative for victims of kidney disease is to receive a kidney transplant. In this procedure, one kidney from a healthy donor is removed and put into the patient. The surgical operation itself is now well developed, but the procedure can still fail because of tissue rejection. This happens when a patient's immune system attacks the new organ because it is not exactly like the patient's own. We will consider this phenomenon further in chapter 11.

Tissue rejection can be minimized by using a kidney from a donor whose cells and tissues are the same "type" as the patient's. Often, the best match is found with a brother, sister, or other close relative of the patient since tissue type is a genetic trait and is therefore likely to be most similar in people who are closely related.

THE RENIN-ANGIOTENSIN PATHWAY

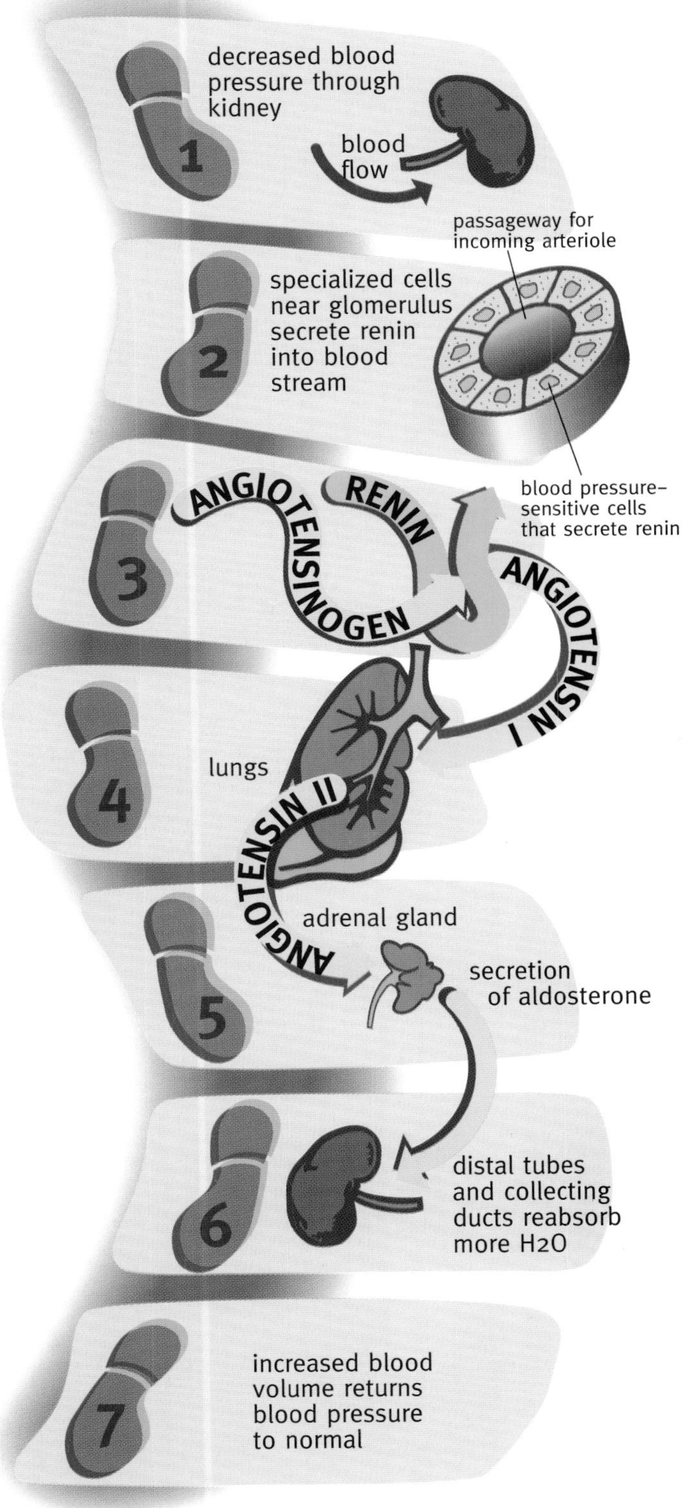

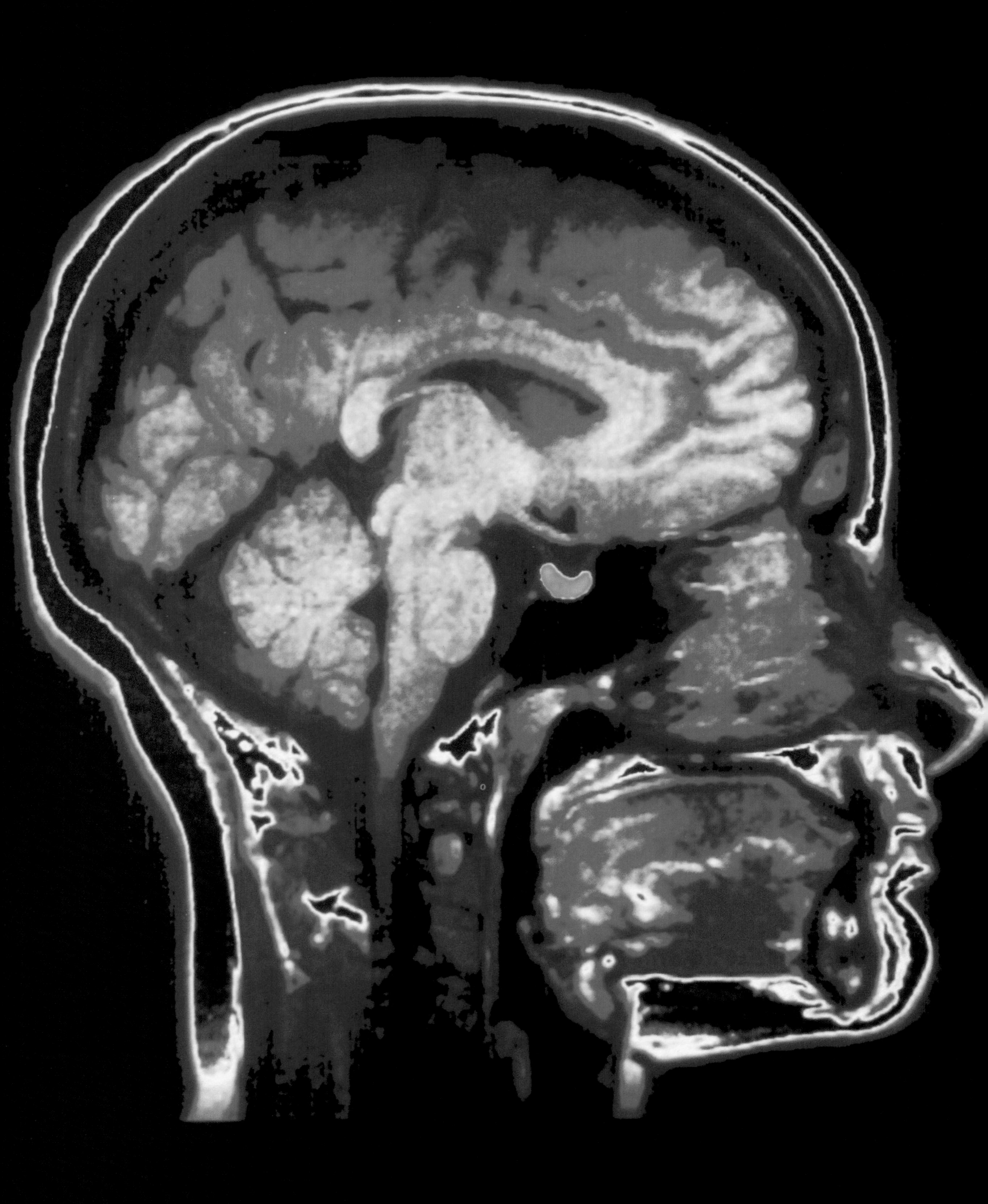

Chapter 10

The Endocrine System

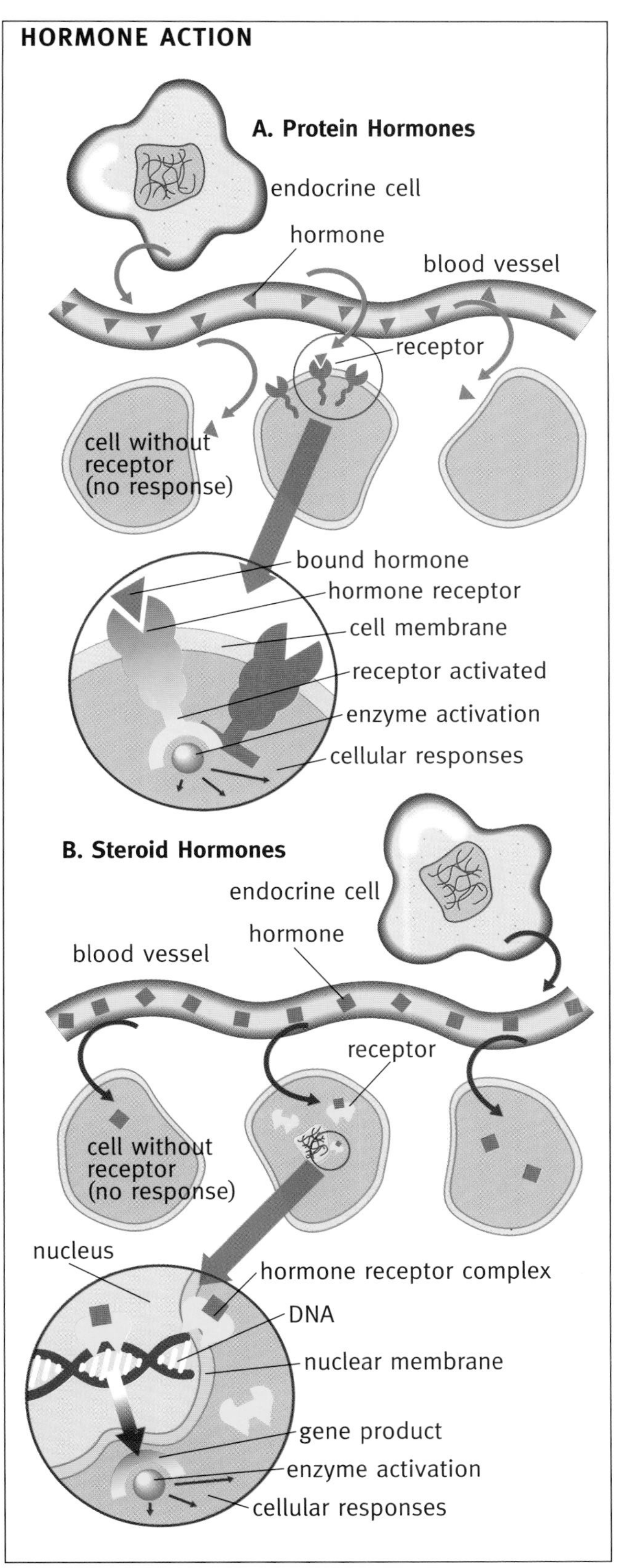

In order for the human body to operate efficiently, its many separate organ systems must be controlled and coordinated so that they work together. When you exercise, for example, your muscles must contract and relax at exactly the right time, the lungs must increase the amount of air taken in, and the circulatory system must deliver extra oxygen to muscle tissues so they can keep going.

The nervous system, which we examined in chapter 5, is responsible for coordinating the activity of many of the body's functions. It uses sensory structures to monitor conditions inside and outside the body, and then sends out electrical impulses that produce immediate reactions. In this way, our bodies can adapt very rapidly to changes.

Because controlling the body's organs, tissues, and even cells is so important, there is another whole system that also directs activities in the body: the endocrine system. This network of regulation is quite different from the nervous system. Whereas neurons use electrical impulses to produce effects, the endocrine glands secrete chemicals known as **hormones** that enter the bloodstream and travel throughout the body to reach various tissues and cells. And while the nervous system brings about strong, very rapid responses, hormones usually take hours to begin working and then continue to influence certain tissues for months and even years.

Thus the endocrine network provides a different kind of regulation than do the neural circuits: The nervous system provides quick responses to current conditions, while the endocrine system pro-

OPPOSITE PAGE:
The brain Computer-enhanced magnetic resonance image of the human brain. This organ is composed of billions of individual nerve cells, all coordinating their activities to control every body function, including the process of thinking. The pituitary gland, which produces numerous chemicals that influence various tissues and organs, is highlighted.

duces sustained, long-lasting changes. Together, these two systems direct the coordinated functions that make our bodies grow and develop, and also help keep them strong and healthy.

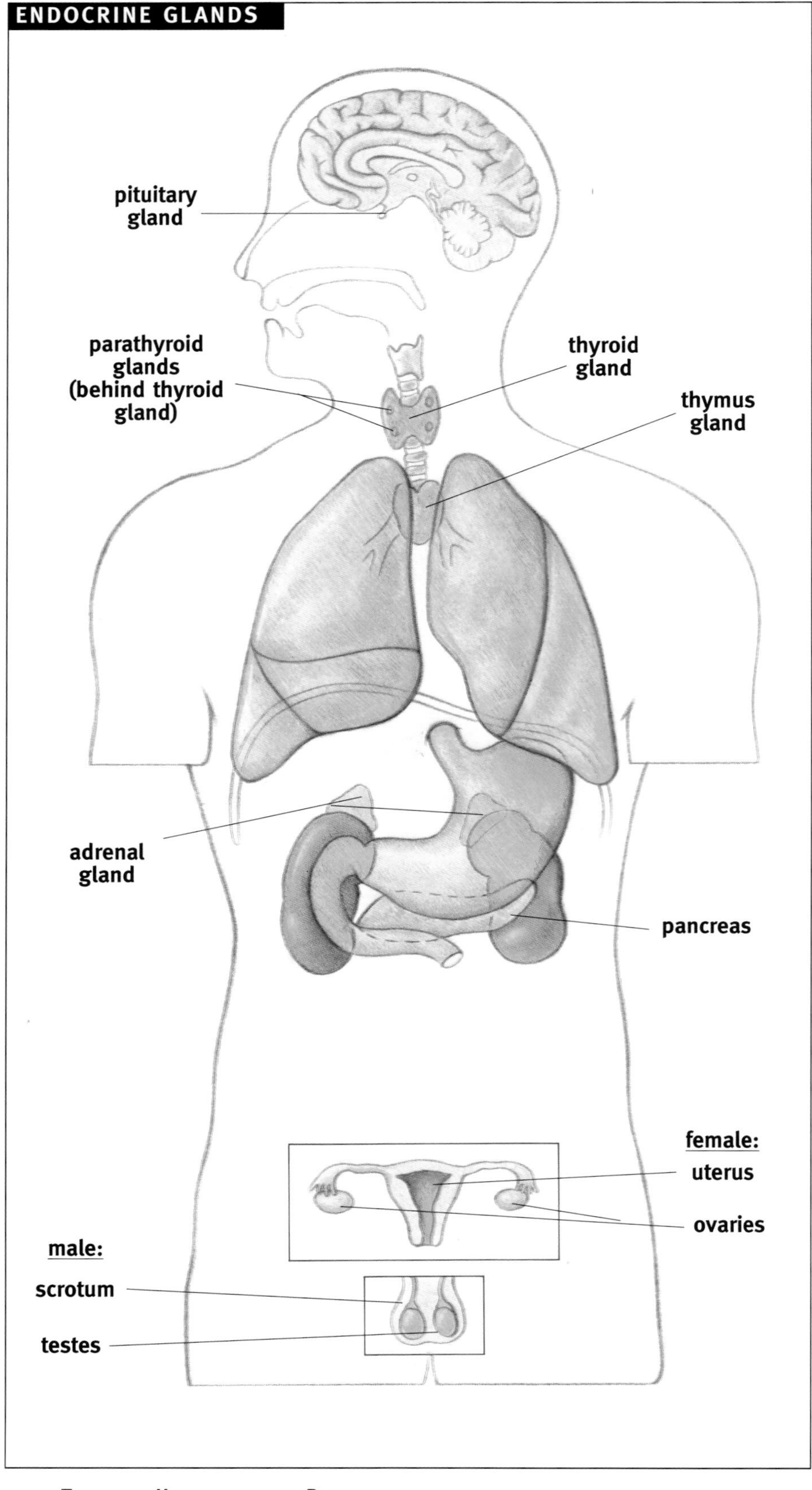

HORMONES

There are two kinds of chemical messengers produced by endocrine tissues: protein hormones and steroid hormones. Let's now consider how these molecules work.

Protein Hormones In chapter 1 we learned how proteins are made inside the cell. Most protein hormones are synthesized in this same way by specific endocrine cells, though some are only a few amino acids long. Others are modified amino acid compounds. Once produced, these molecules are secreted into the bloodstream. They travel throughout the body and pass into the interstitial spaces, where they come in contact with individual cells. But only cells that contain a matching protein called a hormone receptor can respond to hormone molecules. This is why hormones act selectively on just certain tissues: Only those cells containing a receptor to that specific hormone will be affected.

When the hormone reaches a "target" cell, it binds to the outer portion of the cell's receptor, which is embedded in the cell membrane. Binding of the hormone transmits a signal that activates enzymes inside the cell. The activity of these enzymes causes changes within the cell such as growth and division, altered membrane permeability, secretion of other hormones, synthesis of new proteins, or activation of other enzymes. Eventually these cellular activities cause changes in tissues, organs, and the body as a whole.

Steroid Hormones Like protein hormones, steroid hormones are produced by endocrine tissues and secreted into the blood to travel throughout the body. When they reach target cells, however, steroids do not interact with the proteins in the membrane—they simply pass right through it and into the cytoplasm of the cell. Here they bind to specific receptor proteins and the bound complex moves into the nucleus, where the DNA is located. The hormone-receptor complex then binds to very specific places on the DNA and activates certain genes. The products of these genes—various proteins—produce the same kinds of changes in the cell as protein hormones. Like the effects of protein hormones, the final result is altered cell activity that leads to changes in the body.

The structure of steroids is quite different from that of protein hormones. In general, steroid molecules are similar in structure to cholesterol, a molecule that is found commonly in cell membranes and also in many foods we eat. In fact, cholesterol is the base molecule from which steroid hormones are made.

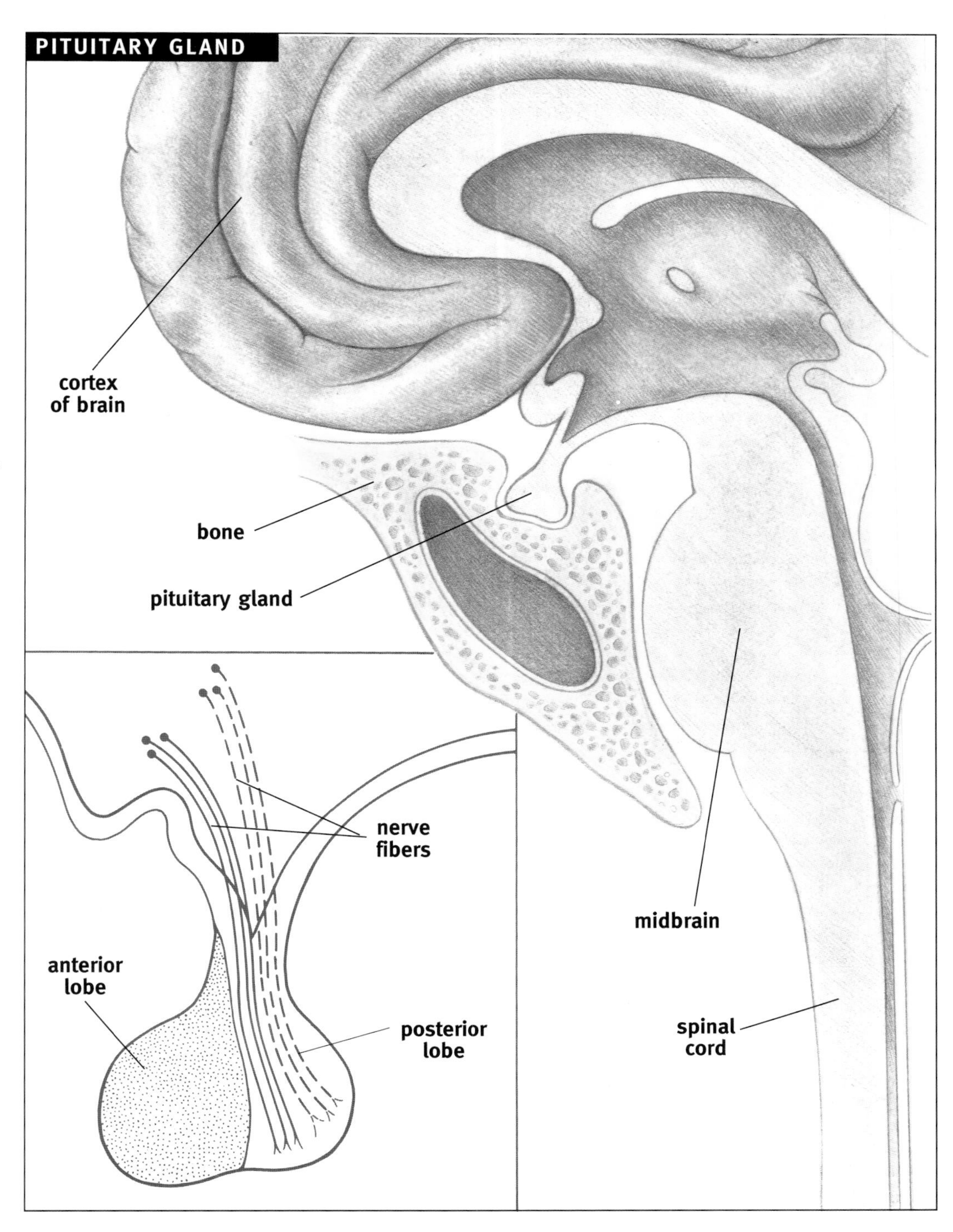

ENDOCRINE GLANDS

The body's endocrine tissues are called **glands** because they secrete materials into the blood. The **pituitary gland**, located in the lower brain, is known as the "master gland" because its hormones direct the other endocrine organs to secrete their products. The **thyroid** and **parathyroid glands** are located in the throat and upper chest. In the abdominal cavity are the **adrenal glands**, which sit on top of the kidneys. The **pancreas** is also included because it contains some endocrine cells along with other tissues that are involved in digestion. The **ovaries** in females and **testes** in males are also endocrine organs.

Pituitary The pituitary gland is very small, measuring about ½ inch (1cm) in diameter. It is made of two parts: the **anterior pituitary** and the **posterior pituitary**.

The anterior pituitary is one of the most complex and active endocrine tissues, secreting seven different hormones:

Growth hormone (GH) influences many different tissues in the body, causing them to grow and then to maintain size and strength once they have developed. GH promotes energy production in cells by speeding up degradation of fat molecules, as well as many other cellular reactions. Growth hormone is particularly stimulating in bone and muscle cells. Absence of this hormone causes dwarfism, a condition that prevents normal growth and results in an unusually short body frame.

Adrenocorticotropic hormone (ACTH) signals cells in the cortex of the adrenal glands to secrete their hormones.

Melanocyte-stimulating hormone (MSH) stimulates melanocytes in the skin to produce and secrete melanin granules.

Thyroid stimulating hormone (TSH) influences the thyroid gland to secrete its hormones.

Prolactin (PRL) is responsible for directing milk production in the mammary glands of pregnant females.

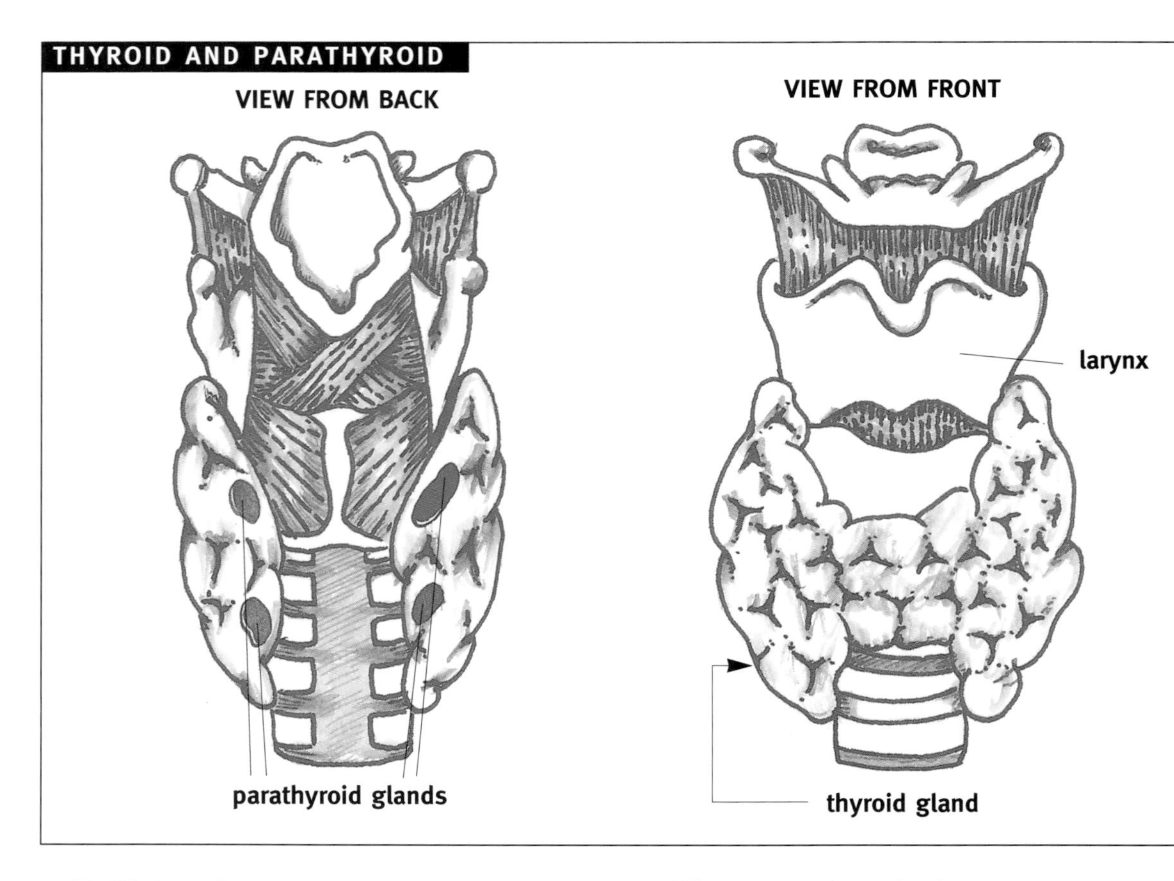

Follicle-stimulating hormone (FSH) stimulates egg production in females, and sperm growth and maturation in males.

Luteinizing hormone (LH) influences several aspects of the reproductive process, including secretion of estrogen and testosterone, the major sexual hormones of females and males.

The posterior pituitary secretes two hormones:

Antidiuretic hormone (ADH) directs the kidney tubules to reabsorb more water when blood volume gets low.

Oxytocin (OT) makes the uterus contract during birth, pushing the new baby through the birth canal.

ANABOLIC STEROIDS

The powerful impact of hormones in the body has led to the creation of synthetic molecules that have the same or even stronger effects. In particular, many artificial anabolic steroids—hormones that build and strengthen cells and tissues—have been chemically produced. Their structures are very similar to the natural hormone testosterone.

Anabolic steroids have important medical uses, including treatment for skeletal diseases and muscle disorders. They are also used to promote healing after surgery, to increase appetite, and to replace natural hormone levels that are too low in some patients. When used properly, synthetic hormones can be effective medicines.

However, sick people are not the only ones who use anabolic steroids. Many professional and even amateur athletes take large doses of synthetic chemicals to artificially build their bones and muscles. This use of steroids can add strength and tone to the body's muscular system—but not without a price.

When very large doses of hormonelike substances are taken into the body, virtually every organ can be affected. Hormones are incredibly powerful molecules, and overloading fragile tissues with high quantities of them can lead to serious health problems. Use of anabolic steroids has been linked to cancer, infertility and degeneration of reproductive organs, birth defects, and liver and kidney diseases. In addition to these potential problems, steroids can also affect the heart, straining it until severe damage of cardiac cells results, which can end in heart failure.

Because the use of steroids confers an unfair advantage, and because steroid abuse results in serious health problems, most amateur and professional athletic associations (including the International Olympic Committee) punish members who are caught using them. Athletic authorities use very sensitive tests that can detect small amounts of synthetic steroids in the blood or urine, even several months after such drugs are taken.

Despite the danger of being kicked out of sports and the chance of developing health problems, some people are still willing to take the enormous risks of using steroids. Perhaps they feel that pursuing athletic superiority is worth the potential harm. It is a dangerous gamble, however, with a very high risk that permanent damage or death will be the result instead of trophies and medals.

THYROID Located in the neck just under the larynx, the thyroid gland secretes two kinds of hormones:

Thyroxine (T_4) and **triiodothreonine (T_3)** are two hormones with slightly different structures that produce the same effects—they increase the rate at which cells in the body use energy. Also, these hormones regulate the activity of the nervous system, and help many parts of the body to grow and develop. Improper thyroid activity during childhood can cause dwarfism and mental retardation.

Calcitonin (CT) decreases the amount of calcium in the blood, probably by inhibiting the activity of osteoclasts (the cells that reabsorb bone matrix).

PARATHYROID The parathyroid glands are four tiny structures embedded in the thyroid gland. They secrete just one product:

Parathyroid hormone (PTH) controls the blood level of calcium, phosphate, and magnesium. PTH increases blood calcium by stimulating osteoclasts to break down bone tissue, which then releases calcium. Thus PTH has the opposite effect of calcitonin. This is an example of dual control over a particular function, which is a common

ADRENALS

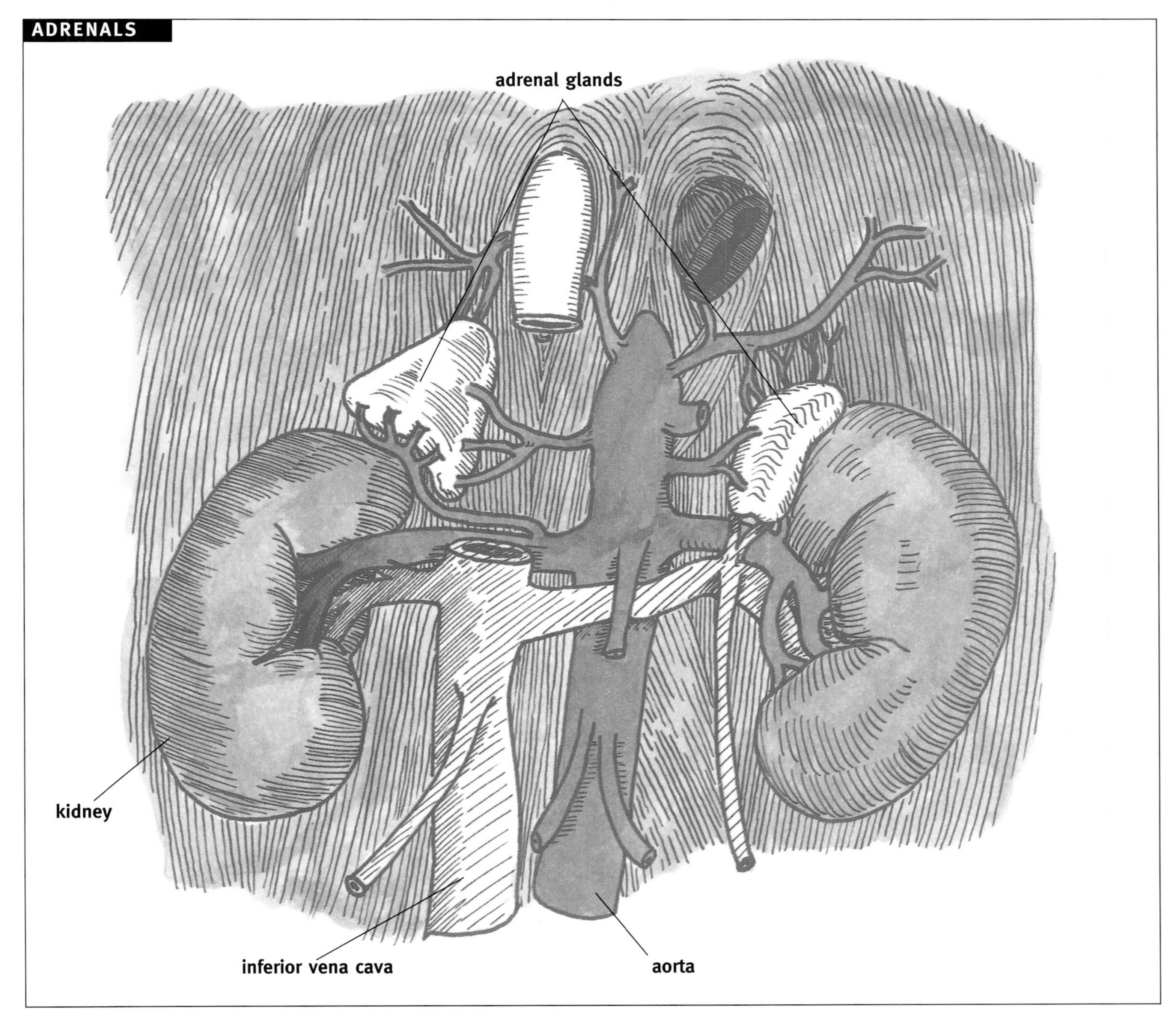

DIABETES MELLITUS

One of the most common diseases of modern times is diabetes mellitus. The name derives from two symptoms of the disease, excessive urination (diabetes is from the Latin for "flowing"), and the presence of sugar in the urine (mellitus means "sweet" or "honey"). Hundreds of millions of people suffer from this disorder, which comes in two forms.

Type I Also called juvenile-onset diabetes, since it usually strikes before the age of twenty, this form accounts for about 10 percent of all cases. The cause is destruction of insulin-producing beta cells in the pancreas. Without insulin present in the body, cells are not signaled to take up glucose, and the concentration of this sugar in the blood rises drastically.

Since glucose is unavailable as an energy source, fat stores are rapidly mobilized, producing several detrimental results. In the short term, breakdown of fats causes a sharp decline in blood pH, which can produce systemic shock and death if not reversed. Over time, the fatty particles being transported in high volume through the blood are deposited on arterial walls. This leads to atherosclerosis, cardiovascular disease, vision problems as vessels in the eye are occluded, and gangrene as various parts of the body receive insufficient blood flow.

This type of diabetes is also called insulin-dependent diabetes because it can be treated with insulin injections. Type I diabetics must receive insulin daily for the duration of their lives. Most insulin is extracted and purified from cow and pig tissues. More recently, scientists have cloned the human insulin gene, expressed this gene in bacteria, and purified the protein for use in treating diabetes. The human form may prove to be a better treatment, since it is less likely to illicit an immune reaction than insulin from nonhuman sources.

Type II The more common form of diabetes, also known as maturity-onset diabetes, type II accounts for 90 percent of all cases. It occurs mainly in people over age forty who are overweight, and it can usually be controlled by adjustments in diet. In this disorder, insulin levels in the blood are normal or sometimes slightly elevated. The cause is most likely a defect in the signaling mechanism of target cells, such as lack of competent insulin receptors, or a defect in the signaling pathway that stimulates glucose uptake.

Because glucose is high in the blood, victims of type II diabetes are prone to the same symptoms and consequences as type I sufferers, but the progress of this ailment is much slower, and it usually responds to improved diet and weight loss.

---

theme in the human body. This arrangement allows tight regulation of crucial functions, and also provides backup systems to compensate when one method fails.

Adrenals The cortex of the adrenal gland secretes four substances:

Aldosterone is part of the renin-angiotensin chemical pathway that signals tubules in the kidney to reabsorb sodium.

Cortisol suppresses inflammation and helps tissues respond to stress.

Estrogen is a female sex hormone, responsible for sexual characteristics and development of reproductive organs.

Androgen is a male sex hormone, responsible for muscle development and development of reproductive organs.

Cells in the medulla of the adrenals produce two closely related hormones:

Epinephrine (adrenaline) and **norepinephrine (noradrenaline)** increase heart rate, respiration, efficiency of muscular contraction, and energy production in cells. Some of the effects of these chemicals are quite rapid, unlike most other hormones. In general, they help the body respond to stress or danger.

Pancreas In addition to its role in digestion, the pancreas also performs endocrine functions. Groups of specialized cells known as pancreatic islets secrete two very important hormones:

Insulin signals all cells to take up glucose from the blood. Lack of insulin causes diabetes, a disease that can be life-threatening and may be treated with insulin injections.

Glucagon increases the amount of glucose in the blood. Glucagon has the opposite effect of insulin.

Ovaries These female reproductive organs produce two hormones:

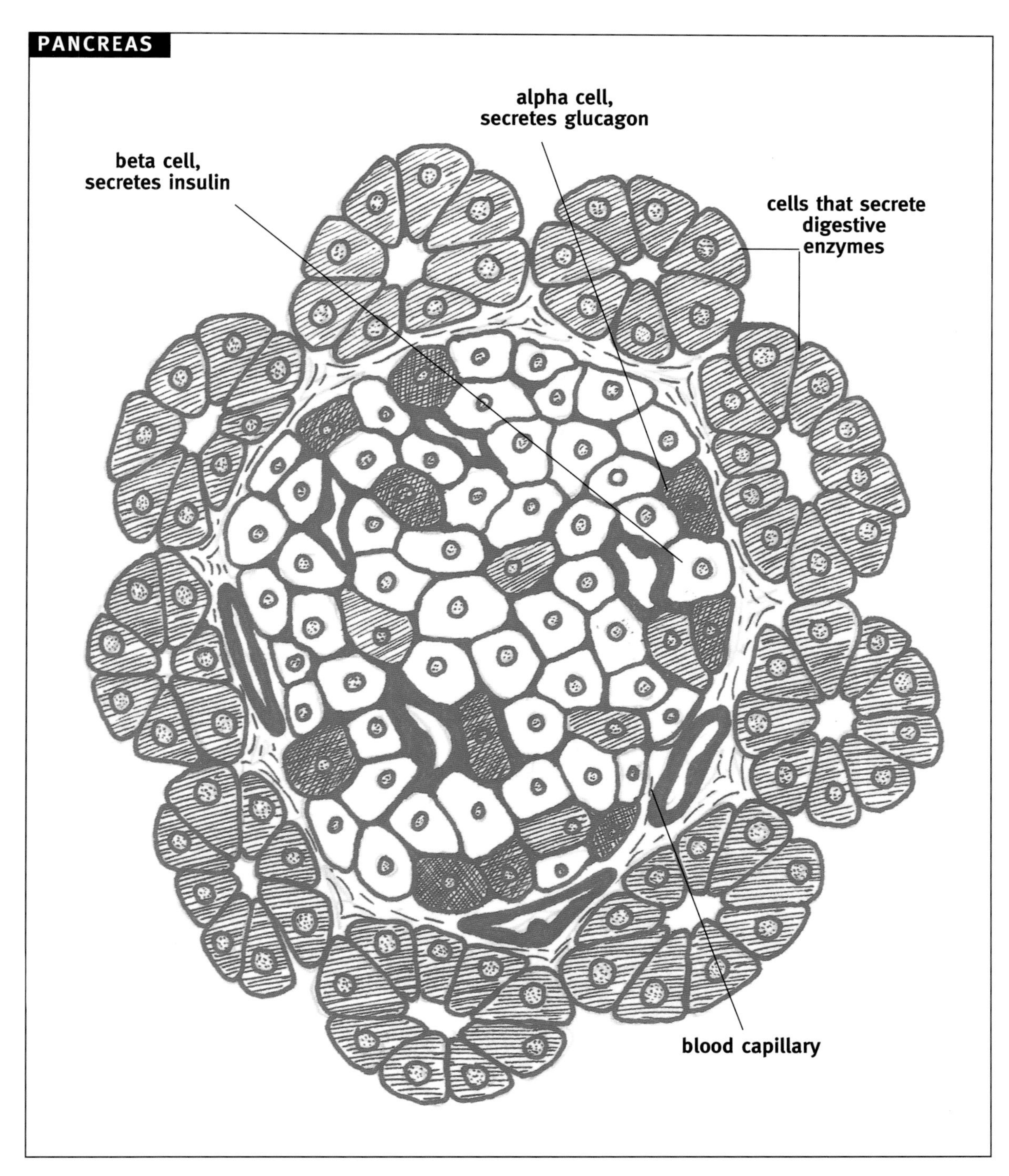

Estrogen produces the sexual characteristics of female anatomy, and directs reproductive activities such as the menstrual cycle, pregnancy, and lactation.

Progesterone also influences female sexual functions.

Testes The male counterpart of the ovaries are the testes, which produce one major hormone.

Testosterone directs growth and development of male sexual characteristics and reproductive organs.

Because hormones are chemical messengers that have powerful effects in the body, they are the subject of much scientific research. In the last several years, investigators have begun to come to an understanding of how these chemical messengers bring about changes in cell activities. This is important because many diseases are caused by improper functioning of various endocrine organs. Understanding how hormones work makes it possible for scientists to design treatments for such diseases, and also to develop better ways to prevent hormone imbalances.

In addition to the hormones considered above, there are several others that have only recently been discovered and are not yet understood very well. In fact, new chemical messengers continue to be discovered every year and are currently being analyzed in scientific laboratories. There are probably many more such hormones waiting to be discovered, and finding them will help us understand more about the complex systems at work in the human body.

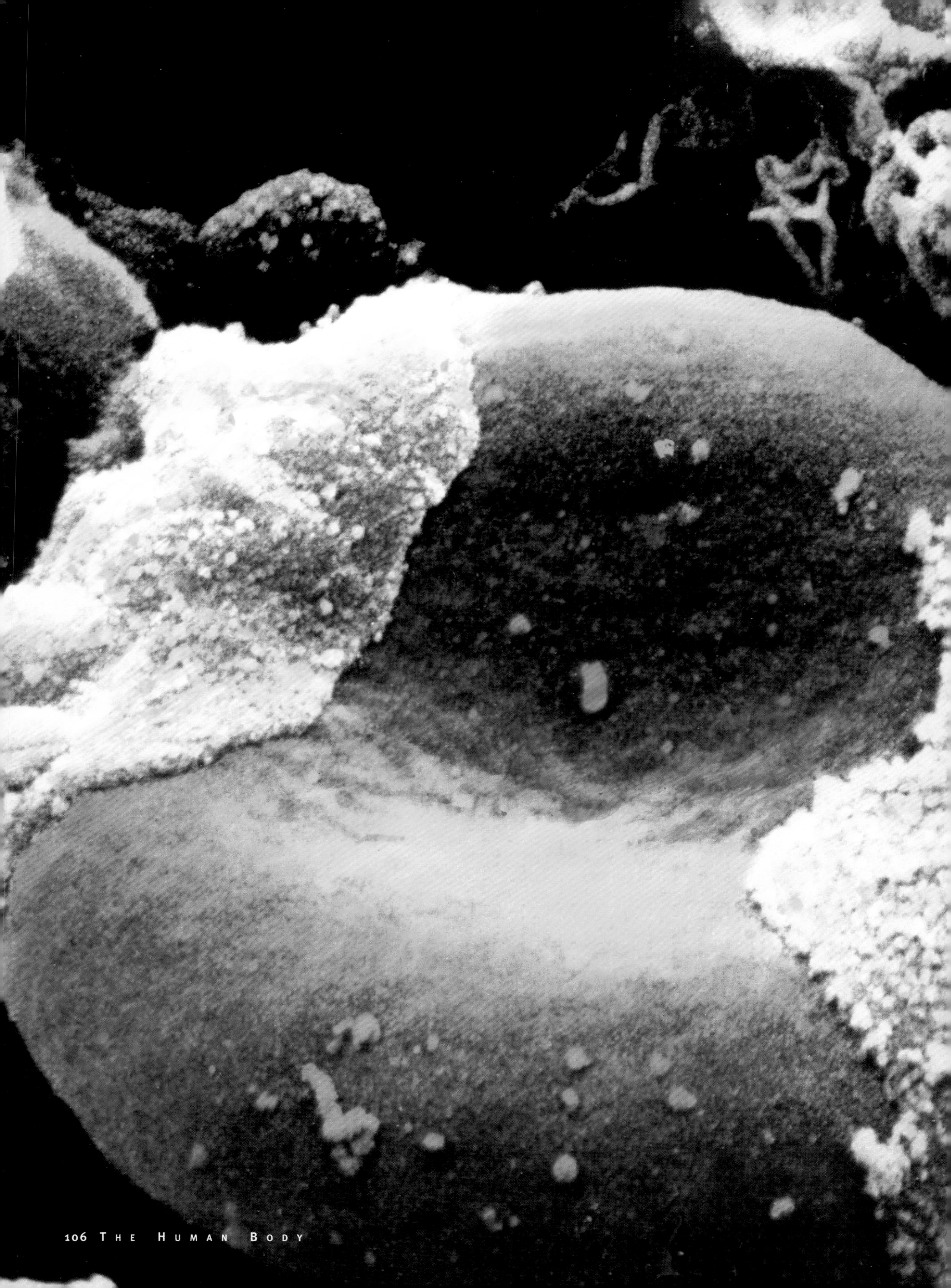

Chapter 11

The Immune System

Considering the complexity and interdependence of many organ systems, it is indeed amazing how well the human body adapts to changes and maintains itself in a healthy condition. As human beings, we are a very "advanced" form of life, meaning we have highly developed physical and mental traits that allow us to perform sophisticated tasks. Our specialized cells, tissues, and organs—particularly our advanced nervous system—have allowed us to develop skills and abilities no other species possess.

OPPOSITE PAGE:
Phagocytosis Electron micrograph showing a a macrophage (yellow and white) engulfing and digesting a worn-out erythrocyte (red), a process known as phagocytosis. Macrophages and other cells of the immune system constantly seek out and eliminate dead and damaged cells, microorganisms, and any foreign particles that might harm the body.

LEUKOCYTES

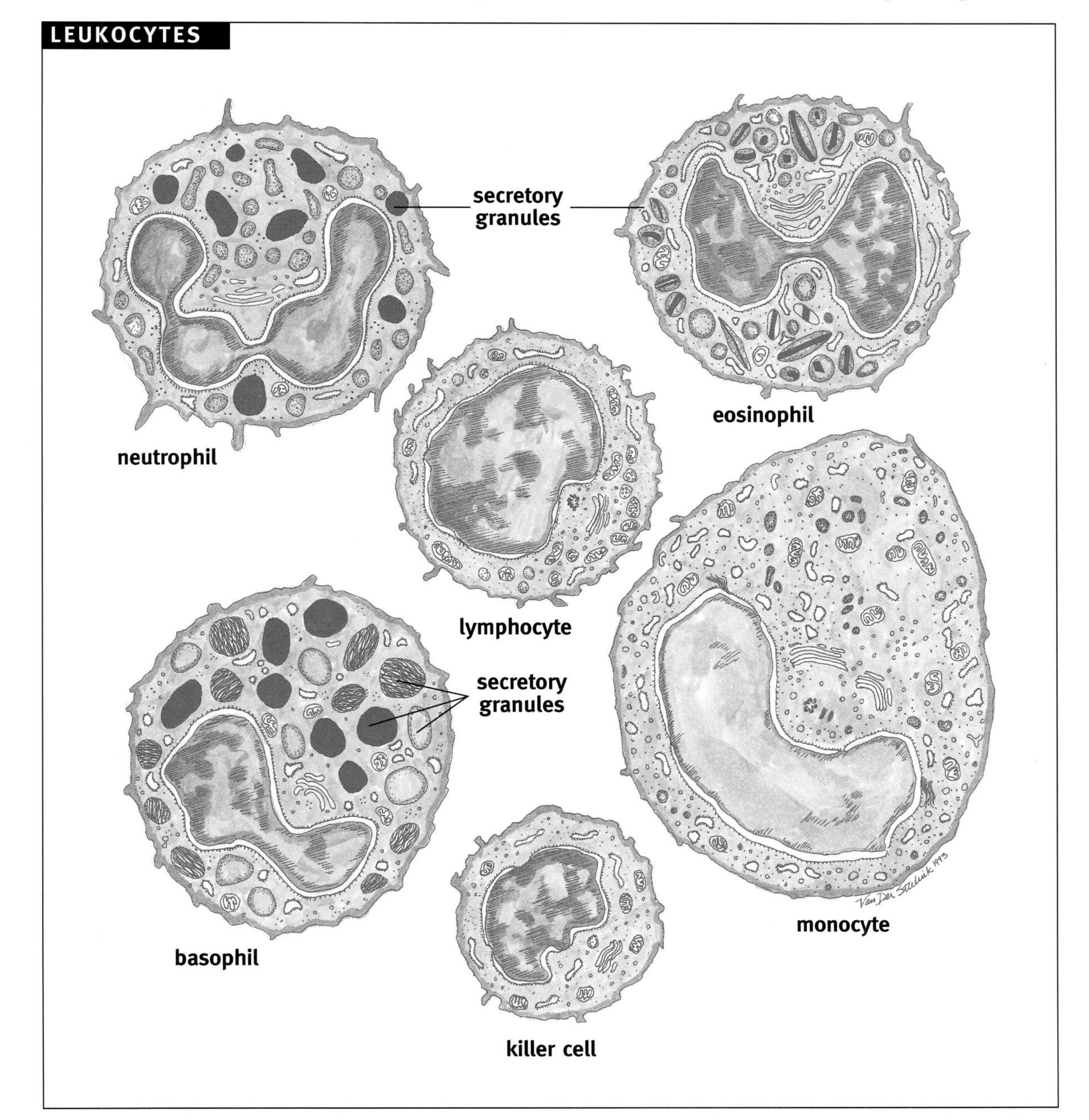

We have already learned that when a cell specializes to perform a particular task, it gives up some basic features and comes to rely on other tissues to provide the missing functions. Nerve cells, for example, rely heavily on the bloodstream to bring them a constant supply of oxygen and nutrients.

Another important feature that many cells in the body lack is the ability to defend themselves from invading microbes. Viruses, bacteria, fungi, and other microscopic organisms are present everywhere. The air we breathe, the food we eat, and almost everything we touch are loaded with billions of these tiny life-forms. Most types of microbes are not harmful, but some species, when they get inside the body, can cause damage. Keeping dangerous microbes out of the body and destroying those that do get in is the job of the immune system.

Immunity to foreign agents is provided in two ways: General resistance refers to structures that keep microbes from getting inside the body; specific resistance is carried out by specialized cells and molecules that deal with the microbes that do manage to enter.

GENERAL RESISTANCE

The Skin The first line of defense against microbes is the body's outer covering of flesh. Hard keratinized layers of dead cells on the outer skin form a tough layer that microbes usually cannot get through. In addition to this physical barrier, sebaceous glands secrete an oily fluid that covers the skin and helps stop the growth of bacteria. Sweat glands also play a role by flushing microbes out of follicle openings.

Mucous Membranes Openings in the skin, such as the mouth and nose, provide a direct entrance for microbes into deeper tissues. To help protect these openings, cells of the inner lining form a sticky fluid called mucus that covers the surface. Incoming microbes that come in contact with mucus get stuck and are eventually carried away. Mucus membranes usually contain hairs, which also collect invading material and keep it from going deeper into the body.

A similar mechanism protects the ear, where a thicker fluid with the texture of wax protects the canal. The sensitive eyes are continuously bathed with fluid from tear glands. This watery substance contains lysozyme, an enzyme that inhibits formation of the cell wall in bacteria.

Gastric Juices The digestive tract is especially open to microbes, since they are carried along with food deep into the body. But the harsh environment of the stomach and intestines destroys harmful organisms by digesting them, too. Saliva also plays a role by constantly washing bacteria down the throat so they cannot attach and grow in the mouth.

These features of general resistance are designed to keep all types of microbial agents from getting into the deeper tissues and cells. Now let's consider what happens when microbes penetrate these barriers and set up within tissues.

SPECIFIC RESISTANCE

The task of fighting off foreign organisms inside the body is carried out by white blood cells, or leukocytes. There are several different types of leukocytes, each of which performs a distinct function.

CELL NAME	MAIN FUNCTION
Neutrophils	Swallow and dissolve bacteria
Eosinophils	Destroy large unicellular parasites
Basophils	Release chemicals to aid immune response
Killer cells	Kill virus-infected cells and some tumors
Monocytes	Turn into macrophages—cells that swallow microbes, dead cells, and other debris
Lymphocytes	Specifically recognize and inactivate all types of foreign organisms and the toxins they produce

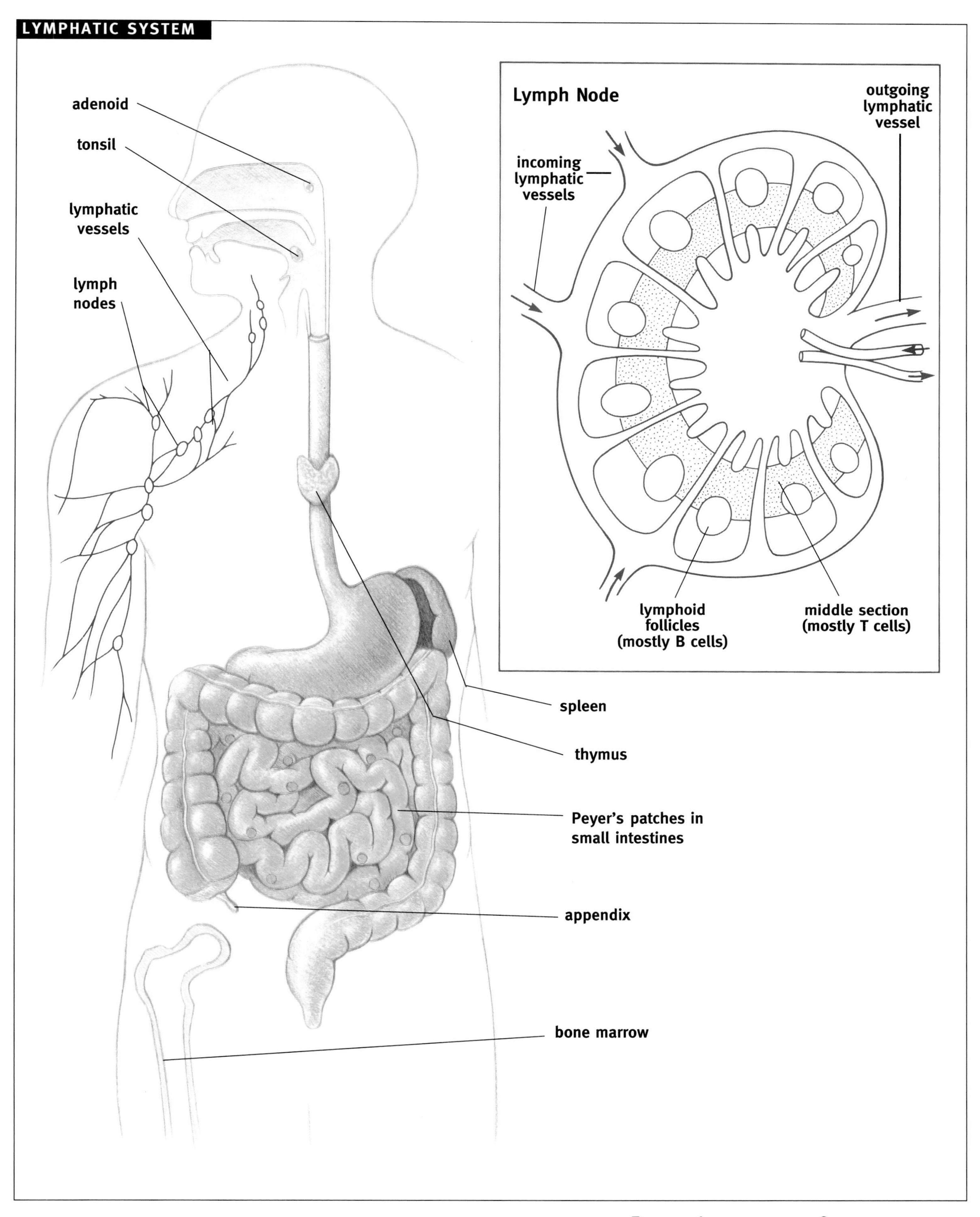
LYMPHATIC SYSTEM
adenoid
tonsil
lymphatic vessels
lymph nodes
Lymph Node
outgoing lymphatic vessel
incoming lymphatic vessels
lymphoid follicles (mostly B cells)
middle section (mostly T cells)
spleen
thymus
Peyer's patches in small intestines
appendix
bone marrow

ALLERGIES

When a foreign substance enters the body, the immune system is signaled to mount a response. That response can proceed in one of three ways: (1) cells of the immune system do not react strongly or quickly enough, allowing irritation or infection to occur; (2) the level of immune response is just right—strong enough to eliminate invaders, but not more; (3) the immune system overreacts, mounting a much larger response than is needed. An example of this third category is allergies.

Since the basic design of the immune system is to monitor all possible chemical shapes and recognize them as either dangerous or harmless, it sometimes happens that a mistake is made. Many biological particles, including food substances, pollen from plants, and fine hair fragments from animals, get into our bodies when we eat and breathe. Such chemicals are not threatening, but they all represent specific chemical shapes the immune system must process and make a decision on. If the system mistakenly recognizes such particles as harmful, it is triggered to respond, and an allergic reaction develops.

The major cell type involved in allergies is the mast cell. This cell type has a fragile membrane and is full of a chemical called histamine. When the immune system is signaled to react to substances like weed pollen or cat hair, these mast cells burst open, spilling histamines into the blood. Histamines produce a number of reactions, including watery eyes, runny nose, sneezing, and swelling—all of which are designed to isolate the foreign particles and expel them from the body.

Because histamines are a major problem in allergic reactions, many treatments for allergies include taking antihistamines, which neutralize the effect of this chemical. Other treatments are aimed at stabilizing the fragile mast cell membranes so that they do not burst easily when foreign chemicals are contacted.

All of these different leukocytes arise from stem cells in the bone marrow that mature into the specialized forms that protect the body from infection. By far the most numerous and important of these are the lymphocytes, which we will now consider in detail.

LYMPHOCYTES The number of lymphocytes in the human body is very large—about 2 trillion in all. Together they would be the size of one of the larger organs such as the liver, but lymphocytes are distributed throughout the entire body as individual cells. Some of them take up residence in structures of the lymphatic system, such as the adenoids, tonsils, appendix, Peyer's patches, spleen, and lymph nodes. All of these organs are filled with lymphocytes and are strategically positioned to intercept and destroy invading organisms. The adenoids and tonsils, for example, are located at the back of the pharynx and battle microbes that enter the mouth and throat. Lymphocytes in the appendix and Peyer's patches destroy bacteria present in food that has been ingested, and white blood cells in the spleen monitor the blood for foreign invaders. Lymph nodes are present at many sites along major vessel routes, where blood and lymph are under constant surveillance for disease-causing agents.

There are two main types of lymphocytes; these are called **B lymphocytes** and **T lymphocytes**.

B Lymphocytes As lymphocytes develop from stem cells in the bone marrow, some of them are programmed to become B lymphocytes (B cells), which specialize in secreting proteins called **antibodies**. These are Y-shaped proteins with ends that recognize and bind to molecules in the invading microbes. Antibodies are numerous, accounting for about 20 percent of total blood protein.

When antibodies come in contact with the surface of a foreign invader, they bind to it very tightly. This tags the microbe as foreign and provides a signal for other cells such as macrophages to engulf and dissolve it. In some cases the bound antibodies also trigger a class of blood proteins to clump together around the undesirable microbe. This clumping reaction,

PHAGOCYTOSIS

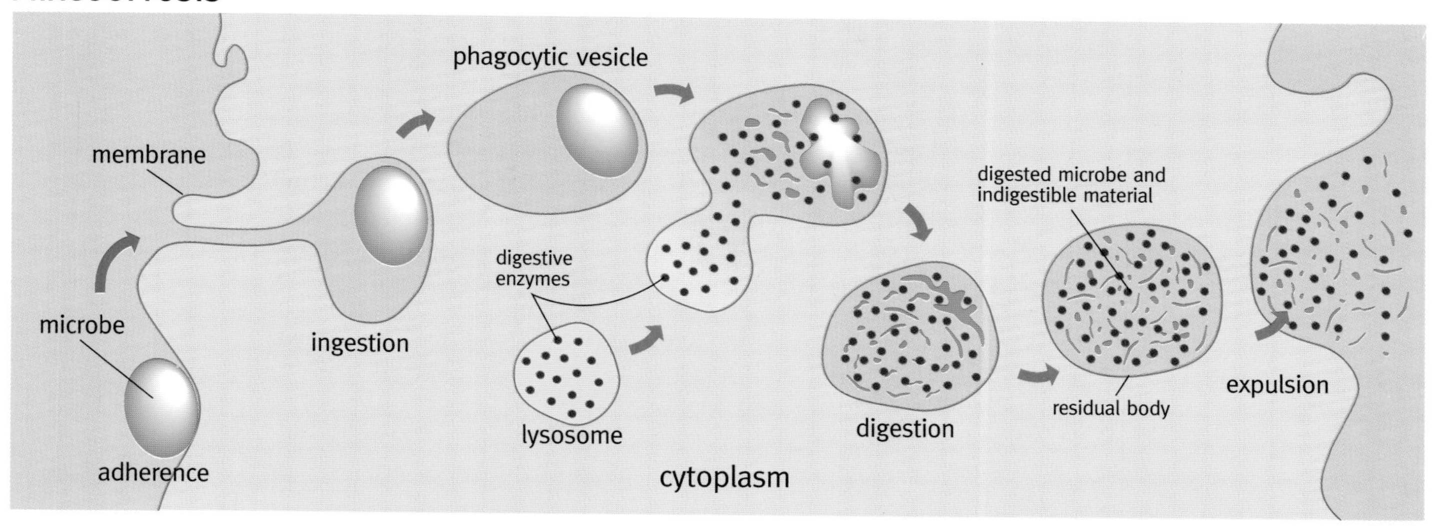

known as **complement formation**, ties up the foreign organism until macrophages arrive to destroy it by a process called **phagocytosis**.

In order for an antibody molecule to bind to a foreign organism, the shape of its binding regions must match perfectly to some part of the microbe. Since foreign particles entering the body can have thousands of different chemical shapes, there needs to be many thousands of different antibodies, so that at least one of them can bind. Since one particular B cell produces only one specific type of antibody, this means there must be a population of different B cells, each producing a different kind of antibody.

The B cells, then, are a collection of lymphocytes, each capable of recognizing a specific chemical shape. They circulate through the lymphatic vessels and the bloodstream, each with a specific antibody type embedded in its outer membrane. When a B cell contacts a chemical structure it can bind, two important changes occur.

First, the B cell begins growing and dividing rapidly, so that a whole group of identical cells are produced. Each of these new cells makes large amounts of the same antibody, which circulates in the blood and binds up identical microbes. This response usually takes care of the current invasion.

Second, some of the activated B cells migrate into lymphoid tissue such as lymph nodes and form a colony of cells.

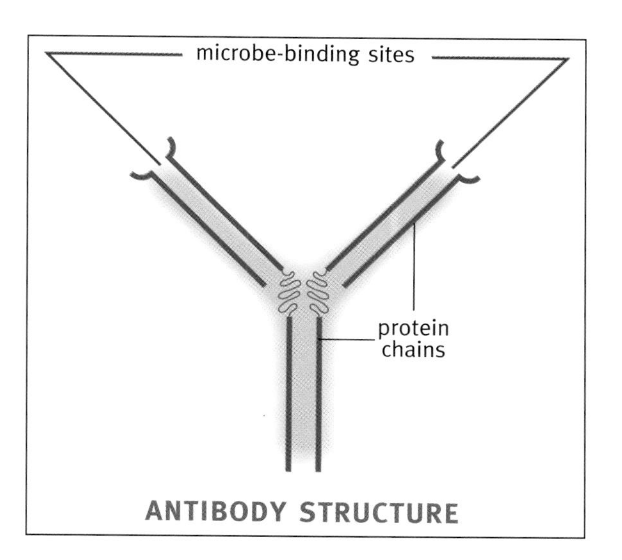

ANTIBODY STRUCTURE

This provides a backup system so that if the same microbe ever invades again, it can be dealt with more quickly. This is why many diseases are experienced just once, or are not as severe in second cases: The immune system has a "memory" of microbes it has already encountered, and can thus respond quickly to a second infection.

T Lymphocytes A portion of the lymphocytes from bone marrow enter the bloodstream and travel to the **thymus**, a lymphoid gland in the neck. Within the thymus these cells are programmed to become T lymphocytes (T cells). Unlike B cells, which produce antibody proteins to fight microbes, T cells bind to foreign particles directly. It is not yet clear if they do this the same way B cells do, but there is definitely a population of T cells that can recognize many different kinds of microbes.

When T cells recognize and bind foreign organisms, they can eliminate them in several ways. In some cases, the T cell itself breaks open the microbe and kills it. In other cases, the T cell holds on to the invader and signals macrophages to come and engulf it. T cells can also signal other T cells and B cells to become active and join in the defense.

Certain groups of T cells serve to control and coordinate the immune response. In the last few years, several chemical messengers—hormonelike compounds that work just on cells of the immune system—have been discovered. T cells secrete some of these compounds, called **lymphokines**, that activate various parts of the immune system. Currently, a lot of research is being done on this class of exciting new chemicals. Indeed, a few lymphokines are already being used to activate the immune systems of patients recovering from certain diseases.

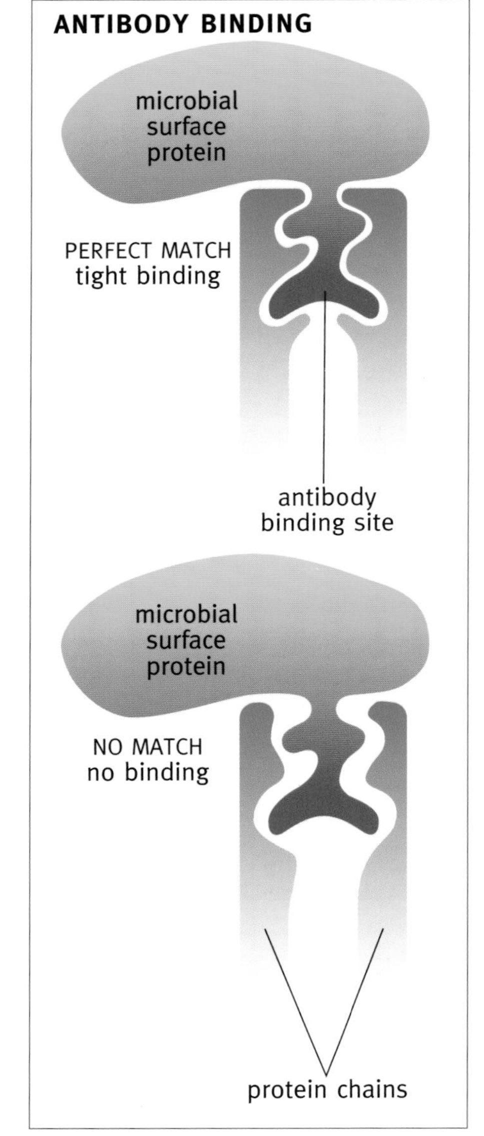

As you can imagine, sorting through thousands and thousands of chemical shapes to identify microbes is tricky business, and sometimes the immune system makes an error. The result is that the body's own tissues can be mistaken as foreign, and an attack is mounted. This produces autoimmune disease, a condition in which lymphocytes destroy other cells and tissues. An example of autoimmune disease is lupus (systemic lupus erythematosus), a disorder in which immune cells attack and destroy blood vessel walls, releasing chemicals that trigger widespread inflammation. Other diseases in this category include rheumatic fever, Graves's disease, thyroiditis, and probably rheumatoid arthritis and some kinds of diabetes. T cells are the component of the immune system responsible for this kind of disorder. The process of transplant rejection—a process in which a replacement organ from another person is attacked by the host's own immune system—is also caused by T cells. A better understanding of how T cells function may one day help solve these two problems.

Both B cells and T cells continue to migrate through the lymph and blood systems throughout life. This constant circulation gives them the best chance of contacting their targets. New lymphocytes continue to be produced at a low

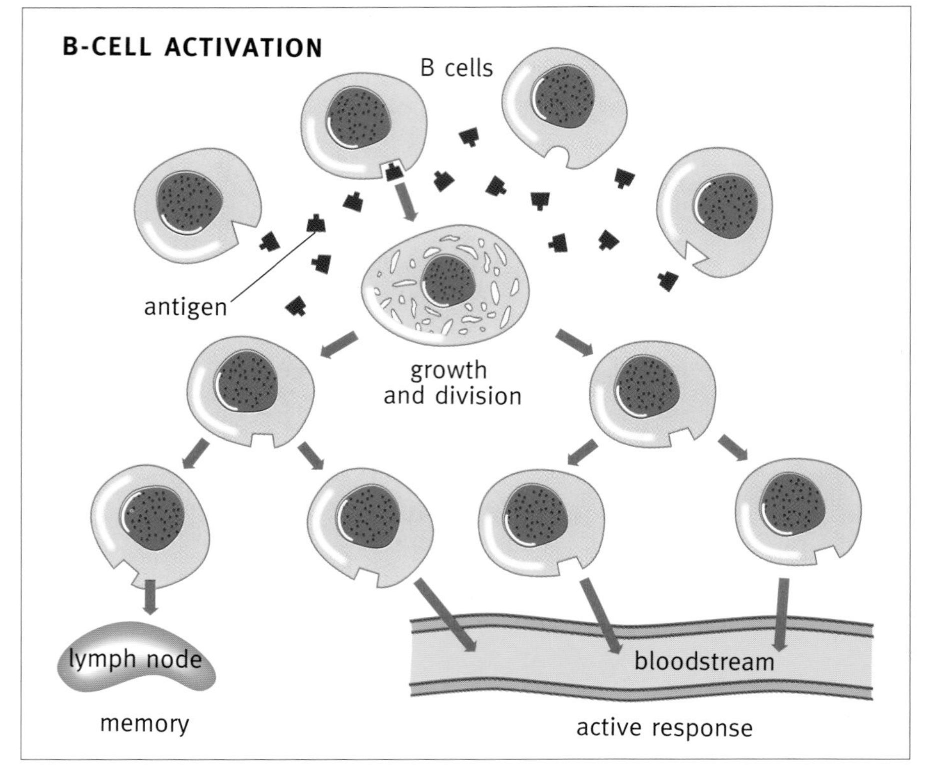

level as we grow, providing us with continued protection.

Chemical Factors In addition to cell-mediated immune responses, there are also chemicals in the body that assist in defense. An example is interferon, a recently discovered compound that displays immune activity. When cells are infected by a virus, they begin synthesizing interferon, which then travels to nearby cells. This signals neighboring cells to produce another protein that blocks viral replication. This helps prevent the virus from spreading to other tissues. Thus, interferon serves as an initial defense against invading viruses.

Since the immune system is so critical to health, many scientists are currently studying how it works. Some of the molecular details of how antibodies work are now well understood, and other aspects of immunity are also yielding to investigation. This knowledge is helping scientists design medicines that stimulate specific parts of the immune response to fight certain diseases.

AIDS

Acquired immunodeficiency syndrome (AIDS) is a disease that directly attacks the immune system. This syndrome is caused by a microorganism known as human immunodeficiency virus (HIV). This microbe can attach specifically to the surface of T lymphocytes, and eventually enter the cell, where it reprograms the cellular machinery and directs the synthesis of new viruses instead of normal cell products. Eventually, the infected T cell dies and breaks apart, releasing thousands of new viruses to infect more cells.

Most AIDS victims—about 75 percent—contract the virus through sexual intercourse with someone infected with HIV. Drug abuse is another source of HIV infection, with about 10 percent of AIDS victims contracting the disease from using virus-contaminated needles for injections. HIV can also be transmitted from an infected mother to her unborn child while it is still in the uterus, accounting for another 10 percent of all cases. About 5 percent of AIDS victims contract the virus from HIV-contaminated blood during transfusions.

HIV is present in the blood and semen of infected individuals, as well as in saliva and tears. However, the number of virus particles in saliva and tears is very low, and studies suggest that it is not possible to contract the virus through casual contact with someone who carries HIV. Experiments have shown also that insects, such as bedbugs, cannot transmit the disease from one person to another. When HIV enters the body, it can remain dormant for weeks, months, or even years. But eventually the virus invades T cells and begins destroying the immune system. The earliest symptoms of the disease—fever, sweating, diarrhea, fatigue, skin infections, and headaches—all result from microbial infections. This is because the damaged immune response of an AIDS victim can no longer combat even the weakest microorganisms.

As AIDS progresses, major organs begin to succumb. Usually pneumonia sets in, along with severe skin disorders, and eventually most of the body's systems are compromised. This disease is one of the most deadly known—it has a 100 percent mortality rate, which means that as of now, anyone who contracts this illness is not expected to live through it. This severe prognosis for HIV infection demonstrates vividly the essential role of the immune system in human health.

Currently, there are several drugs employed to combat AIDS. The most widely used is AZT, a chemical that inhibits viral replication and thus slows the advance of HIV through the immune system. While this is effective at relieving some symptoms and prolonging life, it does not eliminate the virus from the body, and it also produces some detrimental side effects. Scientists all over the world are working frantically to design better treatments, but as of now there is no cure for this disease.

Very accurate tests for detecting the presence of HIV are available from hospitals and medical clinics. With the current epidemic level of this disease in the population and the rapid rate at which it is being transmitted, an AIDS test for oneself and a potential sexual partner should be seriously considered. Additionally, available evidence supports the use of a condom as an effective way to prevent sexual transmission of AIDS.

Chapter 12

The Reproductive System

The hallmark of all living organisms is their ability to reproduce—to create a "copy" of themselves, a new life to continue on through time. For human beings, bearing offspring is also a deeply emotional experience that can bring a sense of fulfillment and happiness. In this chapter we will consider the specialized tissues responsible for reproduction, and how they function to produce a fertilized egg. We will then briefly examine the developmental process that turns a single-celled egg into a complex new baby ready to enter the world.

Humans create offspring by sexual reproduction, a process that requires female and male participation. This process is termed "sexual" because it combines female and male genes together so that the offspring receives a mixture of genetic material, not just an exact duplicate of one parent's genes. The result is that the offspring displays characteristics of both parents, along with brand-new features of its own.

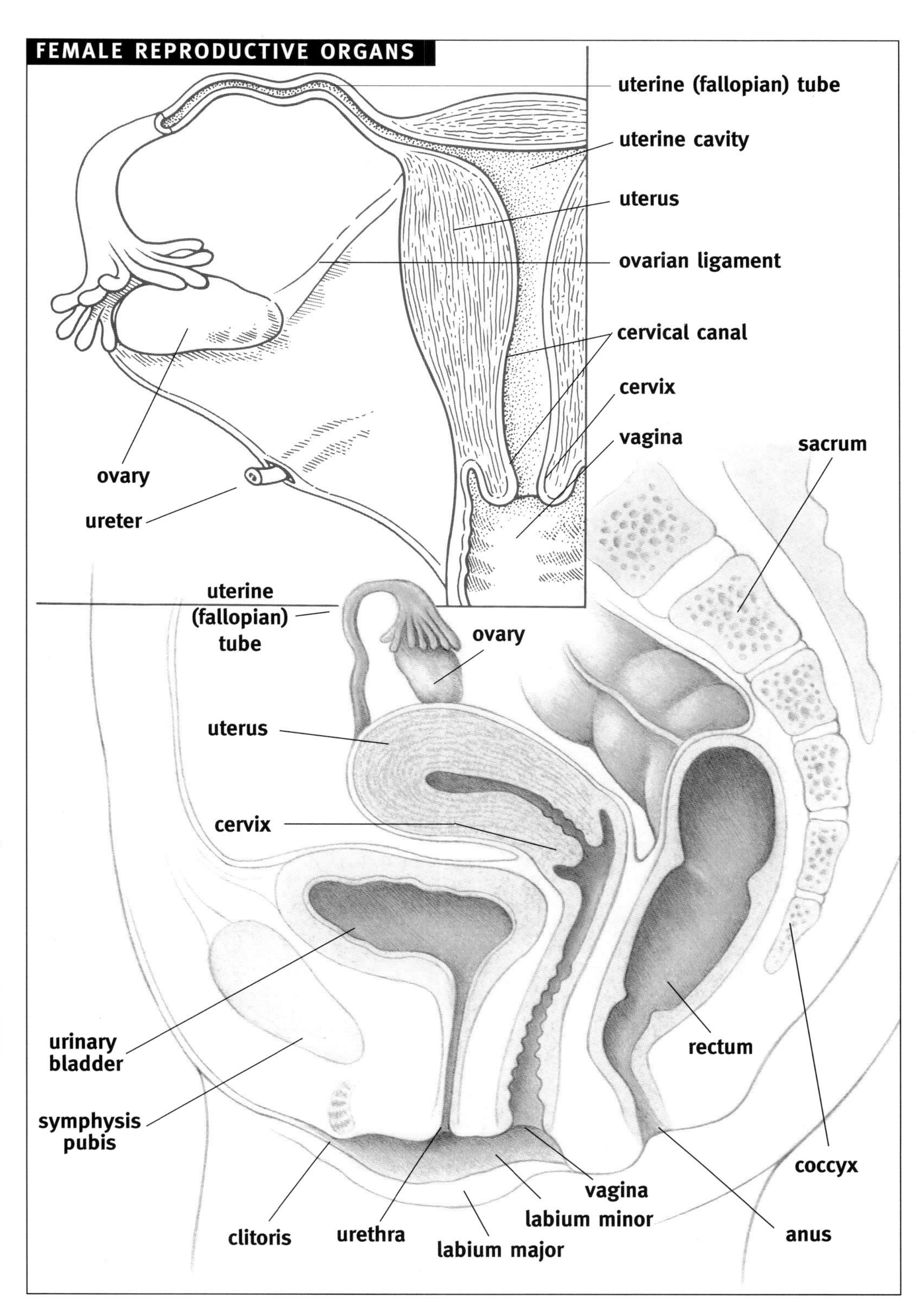

FEMALE REPRODUCTIVE ORGANS

The organs of reproduction in females include the two **ovaries**, oblong-shaped structures positioned in the lower abdomen; the **fallopian tubes**, which open next to the ovaries and connect to the **uterus**, a sacklike organ with very

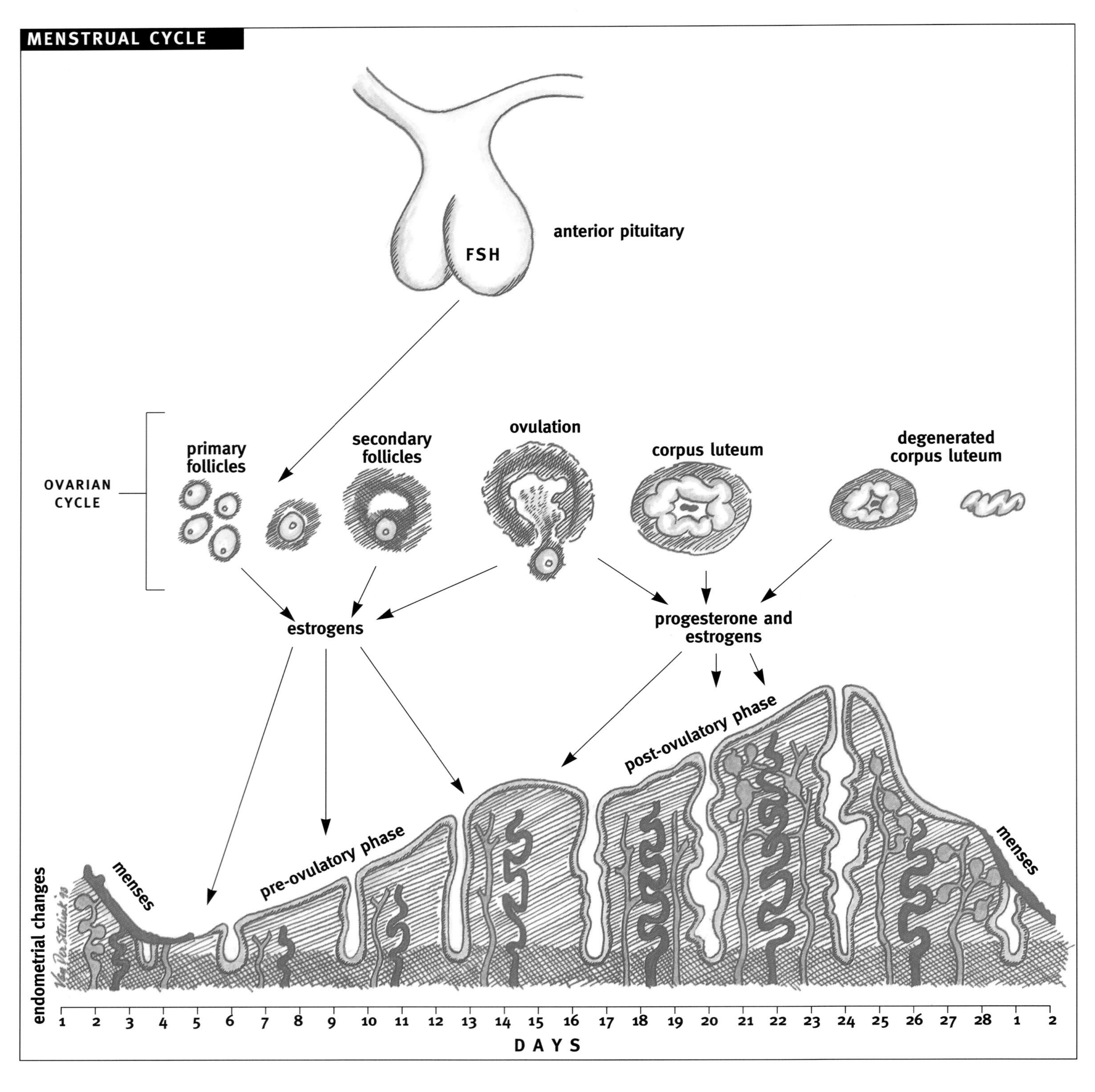

thick muscular walls. The lower mouth of the uterus, called the **cervix**, connects to the **vagina**, which forms a passageway to the outside. Folds of soft tissue that cover the vaginal opening are called the **labia minora** and **labia majora**. Positioned in the upper part of the labia minora is the **clitoris**—a small mass of excitatory tissue. The female **breasts** are also classified as reproductive tissue because they produce milk for the newborn.

Menstrual Cycle Within the ovaries are a large number (about 200,000 at birth) of special cells known as **oocytes**, also called eggs. These egg cells are dormant until **puberty** occurs, usually at about the age of twelve. At this stage in life, a hormone from the pituitary gland called **follicle-stimulating hormone** (FSH) begins to be secreted into the blood and activates eggs withinthe ovaries. During puberty, which takes several years to complete, several other hormones also begin to be secreted. These hormones make the female body capable of reproducing.

As the female anatomy develops during puberty, FSH and other reproductive hormones are secreted in a regular pattern approximately every twenty-eight days. This pattern, known as the **menstrual cycle**, prepares the egg for fertilization and readies the uterus to carry the fertilized egg.

PAGE 114 Human fetus
X-ray image of a fetus inside the uterus. The immature skeleton is visible, including the spinal column, skull bones, long bones of the appendages, and the phalanges. The mother's spine is also visible, at the top edge of the picture.

During the first several days of the menstrual cycle, the menses phase, about twenty-five oocytes begin to grow and develop within the ovary. Most of these primary follicles continue to mature until they become secondary follicles by about the fifth day of the cycle. The secondary follicles consist of oocytes surrounded by layers of protective cells that begin to produce estrogen and progesterone—two important hormones that play key roles in reproduction. In addition, estrogen is responsible for the development of secondary sexual characteristics in females. This includes growth and development of the breasts, broadening of the hips and pelvis, the pattern of hair distribution, and higher pitch of the voice. Thus, estrogen is the main factor that molds the female anatomy into its mature form.

The next ten days—the pre-ovulatory phase—is when all but one of the developing follicles begin to degenerate and die, leaving just one follicle to continue. Under the influence of FSH, this single remaining follicle secretes increasing amounts of hormones and fills with fluid, forcing the egg to one edge. By the end of this phase, the large follicle has migrated to the outer edge of the ovary, usually near the fallopian tube.

INFERTILITY

Among couples who want to have children, about one in six experience difficulty in achieving pregnancy. In former times, it was supposed that the female was usually the partner with reproductive problems, but today's more accurate estimates show that male reproductive insufficiency is to blame about 50 percent of the time. In some cases, physical anomalies in both partners contribute to infertility.

Several types of medical intervention are used to help couples achieve pregnancy. For males, chemicals or drugs that increase sperm count and sperm longevity are prescribed. Vitamin C has been demonstrated to have a positive effect on male fertility. For females, treatment with the drug Clomid, which stimulates ovulation, is effective in many cases.

Another strategy, known as **artificial insemination**, has a success rate of about 25 percent. This procedure involves collection of sperm from the male, sometimes concentrating and storing the sperm ahead of time, and then placing the prepared sperm sample into the female's vagina or uterus. Introducing a large number of sperm directly into the female reproductive tract increases the odds of successful fertilization. In cases where the male partner's sperm count is too low even for this technique, some couples choose artificial insemination with sperm from a donor. This allows for a normal pregnancy and birth, and will produce offspring with a genetic makeup of half its genes from the mother and half its genes contributed by the donor male.

A recent and more complex method now being used to achieve pregnancy is **in-vitro fertilization**. In 1978, Louise Brown—the first "test-tube baby"—was born in England, showing the feasibility of this technique. Since then, several thousand successful pregnancies have resulted from this method. But only about 10 percent of couples who undergo this procedure experience success with the birth of a baby.

In the complicated pathway of human reproduction, there are many different steps that can go wrong and prevent eggs and sperm from joining. In-vitro fertilization eliminates this problem by mixing eggs and sperm together outside of the mother's body. The process involves removing eggs from the female's ovary, collecting sperm from the male, and mixing these components together in a sterile dish. Fertilization of the eggs under these conditions is virtually assured. After about two days, the fertilized ova begin to divide, and at this point the eggs are carefully inserted into the uterus.

For a pregnancy to occur, a fertilized egg must then implant into the uterine wall, and the low efficiency of this occurrence is why in-vitro fertilization has a low success rate. Because successful implantation is rare, doctors usually put several fertilized eggs into the mother's uterus, increasing the probability that at least one will implant. This makes it possible for more than one egg to implant, and multiple births from this procedure have occurred.

Although the success rate of in-vitro fertilization is low, it presents the only alternative for some couples trying to achieve pregnancy. The rate of successful births from in-vitro fertilization is increasing, as doctors and scientists learn more about it and improve various steps of the procedure.

On about day fourteen of the menstrual cycle, ovulation occurs: the follicle bursts open, expelling the egg out of the ovary and into the fallopian tube.

After the egg is gone, the follicle seals back up and continues to secrete hormones that affect the egg and other reproductive structures. This part of the cycle is called the post-ovulatory phase and lasts for about twelve days. The follicle, now called the **corpus luteum**—remains active for most of this phase and then shrivels and degenerates if pregnancy does not occur.

During the menstrual cycle, the uterus is strongly affected. Estrogen from secondary follicles causes the inner lining of the uterus, which is called the **endometrium**, to thicken and become filled with new blood vessels and secretory glands during the first part of the cycle. This change in the endometrium prepares the uterus to receive and nurture the egg if it is fertilized.

After ovulation, the endometrium continues to thicken under the influence of estrogen and progesterone from the corpus luteum. If the egg is not fertilized and does not implant in the endometrium, the built-up endometrium begins to degenerate at the end of the post-ovulatory cycle. The thickened inner layer actually lifts off and is expelled from the uterus through the vagina. This process, called menses, occurs at the end of the menstrual cycle and lasts for about five days—the time when a woman has a "period." About 1.7 ounces (51 ml) of blood are lost during each period.

The menstrual cycle, then, provides an opportunity for reproduction about once a month from the age of about twelve until a

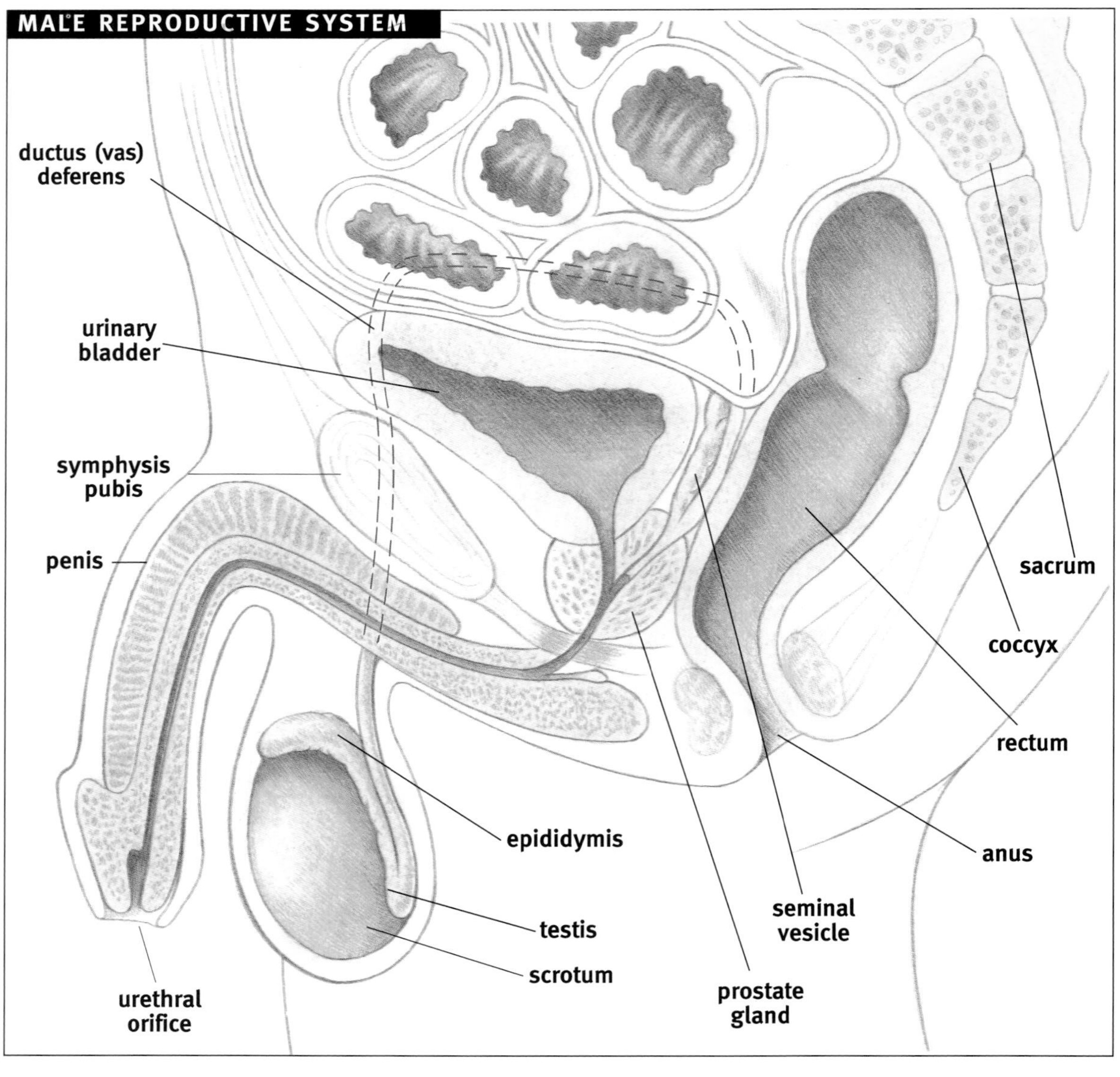

woman experiences **menopause** at about forty-five years of age. A decrease in FSH secretion at this stage of life causes the female reproductive system to gradually shut down. The menstrual cycle eventually stops and a woman can no longer become pregnant.

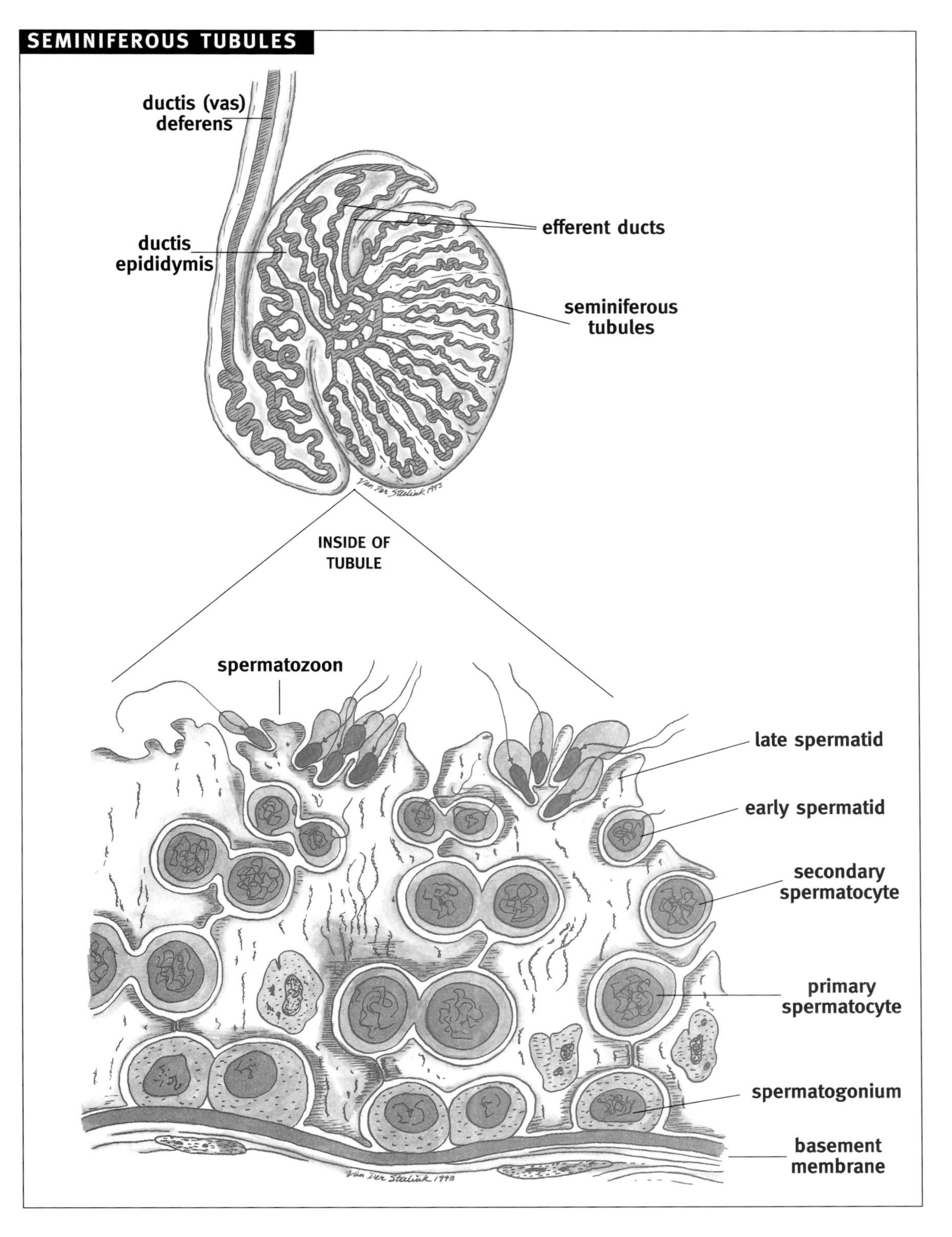

MALE REPRODUCTIVE ORGANS

The organs of the male reproductive system include the two **testes**, where male reproductive cells—**spermatozoa**—are produced. Both testes are enclosed in a sac of skin called the **scrotum**, which helps protect the delicate testes. A tube called the **vas deferens** provides a channel through which sperm travel to exit the body. This duct passes through the **prostate gland**, a structure that secretes a special fluid into the vas deferens that mixes with sperm to form **semen**. The **seminal vesicles** are

TWINS

During a typical menstrual cycle, one egg is released into the fallopian tube at a time. In fact, the two ovaries usually alternate—the left ovary depositing an egg one month, the right ovary releasing an egg the next month. But sometimes, more than one egg is released, either by the same ovary or both ovaries during the same cycle.

When two eggs are available, they can both be fertilized, to produce **fraternal twins,** also known as **dizygotic twins,** since they arise from two separate zygotes, each of which is fertilized by a different sperm.

Physically, fraternal twins are no more related than any other siblings; they can be of the same or different gender, and have different physical features, since their DNAs were always separate. Fraternal twins are like any other brothers or sisters, except that they happened to share their mother's uterus at the same time.

The other type of twins is **maternal** or **monozygotic twins.** In this case, there is just one fertilized egg, and for some reason the zygote splits completely in half very early during embryogenesis. The two embryos then develop separately, but since they both come from identical sets of DNA, all of their genes are the same. This results in identical twins, and produces siblings that are always the same sex and have such similar physical features that they are difficult to tell apart.

another type of gland, which also add fluid to semen.

The vas deferens connects to the **penis**, a muscular organ through which both semen and urine exit the body.

Within each testis there is a system of ducts called the **seminiferous tubules**. It is here that sperm begin to develop and mature when puberty is reached. Special cells known as **spermatogonia** continuously divide to produce primary spermatocytes, which develop into functional sperm. Each sperm cell has a long tail-like structure called a **flagellum**. This structure can whip back and forth, causing the sperm to move. Fully developed testes produce about 300 million functional sperm every day.

Under the influence of FSH, the testes also produce the major sex hormone in males: testosterone. This chemical affects many organs and tissues, and is responsible for secondary sexual characteristics such as muscular development, widening of the shoulders, growth of hair on the chest and face, and enlargement of the larynx, which lowers the pitch of the voice. Testosterone also helps in the final steps of sperm maturation.

FERTILIZATION

Once the reproductive tissues have produced mature eggs and sperm, the process of **fertilization** can occur. Each egg carries one complete copy of DNA from the mother, while each sperm contains one copy of DNA from the father. Thus, these specialized cells are prepared to combine the genetic information from two parents into one new cell.

During sexual intercourse, about 250 million sperm, along with semen, are deposited into the vagina. The sperm then begin "swimming" toward the uterus, propelled by the beating action of their flagella. Most of the sperm die quickly, but a small portion make their way through the cervix and into the uterus. Surviving sperm continue to travel through the uterus and into the fallopian tube.

Within the fallopian tube, sperm contact the egg that has been expelled from the ovary. The sperm then begin to burrow into the egg, breaking through its outer wall with special enzymes. When a sperm successfully penetrates, the outer membrane of the egg, known as the **zone pellucida**, immediately swells and pushes outward, preventing other sperm from getting in. This event is critical because it maintains the right number of copies of DNA inside the egg. If many sperm entered the egg, too many sets of DNA would be present and proper gene functioning could not proceed.

Once the sperm is inside, the egg is considered to be fertilized. The nuclei of the sperm and egg then combine, joining their DNA, and the fertilized cell—now called a **zygote**—begins to divide rapidly, creating two cells, then four, eight, sixteen, and so on. This forms a small mass of cells called an **embryo**. As the embryo continues to grow, it also continues its journey through the fallopian tube and into the uterus.

Fertilization can occur only after the egg is expelled from the ovary, and before it travels completely through the fallopian tubes, a journey that takes about three days. Fertilization usually occurs about twenty-four hours after ovulation, when the egg is about one-third of the way through the fallopian tube. Thus, there are just a few days during the menstrual cycle when a female can become pregnant.

IMPLANTATION

The next step in the reproductive process occurs when the embryo reaches the uterus. Inside this organ, the embryo attaches to the uterine wall and embeds itself in the endometrium. At this time, the endometrium is thick with a network of blood vessels and glandular secretions that supply the embryo with substances to continue growing.

Once established in the endometrium, the growing embryo begins secreting **human chorionic gonadotropin** (HCG),

FERTILIZATION

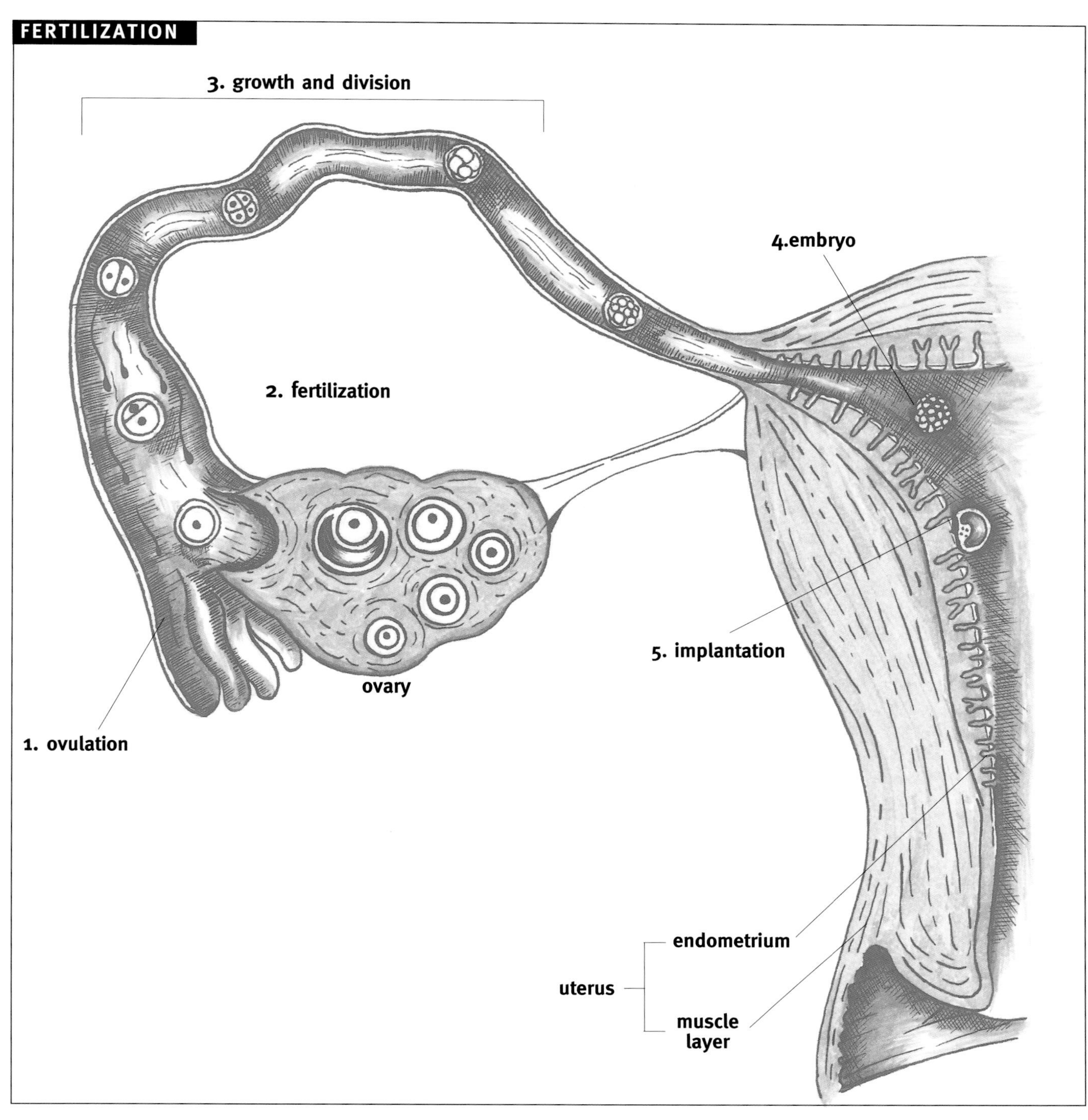

IMPLANTATION

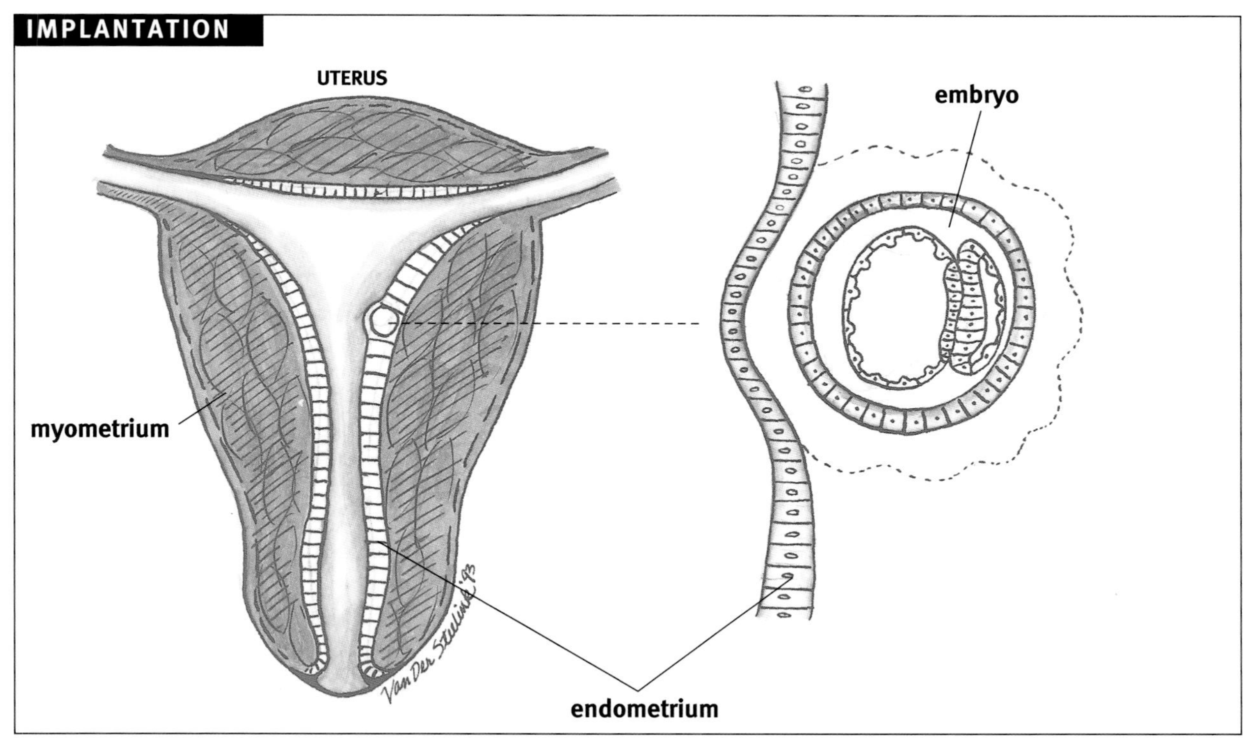

a hormone that stimulates the corpus luteum to continue secreting estrogen and progesterone. HCG stimulates the corpus luteum and keeps it active for the first three to four months of pregnancy. After this, estrogen and progesterone are provided by the **placenta**, an organ of the growing embryo.

DEVELOPMENT

About one month after fertilization, the embryo begins to take shape. The head and spine areas can be seen, along with a pouch that will form the heart. An attached structure called the **yolk sac** provides nutrients, along with the placenta, which connects the embryo to the mother's blood supply. It is through the placenta that the embryo receives both oxygen and nutrients directly from its mother's circulatory system.

At two months, the fetal stage is reached. By this time, all of the major organ systems have begun to form, and the fetus is large enough to create a bulge in the mother's abdomen. The placenta is fully established and provides a rich supply of oxygen and nutrients for continued growth and development.

During the rest of pregnancy, the major activity is simply an increase in size, along with final maturation of all the organ systems. The lungs are one of the last systems to fully develop, and the condition of the lungs is usually the major problem for fetuses that are born early. After about nine months, the fetus is ready to leave the uterus and enter the world.

EMBRYO DEVELOPMENT

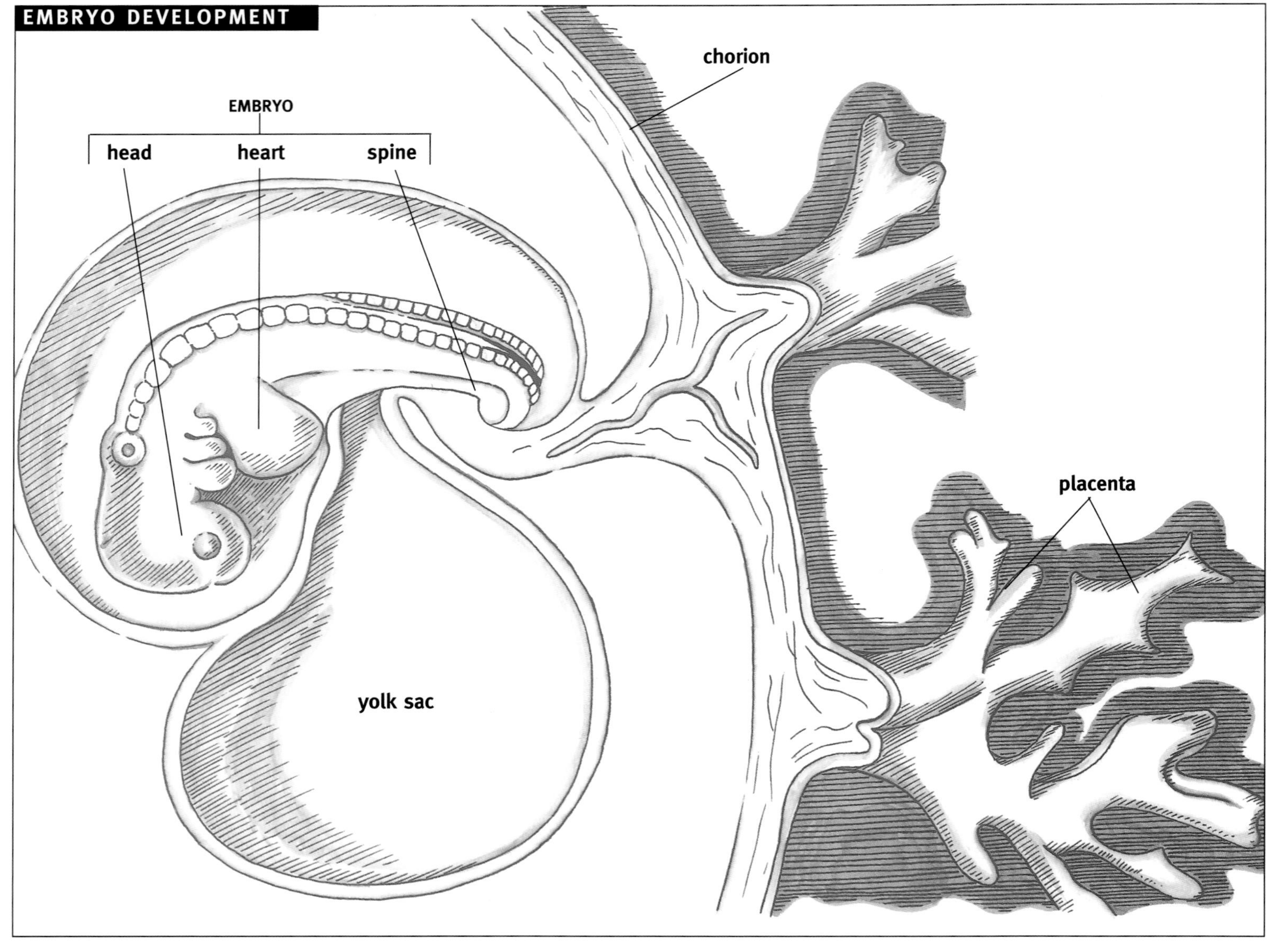

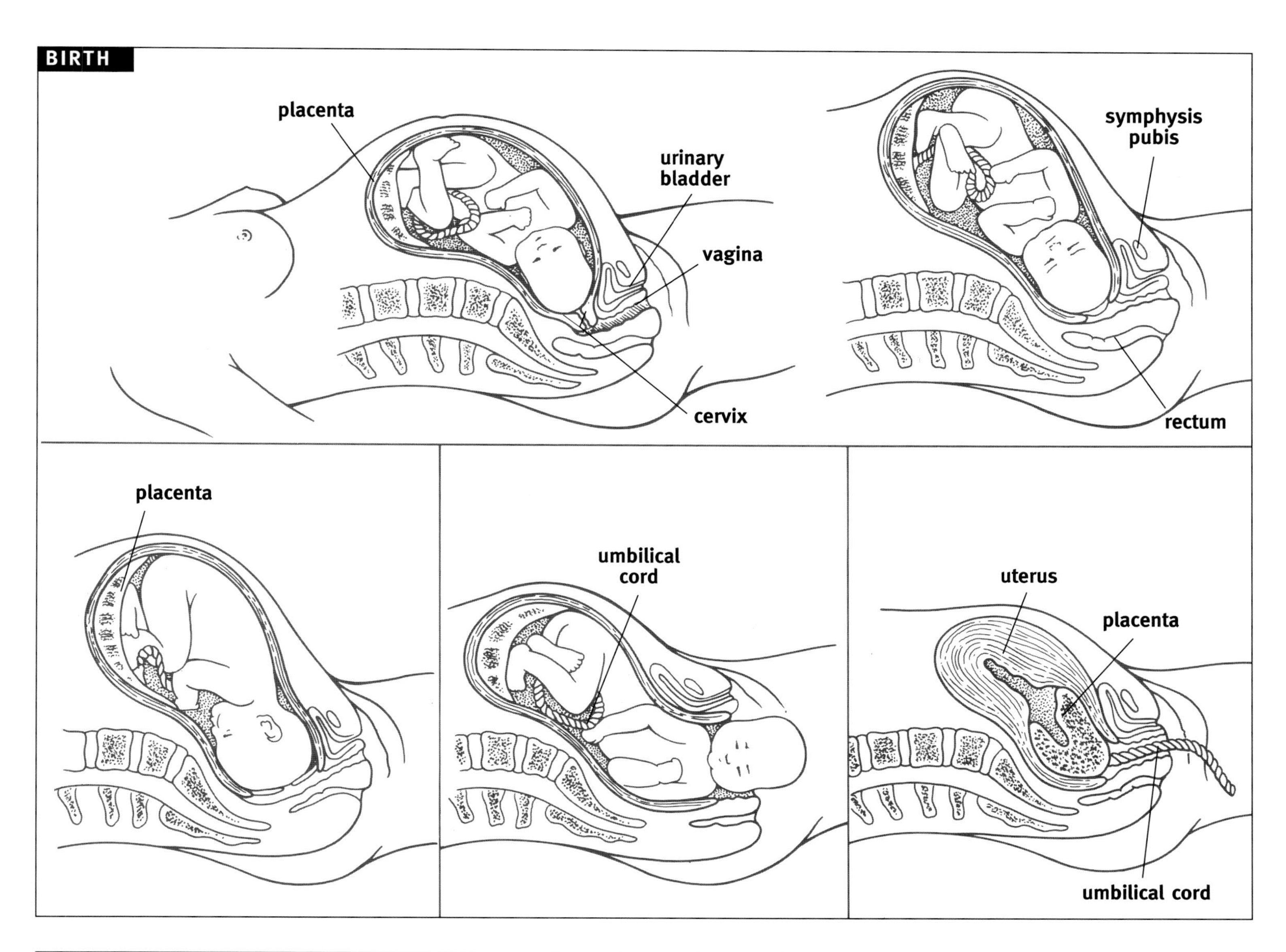

BIRTH

When the fetus is fully grown, it fills a large portion of the mother's abdominal cavity. At this stage, hormonal signals cause the uterus to begin contracting in a rhythmic pattern. These contractions slowly push the fetus down through the mother's pelvis.

As the baby moves downward toward the birth canal, the pelvic bones actually separate slightly to allow the fetus to pass. The **amniotic sac**—the membrane surrounding the fetus—breaks open, and the cervix stretches widely as the fetus is pushed out. The birth process—also called **labor**—usually takes about twelve hours, but can sometimes last much longer. It is a painful and difficult process for the mother and is also stressful for the fetus.

Once the newborn infant has emerged, the placenta is expelled from the uterus, usually about thirty minutes after the baby is out. The **umbilical cord**, which connects the baby to the placenta, is then tied off to stop blood flow, and cut to separate it from the new child.

The reproductive process is complex, involving many steps, and thus is not always successful. Even if fertilization occurs, it is not certain that a pregnancy will result. In fact, as many as 75 percent of all embryos do not survive; some do not implant successfully, and others are not maintained in the uterus for the whole nine-month period. When a fetus does not survive, the mother has a "miscarriage" and the fetus is expelled from the uterus. Miscarriages are not uncommon, and many women who lose a fetus later carry one or more to full term.

Further Reading

Beck, William S. *Human Design.* New York: Harcourt Brace Jovanovich, 1971.

Berne, Robert M., and Matthew N. Levy. *Physiology.* St. Louis: The C.V. Mosby Company, 1987.

Fincham, John R.S. *Genetics.* Portola Valley, Calif.: Jones & Bartlett Publishers, 1983.

Gray, Henry. *Gray's Anatomy,* 30th edition. Edited by Carmine D. Clemente. Philadelphia: Lea & Febiger, 1985.

Lewin, Benjamin. *Genes III.* New York: John Wiley & Sons, 1987.

Singer, Sam, and Henry R. Hilgard. *The Biology of People.* San Francisco: W.H. Freeman & Company, 1978.

Tver, David F., and Percy Russell. *The Nutrition & Health Encyclopedia.* New York: Van Nostrand Reinhold Company, 1981.

Wolfe, Stephen L. *Biology of the Cell.* Belmont, Calif.: Wadsworth Publishing Company Inc., 1972.

Woodburne, Russel T., and William E. Burkel. *Essentials of Human Anatomy.* New York: Oxford University Press, 1988.

INDEX

A

Acne, 24
Actin, 39, 42
Adenine, 11
Adenoids, 110
Adenosine triphosphate, 42, 44, 71, 72, 81, 83
Adrenaline, 68
AIDS, 113
Air passages, *71*, 72–73
Albinoism, 21
Albumin, 65
Aldosterone, 95, 104
Allergies, 110
Alveoli, *75*, 76, 77, 79
Amino acids, 12, *12*, 13, *63*, 65, 81, 83, 84, 89, 93, 94, 95, 96, 100
Amylase, 83, 84, 87
Androgen, 104
Anemia, sickle-cell, 17
Angiotensinogen, 95
Antibodies, *11*, 110, 112, 113
Antihistamines, 110
Aorta, 68, 69
Arteries, 65–66, *66*
  pulmonary, 68, *68*, 69, *69*
  renal, *91*, 92
Arterioles, 66, *67*
Arthritis, 32, 88
Atheroschlerosis, 69
Atoms, 10, 11, 15
ATP. *See* Adenosine triphosphate.
Atrioventricular nodes, 68
Auditory sense, 56, 58
Autonomic nervous system, 54–55, *57*, 68
Axons, 47, 48, 49, 50

B

Biofeedback, 57
Birth, 123, *123*
Blood, 63–66
  cells, 63–64
  clotting, 65, *65*
  color, 64
  flow, 69, 69
  plasma, 65
  platelets, 64–65
  pressure, 57, 65, 88, 95, 96
  vessels, 65, *65*, 66, *68*, *96*
Bone
  funny, 28
  marrow, 27, 64, 110
  matrix, 27, *27*, 28, 45
  remodeling, 28, *29*
  shapes, 28, 30
  tissue, 27–28
Brain, 50–51
  functions, 59–60
  stem, 51, *53*
  structure, *52*
Bronchi, *74*, 75
Bronchioles, 75, *75*

C

Calcium, 25, 27, 28, 35, 42, 44, 65, 95
Cancer, 16, 21
  causes, 14
  and life-style, 13
  lung, 74
  skin, 20
Capillaries, 66, *66*
Carbohydrates, 11, 14–15, 81, 83
Carbon, 10
Carbon dioxide, 65, 72, 76, 78, 91
Carbon monoxide, 78
Carboxypeptidase, 87
Carotene, 21
Carpals, 33, *33*
Cartilage, 31
Cell(s), 9–17
  anatomy, 9–10
  blood, 63–64
  cardiac, 67, *68*
  differentiation, 16–17
  division, 9, 16
  endoplasmic reticulum, 10
  endothelial, 66
  epithelial, 19, 84
  glial, 47
  killer, 108
  mast, 110
  muscle, 37, *37*, 38
  nerve, 108
  nucleus, 10
  plasma membrane, 9, 15, *49*
  Schwann, 47, 48
  special structures, 22–25
Central nervous system, 50-52
Cerebellum, 50, *53*
Cerebrospinal fluid, 51, *53*
Cerebrum, 50, *53*
Cervix, *115*, 116, 120
Cholecalciferol, 25
Cholesterol, 25, 89, 101
Chromosomes, 16, *17*
Chymotrypsin, 87
Circulatory system, 63–69
Clavicle, *32*, 33, *33*
Coccyx, 31, *31*, 34
Cochlea, 56, *58, 59*
Collagen, 22, 27
Cornea, 58
Cortisol, 104
Coughing, 73
Cranium, 30
Crystallin, 14
Cystic fibrosis, 17
Cytoplasm, 10, 12
Cytosine, 11
Cytoskeleton, 10

D

Dendrites, 47, 49, 50, 56
Deoxyribonucleic acid. *See* DNA.
Deoxyribose, 11
Dermis, *19*, 22
Diabetes, 104
Diaphragm, 76, 78
Diencephalon, 51, *53*
Digestive system, 81–89
Digestive tract, 83–84, 87, 89
DNA, 9, 10, *10*, 11, 13, 14, 16, 74, 87, *99*, 100, 120
  double helix, 11
  recombinant therapy, 17
  replication, 16, *17*
Dwarfism, 101

E

Ear structure, 56, 58, *58*
Elastin, 22, 25
Electrocardiogram, 68
Elements, 10
Emphysema, 74, 79

Endocrine system, 99–105
Endoplasmic reticulum, 64
Energy, 15, 22, 44, 71
Enzymes, 14, 16, 25
  antimicrobial, 84
  cellular, 91
  digestive, 83, 84, 87
Epidermis, 19, *19*
Epiglottis, 73
Epithelium, 37
Equilibrium, 58
Erythrocytes, *63*, 64, 77
Esophagus, 73, 84
Estrogen, 104, 105, 117
Exhalation, 77
Eye structure, 58, 59, *61*

F

Fallopian tubes, 115, *115*
Fatty acids, 15, *16*, 22, 65, 81, 89
Femur, 33, *34*
Fertilization, 120, *121*
Fibrinogen, 65
Fibroblasts, 22
Fibula, 33, *34*
Fingers, 33
Freckles, 20

G

Gall bladder, 89
Genes, 12, 13, 15, 17, 100
Genetic code, 11, 13, *13*
Gland(s)
  adrenal, *57*, 68, 95, 101, *103*, 104
  endocrine, *100*, 101–105
  intestinal, 84
  lacrimal, 58
  oil, 22, 23–24
  parathyroid, 101, *102*
  parotid, *57*
  pituitary, 95, 101, *101*
  prostate, *118*, 119
  salivary, *57*, 83
  sebaceous, 108
  sweat, 22, 24, 37, 91, 108
  tear, *57*, 108
  thyroid, 101, *102*, 103
Glomerulus, 92, 93, 94, 95
Glucagon, 104
Glucose, 15, 72, 93, 94
Glutamic acid, 13
Glycerol, 81
Glycine, 12
Glycogen, 15
Glycoproteins, 15
Guanine, 11
Gustatory sense, 55–56

H

Hearing, 56, 58
Heart, *57*, 66–68
  artificial, 67
  chambers, 66
  contractions, 68
  rate, 68
Hematopoiesis, 35
Hemodialysis, 96
Hemoglobin, 14, 15, 17, *63*, 64, 74, 77, 78, 83
Hemophilia, 67
Hiccups, 73
Histidine, 13
Hormone(s), 24, 28
  action, *99*
  adrenocorticotropic, 101
  aldosterone, 104
  anabolic steroid, 102
  androgen, 24, 104
  antidiuretic, 95, 102
  calcitonin, 103
  cortisol, 104
  epinephrine, 104
  estrogen, 104, 105, 117
  follicle-stimulating, 102,116, 117, 120
  glucagon, 104
  growth, 101
  insulin, 104
  luteinizing, 102
  melanocyte-stimulating, 101
  norepinephrine, 104
  oxytocin, 102
  parathyroid, 103
  progesterone, 105, 117
  prolactin, 101
  protein, *99*, 100
  receptors, 100
  steroid, *99*, 100–101
  testosterone, 105
  thryoxine, 103
  thyroid-stimulating, 101
  trilodothreonine, 103
Humerus, 33, *33*
Hydrogen, 10, 15

I

Ilia, 34, *34*
Immune system, 107–113
Incus, 56, *58, 59*
Infertility, 117
Inspiration, 77
Insulin, 104
Integumentary system, 19–22
Interferon, 113
Interstitial fluid, 66
Intestine, 9
  large, *57*, 89
  small, *57*, 84, 87
Iris, 58, 59, *61*

J

Joint(s), 34–35
  ball and socket, 35
  cartilaginous, 34–35
  "double," 35
  fibrous, 34
  hinge, 35
  inflammation, 32
  pivot, 35
  sliding, 35
  synovial, 35

K

Keratin, 19, 20
Keratinocytes, 19, 20, 24
Kidneys, *57*, 91, *91*, 95
  function, 92–96
  stones, 95
  transplants, 97

L

Lactic acid, 44
Lactose intolerance, 86
Larynx, *72*, 73
Learning, 59
Lens, 59, *61*
Leukocytes, *107*, 108, 110
Lipids, 15
Liver, 9, *57*, 69, 87, *88*, 89
Lungs, 9, 31, *57*, 73, *74*, 75–76, 91, 99
Lupus, 112
Lymphatic system, *109*
Lymphatic vessels, 66, *67, 75*
Lymph nodes, 66, *109*, 110, 111
Lymphocytes, 66, 110–113
Lymphokines, 112
Lysozyme, 58, 84, 108

M

Macromolecules, 11, 15, 81, 91
Macrophages, 108, 112

Malleus, 56, *58, 59*
Mandible, 30
Medulla, 96
Megakaryocytes, 64
Melanin, 20, 21
Melanocytes, 20, *20*, 21
Memory, 59
Meninges, 51, *53*
Menopause, 119
Menstrual cycle, 116, *116*, 117
Metacarpals, 33, *33*
Metatarsals, 33, *34*
Methionine, 12
Minerals, 83, 85, 89
Mitochondria, 10, 39, 42, 44
Mitosis, 16, 17, *17*
Molecules, 10, 11, 14
  informational, 11
  steroid, 101
Moles, 21
Motor end plate, *39*, 42
Motor neuron, 42
Mouth, 83–84
  structure, *83*
Mucous membranes, 72, 108
Muscle(s), *40, 41*
  building, 43, 44
  cardiac, 66
  contraction, 42, *42*, 44, 99
  fibers, 39, 42, 44
  function, 44–45
  heart, 37
  intercostal, 76
  myoepithelial, 37
  opposing, *42, 43*, 45
  skeletal, 38, 73, 84
  smooth, 37
  structure, *38*, 44–45
  types, 37–38
Muscular dystrophy, 17
Muscular system, 37–45
Mutations, 16, 17
Myelin sheath, 48, *48*
Myoblasts, 38–39, 39
Myosin, 39, 44

N

Nails, 22, *22*, 24–25
Nasal
  cavity, 73
  passage, 72
Nephrons, 92, *96*
Nerve
  cells, 108
  cochlear, *58, 59*
  cranial, 51
  fibers, 51, 68
  impulse, *49*
  optic, 59, *61*
  parasympathetic, 54–55
  pelvic, *57*
  spinal, 51, *53*
  sympathetic, 54–55
Nervous system, 47–61
  autonomic, 54–55, 57, 68
  central, 50–52
  peripheral, 52–55
  sensory, 52–54
Neurons, 47–50, *51*, 72
  auditory, *59*
  motor, 53, 54
  olfactory, 73
  sensory, 53
Neurotransmitters, 49, 50
Nucleotides, 65, 81, 83

O

Obesity, 88
Olfactory sense, 55, *61*
Organelles, 10, 15, 39
Orginine, 13
Osteoblasts, 27, 28
Osteoclasts, 27, 28
Osteocytes, 27
Osteonectin, 27
Ovaries, 101, 104–105, 115, *115*, 116, 118
Oxygen, 10, 14, 15, 28, 57, 63, 65, 68, 71–72, 76, 78, 83, 99, 108

P

Pain, 53
Pancreas, 9, *57*, 87, *88*, 101, 104, *105*
Patella, 33, *34*
Penis, *118*, 120
Pepsin, 8
Peripheral nervous system, 52–55
Peyer's patches, 110
Phagocytosis, 111, *111*
Phalanges, 33, *33, 34*
Pharynx, *72*, 73
Phosphate, 11
Phospholipids, 15, 89
Pigmentation, 21
Pinna, 56, *58*
Pleura, 75
Polymerase, 12, 14, 16
Progesterone, 105, 117
Proline, 13
Prostate gland, *118*, 119
Proteins, 10, 11–14, 20, 22, 27, 39, 59, 65, 69, 81, 84
  secreted, 22
Puberty, 24

R

Radius, 33, *33*
Rectum, *91*
Reflex arc, 52, *54*
Renin, 95
Reproductive system, 115–123
Resistance
  general, 108
  specific, 108, 110–113
Respiration, 71, 72, 76–78
  control, 78
  reflexes, 73
Respiratory system, 71–79
Retina, 58, 59, *61*
Retin-A, 25
Ribonuclease, 87
Ribonucleic acid. *See* RNA.
Ribosomes, 10, 12, 13, 64
Ribs, 31, *32*
RNA, 12, 14
Rods and cones, 59, *60*

S

Sacrum, 31, *31*, 34, *34*
Sarcolemma, 42
Sarcomere, *38*, 39, 44
Sarcoplasm, 42
Scapula, *32*, 33, *33*
Scrotum, *118*, 119
Semen, 119
Semicircular canal, 58, *59*
Seminal vesicles, *118*, 119
Serine, 13
Sight, 58–59
Sino-atrial nodes, 67
Skeletal system, 27–35, *29*
  function, 35
  joints, 34–35
Skin, 9, 16, 19–22, 37
  cancer, 20
  functions, 25
  regeneration, 19
  structure, 19–22
  wrinkles, 25
Skull, 30, *30*
Smell, 55, *61*
Smoking, 74
Sneezing, 73
Sodium, 65, 93, 94, 95
Sodium pump, 48, *49*